HOLT SCIENCE & TECHNOLOGY

ANNOTATED **T**EACHER'S **E**DITION

Inside the
Restless Earth

HOLT, RINEHART AND WINSTON

A Harcourt Classroom Education Company

Austin · **New York** · **Orlando** · **Atlanta** · **San Francisco** · **Boston** · **Dallas** · **Toronto** · **London**

Acknowledgments

Chapter Writers

Kathleen Meehan Berry
Science Chairman
Canon-McMillan School District
Canonsburg, Pennsylvania

Robert H. Fronk, Ph.D.
Chair of Science and Mathematics Education Department
Florida Institute of Technology
West Melbourne, Florida

Mary Kay Hemenway, Ph.D.
Research Associate and Senior Lecturer
Department of Astronomy
The University of Texas
Austin, Texas

Kathleen Kaska
Life and Earth Science Teacher
Lake Travis Middle School
Austin, Texas

Peter E. Malin, Ph.D.
Professor of Geology
Division of Earth and Ocean Sciences
Duke University
Durham, North Carolina

Karen J. Meech, Ph.D.
Associate Astronomer
Institute for Astronomy
University of Hawaii
Honolulu, Hawaii

Robert J. Sager
Chair and Professor of Earth Sciences
Pierce College
Lakewood, Washington

Lab Writers

Kenneth Creese
Science Teacher
White Mountain Junior High School
Rock Springs, Wyoming

Linda A. Culp
Science Teacher and Dept. Chair
Thorndale High School
Thorndale, Texas

Bruce M. Jones
Science Teacher and Dept. Chair
The Blake School
Minneapolis, Minnesota

Shannon Miller
Science and Math Teacher
Llano Junior High School
Llano, Texas

Robert Stephen Ricks
Special Services Teacher
Department of Classroom Improvement
Alabama State Department of Education
Montgomery, Alabama

James J. Secosky
Science Teacher
Bloomfield Central School
Bloomfield, New York

Academic Reviewers

Mead Allison, Ph.D.
Assistant Professor of Oceanography
Texas A&M University
Galveston, Texas

Alissa Arp, Ph.D.
Director and Professor of Environmental Studies
Romberg Tiburon Center
San Francisco State University
Tiburon, California

Paul D. Asimow, Ph.D.
Assistant Professor of Geology and Geochemistry
Department of Physics and Planetary Sciences
California Institute of Technology
Pasadena, California

G. Fritz Benedict, Ph.D.
Senior Research Scientist and Astronomer
McDonald Observatory
The University of Texas
Austin, Texas

Russell M. Brengelman, Ph.D.
Professor of Physics
Morehead State University
Morehead, Kentucky

John A. Brockhaus, Ph.D.
Director—Mapping, Charting, and Geodesy Program
Department of Geography and Environmental Engineering
United States Military Academy
West Point, New York

Michael Brown, Ph.D.
Assistant Professor of Planetary Astronomy
Department of Physics and Astronomy
California Institute of Technology
Pasadena, California

Wesley N. Colley, Ph.D.
Postdoctoral Fellow
Harvard-Smithsonian Center for Astrophysics
Cambridge, Massachusetts

Andrew J. Davis, Ph.D.
Manager—ACE Science Data Center
Physics Department
California Institute of Technology
Pasadena, California

Peter E. Demmin, Ed.D.
Former Science Teacher and Department Chair
Amherst Central High School
Amherst, New York

James Denbow, Ph.D.
Associate Professor
Department of Anthropology
The University of Texas
Austin, Texas

Roy W. Hann, Jr., Ph.D.
Professor of Civil Engineering
Texas A&M University
College Station, Texas

Frederick R. Heck, Ph.D.
Professor of Geology
Ferris State University
Big Rapids, Michigan

Richard Hey, Ph.D.
Professor of Geophysics
Hawaii Institute of Geophysics and Planetology
University of Hawaii
Honolulu, Hawaii

John E. Hoover, Ph.D.
Associate Professor of Biology
Millersville University
Millersville, Pennsylvania

Robert W. Houghton, Ph.D.
Senior Staff Associate
Lamont-Doherty Earth Observatory
Columbia University
Palisades, New York

Steven A. Jennings, Ph.D.
Assistant Professor
Department of Geography & Environmental Studies
University of Colorado
Colorado Springs, Colorado

Eric L. Johnson, Ph.D.
Assistant Professor of Geology
Central Michigan University
Mount Pleasant, Michigan

John Kermond, Ph.D.
Visiting Scientist
NOAA–Office of Global Programs
Silver Spring, Maryland

Zavareh Kothavala, Ph.D.
Postdoctoral Associate Scientist
Department of Geology and Geophysics
Yale University
New Haven, Connecticut

Karen Kwitter, Ph.D.
Ebenezer Fitch Professor of Astronomy
Williams College
Williamstown, Massachusetts

Valerie Lang, Ph.D.
Project Leader of Environmental Programs
The Aerospace Corporation
Los Angeles, California

Philip LaRoe
Professor
Helena College of Technology
Helena, Montana

Julie Lutz, Ph.D.
Astronomy Program
Washington State University
Pullman, Washington

Acknowledgments (cont.)

Duane F. Marble, Ph.D.
Professor Emeritus
Department of Geography and Natural Resources
Ohio State University
Columbus, Ohio

Joseph A. McClure, Ph.D.
Associate Professor
Department of Physics
Georgetown University
Washington, D.C.

Frank K. McKinney, Ph.D.
Professor of Geology
Appalachian State University
Boone, North Carolina

Joann Mossa, Ph.D.
Associate Professor of Geography
University of Florida
Gainesville, Florida

LaMoine L. Motz, Ph.D.
Coordinator of Science Education
Department of Learning Services
Oakland County Schools
Waterford, Michigan

Barbara Murck, Ph.D.
Assistant Professor of Earth Science
Erindale College
University of Toronto
Mississauga, Ontario CANADA

Hilary Clement Olson, Ph.D.
Research Associate
Institute for Geophysics
The University of Texas
Austin, Texas

Andre Potochnik
Geologist
Grand Canyon Field Institute
Flagstaff, Arizona

John R. Reid, Ph.D.
Professor Emeritus
Department of Geology and Geological Engineering
University of North Dakota
Grand Forks, North Dakota

Gary Rottman, Ph.D.
Associate Director
Laboratory for Atmosphere and Space Physics
University of Colorado
Boulder, Colorado

Dork L. Sahagian, Ph.D.
Professor
Institute for the Study of Earth, Oceans, and Space
University of New Hampshire
Durham, New Hampshire

Peter Sheridan, Ph.D.
Professor of Chemistry
Colgate University
Hamilton, New York

David Sprayberry, Ph.D.
Assistant Director for Observing Support
W.M. Keck Observatory
California Association for Research in Astronomy
Kamuela, Hawaii

Lynne Talley, Ph.D.
Professor
Scripps Institution of Oceanography
University of California
La Jolla, California

Glenn Thompson, Ph.D.
Scientist
Geophysical Institute
University of Alaska
Fairbanks, Alaska

Martin VanDyke, Ph.D.
Professor of Chemistry, Emeritus
Front Range Community College
Westminister, Colorado

Thad A. Wasklewicz, Ph.D.
Assistant Professor of Geography
University of Memphis
Memphis, Tennessee

Hans Rudolf Wenk, Ph.D.
Professor of Geology and Geophysical Sciences
University of California
Berkeley, California

Lisa D. White, Ph.D.
Associate Professor of Geosciences
San Francisco State University
San Francisco, California

Lorraine W. Wolf, Ph.D.
Associate Professor of Geology
Auburn University
Auburn, Alabama

Charles A. Wood, Ph.D.
Chairman and Professor of Space Studies
University of North Dakota
Grand Forks, North Dakota

Safety Reviewer

Jack Gerlovich, Ph.D.
Associate Professor
School of Education
Drake University
Des Moines, Iowa

Teacher Reviewers

Barry L. Bishop
Science Teacher and Dept. Chair
San Rafael Junior High School
Ferron, Utah

Yvonne Brannum
Science Teacher and Dept. Chair
Hine Junior High School
Washington, D.C.

Daniel L. Bugenhagen
Science Teacher and Dept. Chair
Yutan Junior & Senior High School
Yutan, Nebraska

Kenneth Creese
Science Teacher
White Mountain Junior High School
Rock Springs, Wyoming

Linda A. Culp
Science Teacher and Dept. Chair
Thorndale High School
Thorndale, Texas

Alonda Droege
Science Teacher
Pioneer Middle School
Steilacom, Washington

Laura Fleet
Science Teacher
Alice B. Landrum Middle School
Ponte Vedra Beach, Florida

Susan Gorman
Science Teacher
Northridge Middle School
North Richland Hills, Texas

C. John Graves
Science Teacher
Monforton Middle School
Bozeman, Montana

Janel Guse
Science Teacher and Dept. Chair
West Central Middle School
Hartford, South Dakota

Gary Habeeb
Science Mentor
Sierra–Plumas Joint Unified School District
Downieville, California

Dennis Hanson
Science Teacher and Dept. Chair
Big Bear Middle School
Big Bear Lake, California

Norman E. Holcomb
Science Teacher
Marion Local Schools
Maria Stein, Ohio

Tracy Jahn
Science Teacher
Berkshire Junior-Senior High School
Canaan, New York

David D. Jones
Science Teacher
Andrew Jackson Middle School
Cross Lanes, West Virginia

Howard A. Knodle
Science Teacher
Belvidere High School
Belvidere, Illinois

Michael E. Kral
Science Teacher
West Hardin Middle School
Cecilia, Kentucky

Kathy LaRoe
Science Teacher
East Valley Middle School
East Helena, Montana

Scott Mandel, Ph.D.
Director and Educational Consultant
Teachers Helping Teachers
Los Angeles, California

Kathy McKee
Science Teacher
Hoyt Middle School
Des Moines, Iowa

Michael Minium
Vice President of Program Development
United States Orienteering Federation
Forest Park, Georgia

Jan Nelson
Science Teacher
East Valley Middle School
East Helena, Montana

Dwight C. Patton
Science Teacher
Carroll T. Welch Middle School
Horizon City, Texas

Joseph Price
Chairman—Science Department
H. M. Brown Junior High School
Washington, D.C.

Terry J. Rakes
Science Teacher
Elmwood Junior High School
Rogers, Arkansas

Steven Ramig
Science Teacher
West Point High School
West Point, Nebraska

Helen P. Schiller
Science Teacher
Northwood Middle School
Taylors, South Carolina

Bert J. Sherwood
Science Teacher
Socorro Middle School
El Paso, Texas

Larry Tackett
Science Teacher and Dept. Chair
Andrew Jackson Middle School
Cross Lanes, West Virginia

Walter Woolbaugh
Science Teacher
Manhattan Junior High School
Manhattan, Montana

Alexis S. Wright
Middle School Science Coordinator
Rye Country Day School
Rye, New York

Gordon Zibelman
Science Teacher
Drexel Hill Middle School
Drexel Hill, Pennsylvania

F Inside the Restless Earth

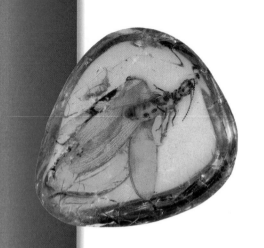

Skills Development

Process Skills

QuickLabs

Chapter Labs

Skills Development

Research and Critical Thinking Skills

Apply

Feature Articles

Weird Science

Science Fiction

Science, Technology, and Society

Health Watch

Careers

Scientific Debate

Eye on the Environment

Across the Sciences

Connections

Biology Connection

Physics Connection

Mathematics

Program Scope and Sequence

Selecting the right books for your course is easy. Just review the topics presented in each book to determine the best match to your district curriculum.

	A MICROORGANISMS, FUNGI, AND PLANTS	**B** ANIMALS
CHAPTER 1	**It's Alive!! Or, Is It?** ❑ Characteristics of living things ❑ Homeostasis ❑ Heredity and DNA ❑ Producers, consumers, and decomposers ❑ Biomolecules	**Animals and Behavior** ❑ Characteristics of animals ❑ Classification of animals ❑ Animal behavior ❑ Hibernation and estivation ❑ The biological clock ❑ Animal communication ❑ Living in groups
CHAPTER 2	**Bacteria and Viruses** ❑ Binary fission ❑ Characteristics of bacteria ❑ Nitrogen-fixing bacteria ❑ Antibiotics ❑ Pathogenic bacteria ❑ Characteristics of viruses ❑ Lytic cycle	**Invertebrates** ❑ General characteristics of invertebrates ❑ Types of symmetry ❑ Characteristics of sponges, cnidarians, arthropods, and echinoderms ❑ Flatworms versus roundworms ❑ Types of circulatory systems
CHAPTER 3	**Protists and Fungi** ❑ Characteristics of protists ❑ Types of algae ❑ Types of protozoa ❑ Protist reproduction ❑ Characteristics of fungi and lichens	**Fishes, Amphibians, and Reptiles** ❑ Characteristics of vertebrates ❑ Structure and kinds of fishes ❑ Development of lungs ❑ Structure and kinds of amphibians and reptiles ❑ Function of the amniotic egg
CHAPTER 4	**Introduction to Plants** ❑ Characteristics of plants and seeds ❑ Reproduction and classification ❑ Angiosperms versus gymnosperms ❑ Monocots versus dicots ❑ Structure and functions of roots, stems, leaves, and flowers	**Birds and Mammals** ❑ Structure and kinds of birds ❑ Types of feathers ❑ Adaptations for flight ❑ Structure and kinds of mammals ❑ Function of the placenta
CHAPTER 5	**Plant Processes** ❑ Pollination and fertilization ❑ Dormancy ❑ Photosynthesis ❑ Plant tropisms ❑ Seasonal responses of plants	
CHAPTER 6		
CHAPTER 7		

Life Science

C CELLS, HEREDITY, & CLASSIFICATION

Cells: The Basic Units of Life
- ❏ Cells, tissues, and organs
- ❏ Populations, communities, and ecosystems
- ❏ Cell theory
- ❏ Surface-to-volume ratio
- ❏ Prokaryotic versus eukaryotic cells
- ❏ Cell organelles

The Cell in Action
- ❏ Diffusion and osmosis
- ❏ Passive versus active transport
- ❏ Endocytosis versus exocytosis
- ❏ Photosynthesis
- ❏ Cellular respiration and fermentation
- ❏ Cell cycle

Heredity
- ❏ Dominant versus recessive traits
- ❏ Genes and alleles
- ❏ Genotype, phenotype, the Punnett square and probability
- ❏ Meiosis
- ❏ Determination of sex

Genes and Gene Technology
- ❏ Structure of DNA
- ❏ Protein synthesis
- ❏ Mutations
- ❏ Heredity disorders and genetic counseling

The Evolution of Living Things
- ❏ Adaptations and species
- ❏ Evidence for evolution
- ❏ Darwin's work and natural selection
- ❏ Formation of new species

The History of Life on Earth
- ❏ Geologic time scale and extinctions
- ❏ Plate tectonics
- ❏ Human evolution

Classification
- ❏ Levels of classification
- ❏ Cladistic diagrams
- ❏ Dichotomous keys
- ❏ Characteristics of the six kingdoms

D HUMAN BODY SYSTEMS & HEALTH

Body Organization and Structure
- ❏ Homeostasis
- ❏ Types of tissue
- ❏ Organ systems
- ❏ Structure and function of the skeletal system, muscular system, and integumentary system

Circulation and Respiration
- ❏ Structure and function of the cardiovascular system, lymphatic system, and respiratory system
- ❏ Respiratory disorders

The Digestive and Urinary Systems
- ❏ Structure and function of the digestive system
- ❏ Structure and function of the urinary system

Communication and Control
- ❏ Structure and function of the nervous system and endocrine system
- ❏ The senses
- ❏ Structure and function of the eye and ear

Reproduction and Development
- ❏ Asexual versus sexual reproduction
- ❏ Internal versus external fertilization
- ❏ Structure and function of the human male and female reproductive systems
- ❏ Fertilization, placental development, and embryo growth
- ❏ Stages of human life

Body Defenses and Disease
- ❏ Types of diseases
- ❏ Vaccines and immunity
- ❏ Structure and function of the immune system
- ❏ Autoimmune diseases, cancer, and AIDS

Staying Healthy
- ❏ Nutrition and reading food labels
- ❏ Alcohol and drug effects on the body
- ❏ Hygiene, exercise, and first aid

E ENVIRONMENTAL SCIENCE

Interactions of Living Things
- ❏ Biotic versus abiotic parts of the environment
- ❏ Producers, consumers, and decomposers
- ❏ Food chains and food webs
- ❏ Factors limiting population growth
- ❏ Predator-prey relationships
- ❏ Symbiosis and coevolution

Cycles in Nature
- ❏ Water cycle
- ❏ Carbon cycle
- ❏ Nitrogen cycle
- ❏ Ecological succession

The Earth's Ecosystems
- ❏ Kinds of land and water biomes
- ❏ Marine ecosystems
- ❏ Freshwater ecosystems

Environmental Problems and Solutions
- ❏ Types of pollutants
- ❏ Types of resources
- ❏ Conservation practices
- ❏ Species protection

Energy Resources
- ❏ Types of resources
- ❏ Energy resources and pollution
- ❏ Alternative energy resources

Scope and Sequence *(continued)*

	F INSIDE THE RESTLESS EARTH	**G** EARTH'S CHANGING SURFACE
CHAPTER 1	**Minerals of the Earth's Crust** ❏ Mineral composition and structure ❏ Types of minerals ❏ Mineral identification ❏ Mineral formation and mining	**Maps as Models of the Earth** ❏ Structure of a map ❏ Cardinal directions ❏ Latitude, longitude, and the equator ❏ Magnetic declination and true north ❏ Types of projections ❏ Aerial photographs ❏ Remote sensing ❏ Topographic maps
CHAPTER 2	**Rocks: Mineral Mixtures** ❏ Rock cycle and types of rocks ❏ Rock classification ❏ Characteristics of igneous, sedimentary, and metamorphic rocks	**Weathering and Soil Formation** ❏ Types of weathering ❏ Factors affecting the rate of weathering ❏ Composition of soil ❏ Soil conservation and erosion prevention
CHAPTER 3	**The Rock and Fossil Record** ❏ Uniformitarianism versus catastrophism ❏ Superposition ❏ The geologic column and unconformities ❏ Absolute dating and radiometric dating ❏ Characteristics and types of fossils ❏ Geologic time scale	**Agents of Erosion and Deposition** ❏ Shoreline erosion and deposition ❏ Wind erosion and deposition ❏ Erosion and deposition by ice ❏ Gravity's effect on erosion and deposition
CHAPTER 4	**Plate Tectonics** ❏ Structure of the Earth ❏ Continental drifts and sea floor spreading ❏ Plate tectonics theory ❏ Types of boundaries ❏ Types of crust deformities	
CHAPTER 5	**Earthquakes** ❏ Seismology ❏ Features of earthquakes ❏ P and S waves ❏ Gap hypothesis ❏ Earthquake safety	
CHAPTER 6	**Volcanoes** ❏ Types of volcanoes and eruptions ❏ Types of lava and pyroclastic material ❏ Craters versus calderas ❏ Sites and conditions for volcano formation ❏ Predicting eruptions	

Earth Science

Scope and Sequence (continued)

	K INTRODUCTION TO MATTER	**L INTERACTIONS OF MATTER**
CHAPTER 1	**The Properties of Matter** ❏ Definition of matter ❏ Mass and weight ❏ Physical and chemical properties ❏ Physical and chemical change ❏ Density	**Chemical Bonding** ❏ Types of chemical bonds ❏ Valence electrons ❏ Ions versus molecules ❏ Crystal lattice
CHAPTER 2	**States of Matter** ❏ States of matter and their properties ❏ Boyle's and Charles's laws ❏ Changes of state	**Chemical Reactions** ❏ Writing chemical formulas and equations ❏ Law of conservation of mass ❏ Types of reactions ❏ Endothermic versus exothermic reactions ❏ Law of conservation of energy ❏ Activation energy ❏ Catalysts and inhibitors
CHAPTER 3	**Elements, Compounds, and Mixtures** ❏ Elements and compounds ❏ Metals, nonmetals, and metalloids (semiconductors) ❏ Properties of mixtures ❏ Properties of solutions, suspensions, and colloids	**Chemical Compounds** ❏ Ionic versus covalent compounds ❏ Acids, bases, and salts ❏ pH ❏ Organic compounds ❏ Biomolecules
CHAPTER 4	**Introduction to Atoms** ❏ Atomic theory ❏ Atomic model and structure ❏ Isotopes ❏ Atomic mass and mass number	**Atomic Energy** ❏ Properties of radioactive substances ❏ Types of decay ❏ Half-life ❏ Fission, fusion, and chain reactions
CHAPTER 5	**The Periodic Table** ❏ Structure of the periodic table ❏ Periodic law ❏ Properties of alkali metals, alkaline-earth metals, halogens, and noble gases	
CHAPTER 6		

Physical Science

M FORCES, MOTION, AND ENERGY

Matter in Motion
- Speed, velocity, and acceleration
- Measuring force
- Friction
- Mass versus weight

Forces in Motion
- Terminal velocity and free fall
- Projectile motion
- Inertia
- Momentum

Forces in Fluids
- Properties in fluids
- Atmospheric pressure
- Density
- Pascal's principle
- Buoyant force
- Archimedes' principle
- Bernoulli's principle

Work and Machines
- Measuring work
- Measuring power
- Types of machines
- Mechanical advantage
- Mechanical efficiency

Energy and Energy Resources
- Forms of energy
- Energy conversions
- Law of conservation of energy
- Energy resources

Heat and Heat Technology
- Heat versus temperature
- Thermal expansion
- Absolute zero
- Conduction, convection, radiation
- Conductors versus insulators
- Specific heat capacity
- Changes of state
- Heat engines
- Thermal pollution

N ELECTRICITY AND MAGNETISM

Introduction to Electricity
- Law of electric charges
- Conduction versus induction
- Static electricity
- Potential difference
- Cells, batteries, and photocells
- Thermocouples
- Voltage, current, and resistance
- Electric power
- Types of circuits

Electromagnetism
- Properties of magnets
- Magnetic force
- Electromagnetism
- Solenoids and electric motors
- Electromagnetic induction
- Generators and transformers

Electronic Technology
- Properties of semiconductors
- Integrated circuits
- Diodes and transistors
- Analog versus digital signals
- Microprocessors
- Features of computers

O SOUND AND LIGHT

The Energy of Waves
- Properties of waves
- Types of waves
- Reflection and refraction
- Diffraction and interference
- Standing waves and resonance

The Nature of Sound
- Properties of sound waves
- Structure of the human ear
- Pitch and the Doppler effect
- Infrasonic versus ultrasonic sound
- Sound reflection and echolocation
- Sound barrier
- Interference, resonance, diffraction, and standing waves
- Sound quality of instruments

The Nature of Light
- Electromagnetic waves
- Electromagnetic spectrum
- Law of reflection
- Absorption and scattering
- Reflection and refraction
- Diffraction and interference

Light and Our World
- Luminosity
- Types of lighting
- Types of mirrors and lenses
- Focal point
- Structure of the human eye
- Lasers and holograms

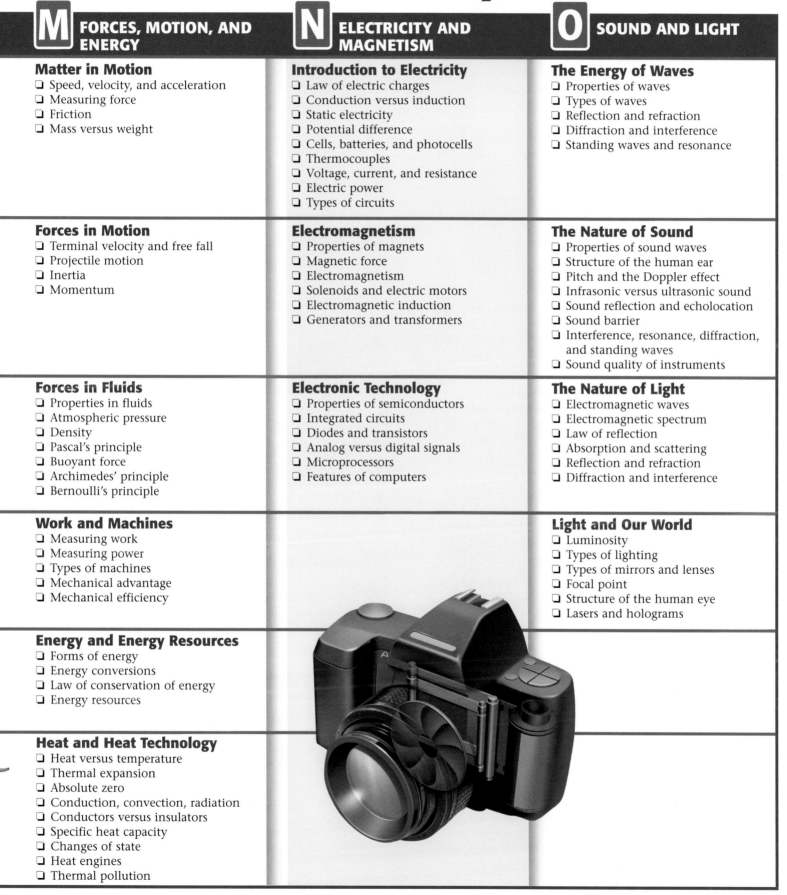

HOLT SCIENCE & TECHNOLOGY
Components Listing

Effective planning starts with all the resources you need in an easy-to-use package for each short course.

Directed Reading Worksheets Help students develop and practice fundamental reading comprehension skills and provide a comprehensive review tool for students to use when studying for an exam.

Study Guide Vocabulary & Notes Worksheets and Chapter Review Worksheets are reproductions of the Chapter Highlights and Chapter Review sections that follow each chapter in the textbook.

Science Puzzlers, Twisters & Teasers Use vocabulary and concepts from each chapter of the Pupil's Editions as elements of rebuses, anagrams, logic puzzles, daffy definitions, riddle poems, word jumbles, and other types of puzzles.

Reinforcement and Vocabulary Review Worksheets Approach a chapter topic from a different angle with an emphasis on different learning modalities to help students that are frustrated by traditional methods.

Critical Thinking & Problem Solving Worksheets Develop the following skills: distinguishing fact from opinion, predicting consequences, analyzing information, and drawing conclusions. Problem Solving Worksheets develop a step-by-step process of problem analysis including gathering information, asking critical questions, identifying alternatives, and making comparisons.

Math Skills for Science Worksheets Each activity gives a brief introduction to a relevant math skill, a step-by-step explanation of the math process, one or more example problems, and a variety of practice problems.

Science Skills Worksheets Help your students focus specifically on skills such as measuring, graphing, using logic, understanding statistics, organizing research papers, and critical thinking options.

LAB ACTIVITIES

ALL LABS ARE CLASSROOM TESTED & APPROVED

Datasheets for Labs These worksheets are the labs found in the *Holt Science & Technology* textbook. Charts, tables, and graphs are included to make data collection and analysis easier, and space is provided to write observations and conclusions.

Whiz-Bang Demonstrations Discovery or Making Models experiences label each demo as one in which students discover an answer or use a scientific model.

Calculator-Based Labs Give students the opportunity to use graphing-calculator probes and sensors to collect data using a TI graphing calculator, Vernier sensors, and a TI CBL 2™ or Vernier Lab Pro interface.

EcoLabs and Field Activities Focus on educational outdoor projects, such as wildlife observation, nature surveys, or natural history.

Inquiry Labs Use the scientific method to help students find their own path in solving a real-world problem.

Long-Term Projects and Research Ideas Provide students with the opportunity to go beyond library and Internet resources to explore science topics.

ASSESSMENT

Chapter Tests Each four-page chapter test consists of a variety of item types including Multiple Choice, Using Vocabulary, Short Answer, Critical Thinking, Math in Science, Interpreting Graphics, and Concept Mapping.

Performance-Based Assessments Evaluate students' abilities to solve problems using the tools, equipment, and techniques of science. Rubrics included for each assessment make it easy to evaluate student performance.

TEACHER RESOURCES

Lesson Plans Integrate all of the great resources in the *Holt Science & Technology* program into your daily teaching. Each lesson plan includes a correlation of the lesson activities to the National Science Education Standards.

Teaching Transparencies Each transparency is correlated to a particular lesson in the Chapter Organizer.

Concept Mapping Transparencies, Worksheets, and Answer Key
Give students an opportunity to complete their own concept maps to study the concepts within each chapter and form logical connections. Student worksheets contain a blank concept map with linking phrases and a list of terms to be used by the student to complete the map.

TECHNOLOGY RESOURCES

One-Stop Planner CD-ROM
Finding the right resources is easy with the One-Stop Planner CD-ROM. You can view and print any resource with just the click of a mouse. Customize the suggested lesson plans to match your daily or weekly calendar and your district's requirements. Powerful test generator software allows you to create customized assessments using a databank of items.

The One-Stop Planner for each level includes the following:

- All materials from the Teaching Resources
- Bellringer Transparency Masters
- Block Scheduling Tools
- Standards Correlations
- Lab Inventory Checklist
- Safety Information
- Science Fair Guide
- Parent Involvement Tools
- Spanish Audio Scripts
- Spanish Glossary
- Assessment Item Listing
- Assessment Checklists and Rubrics
- Test Generator

 sciLINKS
sciLINKS numbers throughout the text take you and your students to some of the best on-line resources available. Sites are constantly reviewed and updated by the National Science Teachers Association. Special "teacher only" sites are available to you once you register with the service.

 go.hrw.com
To access Holt, Rinehart and Winston Web resources, use the home page codes for each level found on page 1 of the Pupil's Editions. The codes shown on the Chapter Organizers for each chapter in the Annotated Teacher's Edition take you to chapter-specific resources.

 Smithsonian Institution
Find lesson plans, activities, interviews, virtual exhibits, and just general information on a wide variety of topics relevant to middle school science.

CNNfyi.com
Find the latest in late-breaking science news for students. Featured news stories are supported with lesson plans and activities.

 Presents Science in the News Video Library
Bring relevant science news stories into the classroom. Each video comes with a Teacher's Guide and set of Critical Thinking Worksheets that develop listening and media analysis skills. Tapes in the series include:

- Eye on the Environment
- Multicultural Connections
- Scientists in Action
- Science, Technology & Society

 Guided Reading Audio CD Program
Students can listen to a direct read of each chapter and follow along in the text. Use the program as a content bridge for struggling readers and students for whom English is not their native language.

 Interactive Explorations CD-ROM
Turn a computer into a virtual laboratory. Students act as lab assistants helping Dr. Crystal Labcoat solve real-world problems. Activities develop students' inquiry, analysis, and decision-making skills.

Interactive Science Encyclopedia CD-ROM
Give your students access to more than 3,000 cross-referenced scientific definitions, in-depth articles, science fair project ideas, activities, and more.

ADDITIONAL COMPONENTS

Holt Anthology of Science Fiction
Science Fiction features in the Pupil's Edition preview the stories found in the anthology. Each story begins with a Reading Prep guide and closes with Think About It questions.

Professional Reference for Teachers
Articles written by leading educators help you learn more about the National Science Education Standards, block scheduling, classroom management techniques, and more. A bibliography of professional references is included.

Holt Science Posters
Seven wall posters highlight interesting topics, such as the Physics of Sports, or useful reference material, such as the Scientific Method.

 Holt Science Skills Workshop: Reading in the Content Area
Use a variety of in-depth skills exercises to help students learn to read science materials strategically.

Key
These materials are blackline masters.
All titles shown in green are found in the *Teaching Resources* booklets for each course.

Science & Math Skills Worksheets

The *Holt Science and Technology* program helps you meet the needs of a wide variety of students, regardless of their skill level. The following pages provide examples of the worksheets available to improve your students' science and math skills, whether they already have a strong science and math background or are weak in these areas. Samples of assessment checklists and rubrics are also provided.

In addition to the skills worksheets represented here, *Holt Science and Technology* provides a variety of worksheets that are correlated directly with each chapter of the program. Representations of these worksheets are found at the beginning of each chapter in this Annotated Teacher's Edition. Specific worksheets related to each chapter are listed in the Chapter Organizer. Worksheets and transparencies are found in the softcover *Teaching Resources* for each course.

Many worksheets are also available on the HRW Web site. The address is **go.hrw.com.**

Science Skills Worksheets: Thinking Skills

BEING FLEXIBLE
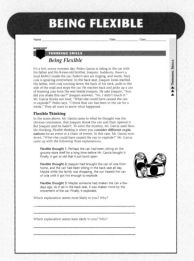

USING YOUR SENSES

THINKING OBJECTIVELY
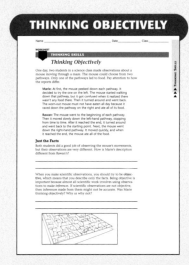

UNDERSTANDING BIAS
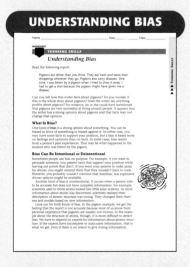

USING LOGIC

BOOSTING YOUR MEMORY
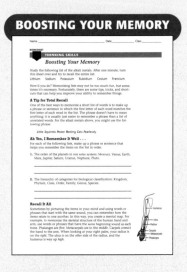

IMPROVING YOUR STUDY HABITS

READING A SCIENCE TEXTBOOK
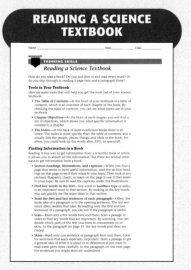

Science Skills Worksheets: Experimenting Skills

SAFETY RULES!
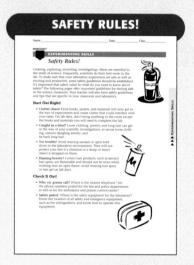

DOING A LAB WRITE-UP
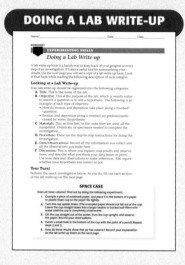

UNDERSTANDING VARIABLES

WORKING WITH HYPOTHESES
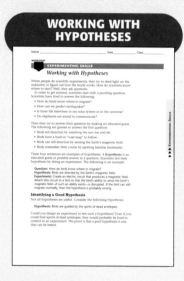

DESIGNING AN EXPERIMENT

USING THE INTERNATIONAL SYSTEM OF UNITS (SI)

MEASURING
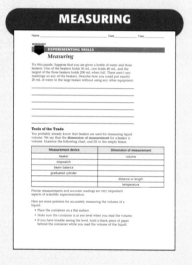

Science Skills Worksheets: Researching Skills

CHOOSING YOUR TOPIC
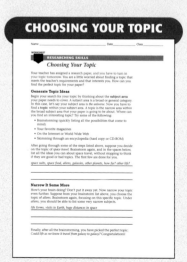

ORGANIZING YOUR RESEARCH
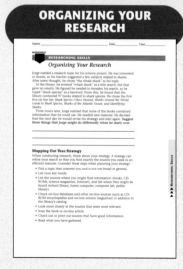

FINDING USEFUL SOURCES
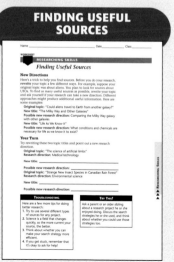

RESEARCHING ON THE WEB
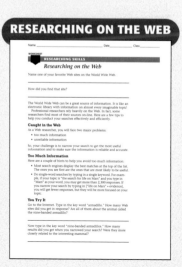

Science & Math Skills Worksheets (continued)

Science Skills Worksheets: Researching Skills (continued)

IDENTIFYING BIAS

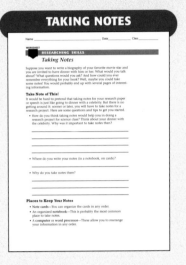

TAKING NOTES

SCIENCE WRITING

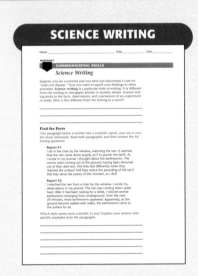

Science Skills Worksheets: Communicating Skills

SCIENCE DRAWING

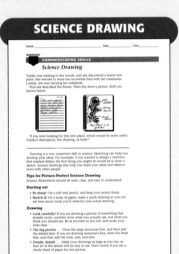

USING MODELS TO COMMUNICATE

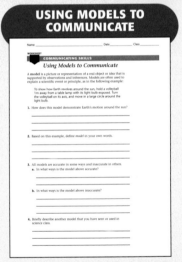

INTRODUCTION TO GRAPHS

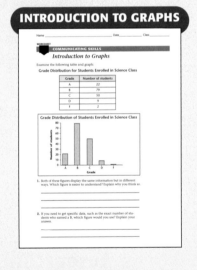

GRASPING GRAPHING

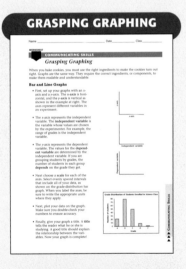

INTERPRETING YOUR DATA

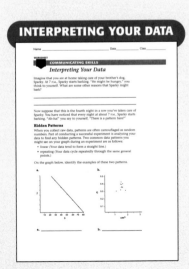

RECOGNIZING BIAS IN GRAPHS

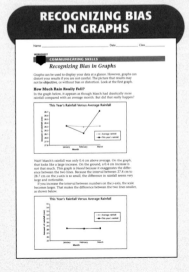

MAKING DATA MEANINGFUL

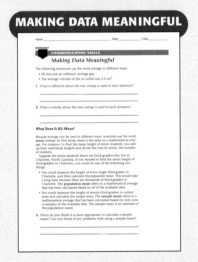

HINTS FOR ORAL PRESENTATIONS

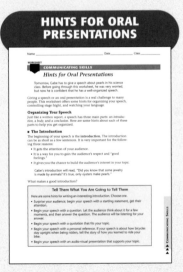

Math Skills for Science

ADDITION AND SUBTRACTION

MULTIPLICATION

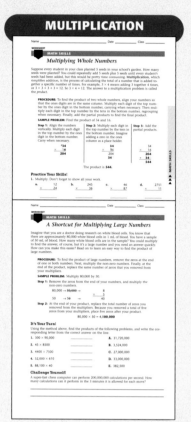

DIVISION

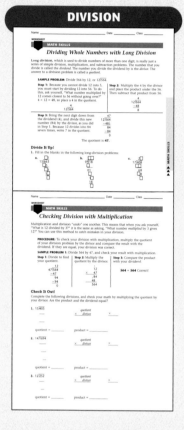

AVERAGES

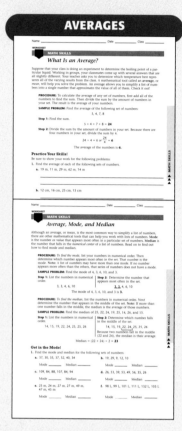

POSITIVE AND NEGATIVE NUMBERS

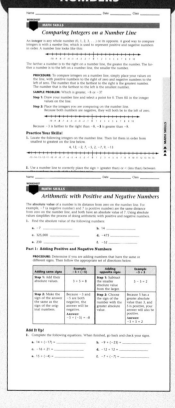

FRACTIONS

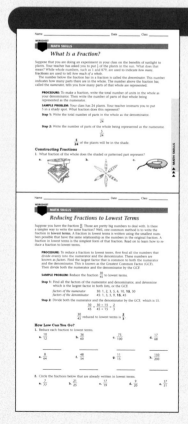

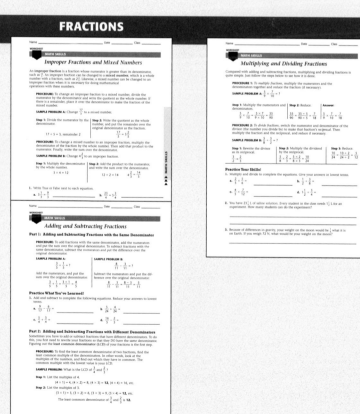

Math Skills for Science (continued)

RATIOS AND PROPORTIONS

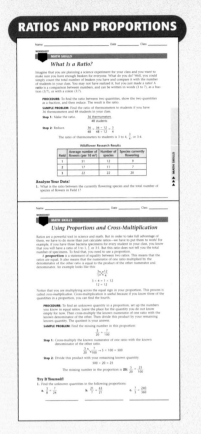

DECIMALS

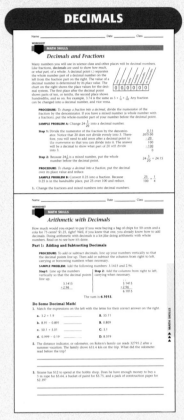

PERCENTAGES

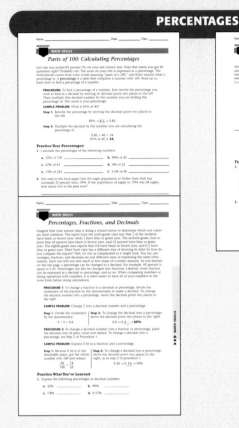

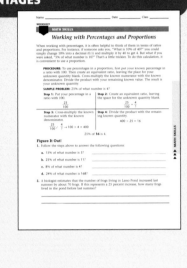

POWERS OF 10

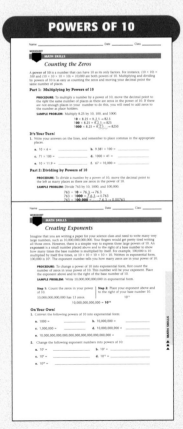

SCIENTIFIC NOTATION

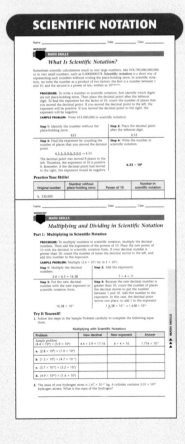

SI MEASUREMENT AND CONVERSION

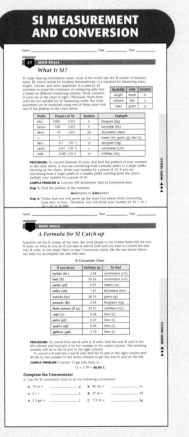

Math Skills for Science (continued)

GEOMETRY

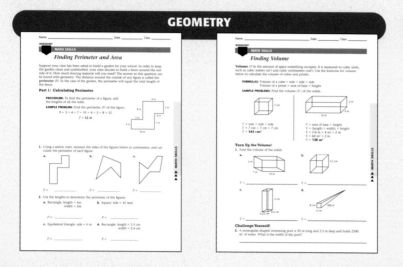

THE UNIT FACTOR AND DIMENSIONAL ANALYSIS

MATH IN SCIENCE: INTEGRATED SCIENCE

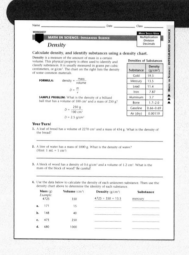

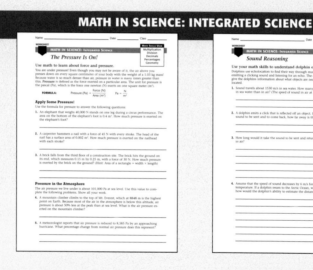

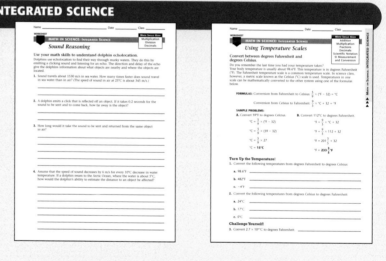

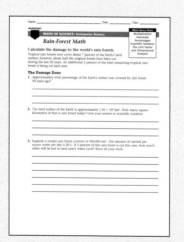

Math Skills for Science (continued)

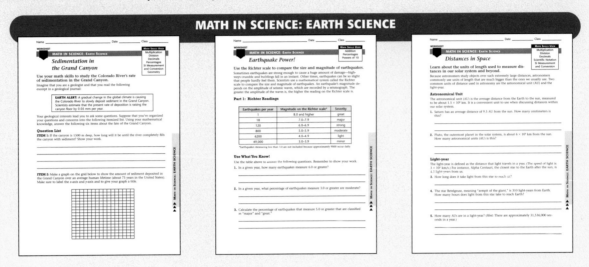

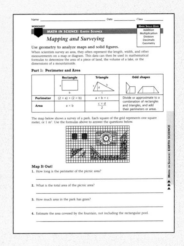

Assessment Checklist & Rubrics

The following is just a sample of over 50 checklists and rubrics contained in this booklet.

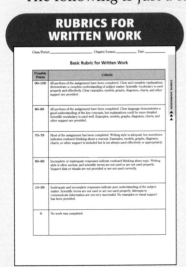

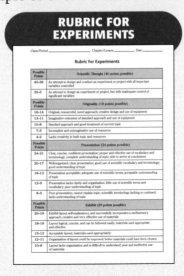

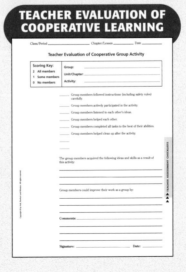

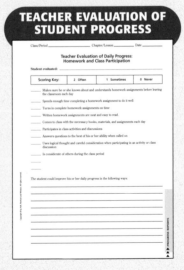

HOLT SCIENCE & TECHNOLOGY

EARTH SCIENCE NATIONAL SCIENCE EDUCATION STANDARDS CORRELATIONS

The following lists show the chapter correlation of **Holt Science and Technology: Inside the Restless Earth** with the *National Science Education Standards* (grades 5-8)

UNIFYING CONCEPTS AND PROCESSES

Standard	Chapter Correlation	
Systems, order, and organization Code: UCP 1	Chapter 1	1.1, 1.2
	Chapter 2	2.1, 2.2, 2.3, 2.4
	Chapter 3	3.2, 3.3, 3.5
Evidence, models, and explanation Code: UCP 2	Chapter 2	2.2, 2.3, 2.4
	Chapter 3	3.1, 3.2, 3.5
	Chapter 4	4.1, 4.2, 4.3, 4.4
	Chapter 5	5.1, 5.3
Change, constancy, and measurement Code: UCP 3	Chapter 3	3.2, 3.3, 3.4, 3.5
	Chapter 5	5.2, 5.3
	Chapter 6	6.3
Evolution and equilibrium Code: UCP 4	Chapter 3	3.1, 3.2, 3.5
Form and function Code: UCP 5	Chapter 1	1.1, 1.2, 1.3
	Chapter 5	5.3

SCIENCE IN PERSONAL AND SOCIAL PERSPECTIVES

Standard	Chapter Correlation	
Personal health Code: SPSP 1	Chapter 5	5.3
Populations, resources, and environments Code: SPSP 2	Chapter 1	1.3
Natural hazards Code: SPSP 3	Chapter 6	6.2
Risks and benefits Code: SPSP 4	Chapter 1	1.3
	Chapter 4	4.3
	Chapter 5	5.2, 5.3
	Chapter 6	6.2
Science and technology in society Code: SPSP 5	Chapter 2	2.1
	Chapter 3	3.4
	Chapter 4	4.1, 4.3
	Chapter 5	5.3
	Chapter 6	6.2, 6.3

SCIENCE AS INQUIRY

Standard	Chapter Correlation	
Abilities necessary to do scientific inquiry Code: SAI 1	Chapter 1	1.2, 1.3
	Chapter 2	2.1, 2.2, 2.3, 2.4
	Chapter 3	3.1, 3.2, 3.3, 3.5
	Chapter 4	4.1, 4.3, 4.4
	Chapter 5	5.1, 5.2, 5.3
	Chapter 6	6.1, 6.2, 6.3
Understandings about scientific inquiry Code: SAI 2	Chapter 3	3.2
	Chapter 5	5.2

SCIENCE AND TECHNOLOGY

Standard	Chapter Correlation	
Abilities of technological design Code: ST 1	Chapter 4	4.3
	Chapter 5	5.3
Understandings about science and technology Code: ST 2	Chapter 2	2.1, 2.4
	Chapter 3	3.4
	Chapter 4	4.1, 4.2, 4.3
	Chapter 6	6.2, 6.3

HISTORY AND NATURE OF SCIENCE

Standard	Chapter Correlation	
Science as a human endeavor Code: HNS 1	Chapter 2	2.1
	Chapter 3	3.1
	Chapter 4	4.2, 4.3
	Chapter 5	5.1, 5.2
	Chapter 6	6.2
Nature of science Code: HNS 2	Chapter 3	3.1
	Chapter 5	5.4
	Chapter 6	6.1
History of science Code: HNS 3	Chapter 2	2.4
	Chapter 3	3.1
	Chapter 4	4.3
	Chapter 5	5.2
	Chapter 6	6.2

EARTH SCIENCE National Science Education Content Standards

STRUCTURE OF THE EARTH SYSTEM

Standard	Chapter Correlation	
The solid earth is layered with a lithosphere; hot, convecting mantle; and dense metallic core. Code: ES 1a	**Chapter 4** **Chapter 5**	4.1 5.4
Lithospheric plates on the scales of continents and oceans constantly move at rates of centimeters per year in response to movements in the mantle. Major geological events, such as earthquakes, volcanic eruptions, and mountain building result from these plate motions. Code: ES 1b	**Chapter 4** **Chapter 5** **Chapter 6**	4.3, 4.4 5.1 6.3
Land forms are the result of a combination of constructive and destructive forces. Constructive forces include crustal deformation, volcanic eruption, and deposition of sediment, while destructive forces include weathering and erosion. Code: ES 1c	**Chapter 2** **Chapter 4** **Chapter 6**	2.2, 2.3 4.4 6.1, 6.2, 6.3
Some changes in the solid earth can be described as the "rock cycle." Old rocks at the earth's surface weather, forming sediments that are buried, then compacted, heated, and often recrystallized into new rock. Eventually, those new rocks may be brought to the earth's surface by the forces that drive plate motions, and the rock cycle continues. Code: ES 1d	**Chapter 2**	2.1, 2.2, 2.3, 2.4
Living organisms have played many roles in the earth system, including affecting the composition of the atmosphere, producing some types of rocks, and contributing to the weathering of rocks. Code: ES 1k	**Chapter 2** **Chapter 3**	2.1, 2.3 3.4

EARTH'S HISTORY

Standard	Chapter Correlation	
The earth processes we see today, including erosion, movement of lithospheric plates, and changes in atmospheric composition, are similar to those that occurred in the past. Earth history is also influenced by occasional catastrophes, such as the impact of an asteroid or comet. Code: ES 2a	**Chapter 3** **Chapter 4**	3.1 4.2, 4.4
Fossils provide important evidence of how life and environmental conditions have changed. Code: ES 2b	**Chapter 2** **Chapter 3**	2.1, 2.3 3.2, 3.4, 3.5

Master Materials List

For added convenience, Science Kit® provides materials-ordering software on CD-ROM designed specifically for *Holt Science and Technology*. Using this software, you can order complete kits or individual items, quickly and efficiently.

CONSUMABLE MATERIALS	AMOUNT	PAGE
Aluminum can (or small pan)	1	46
Aluminum foil, approx. 20 x 40 cm	1	178
Bag, paper lunch	1	55
Baking soda	15 mL	186
Baking soda	10 mL	147
Bottle, soda, 3 L (or jar) with lid	1	182
Cardboard, corrugated, 20 x 20 cm (or plywood)	2	181
Clay, modeling	2 sticks	181
Clay, modeling (3 colors)	2 sticks of each	174
Clay, modeling (4 colors)	1 stick of each	110
Clothes hanger, plastic	1	119
Clothes hanger, wire	1	119
Cornstarch	150 mL	156
Epsom salt	15 mL	178
Gelatin square, 8 x 8 cm	1	138

CONSUMABLE MATERIALS	AMOUNT	PAGE
Gloves, protective	1	16
Gravel	250 mL	182
Honey	1 jar	150
Limewater	1 L	186
Liquid dish soap	1	147
Marker, colored (dark)	1	178
Marker, permanent black	1	77
Markers (green, blue, red, yellow)	1 each	77
Marshmallow	10	138
Microscope slides, glass	10	16
Newspaper	2–3 sheets	110
Paper, adding-machine, approx. 50 cm	1	77
Paper, 1 cm stack	2	87
Paper, graphing	1 sheet	162
Paper, heavy white	1 sheet	78
Pencil, assorted, colored	1 box	78

CONSUMABLE MATERIALS	AMOUNT	PAGE
Pencil, colored (or marker)	3	174
Pencil, colored	4	110
Pencil, colored (red, orange, yellow)	3	162
Plate, paper	1	138
Poster board, square, 5 x 5 cm	2	110
Poster board strip, 5 x 15 cm	1	110
Sand	250 mL	182
Soil, clay-rich	250 mL	182
Stick, small wooden	1	119
Straw, flexible	1	186
Straw, straight plastic	2	150, 176
String	1 ball	176
Tape, masking	1 roll	178
Tape, transparent	1 roll	78
Tissue, bathroom	1–2 sheets	147, 186
Toothpick	10	138
Vinegar	50 mL	147
Vinegar, white	140 mL	186
Water, distilled	50 mL	178
Wax mold	1	46
Wax shavings, candle or crayon	1 pile	46

NONCONSUMABLE EQUIPMENT	AMOUNT	PAGE
Balance, triple-beam, metric	1	176
Beaker, 200 mL	1	147
Beaker, 400 mL	1	176, 178
Bottle, 16 fl oz	1	186
Bowl, clear plastic, 3 gal	1	156
Bowl, mixing, 3 L	1	182
Box (or stand), for cup	1	186
Box (or pan), nontransparent, approx. 30 x 50 cm	1	174
Calculator, scientific	1	184

NONCONSUMABLE EQUIPMENT	AMOUNT	PAGE
Clay, modeling	1 lb	55
Clay, modeling	1 stick	147, 186
Coin	1	186
Compass, drawing	1	184
Container, clear plastic storage	1	93
Cup, plastic	1	156
Cup, plastic	2	150
Cup, plastic, 9 oz	1	186
Dropper pipet	1	182
Funnel, plastic	1	147
Gloves, heat-resistant	2	178
Graduated cylinder, 100 mL	1	186
Hot plate	1	46, 178
Iron filings	1/4 cup	16
Knife, plastic	1	46, 110, 174, 181
Laboratory scoop, pointed	1	178
Magnifying lens	1	178, 182
Mineral, biotite sample	1	16
Mineral, feldspar (pink) sample	1	16
Mineral, galena sample	1	16, 176
Mineral, garnet sample	1	16
Mineral, graphite sample	1	16
Mineral, gypsum sample	1	16
Mineral, hematite sample	1	16
Mineral, hornblende sample	1	16
Mineral, magnetite sample	1	16
Mineral, muscovite sample	1	16
Mineral, pyrite sample	1	176
Mineral, quartz sample	1	16
Pan, aluminum pie	1	147
Penny	1	10
Pipe, PVC, 1.3 cm diam., approx. 20 cm long	1	174

Nonconsumable Equipment	Amount	Page
Protractor	1	119
Putty, plastic play	1 ball	42
Ring stand	1	176
Rock, basalt sample	1	178
Rock, granite sample	1	178
Rock, pumice sample	1	178
Rolling pin, wood	1	110
Ruler, metric	1	77, 78, 162, 184
Scale, spring	1	176
Scissors	1	77, 78, 182

Nonconsumable Equipment	Amount	Page
Sequins	1 sm. pkg.	181
Spoon, plastic	1	156
Spring toy, coiled	1	125
Stopwatch	1	147, 178
Streak plate	1	16
Test tube, medium	1	178
Thermometer, Celsius	1	178
Tongs, test-tube	1	178
Wood, block, approx. 5 x 10 x 20 cm	1	93
Wooden objects, various weights	6	93

Answers to Concept Mapping Questions

The following pages contain sample answers to all of the concept mapping questions that appear in the Chapter Reviews. Because there is more than one way to do a concept map, your students' answers may vary.

CHAPTER 1 Minerals of the Earth's Crust

17.

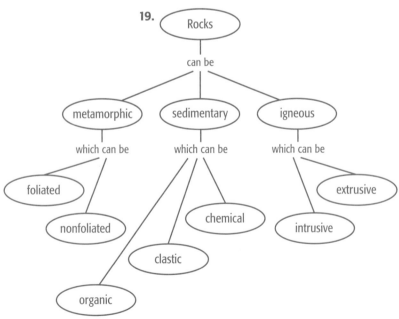

CHAPTER 2 Rocks: Mineral Mixtures

19.

CHAPTER 3 The Rock and Fossil Record

17.

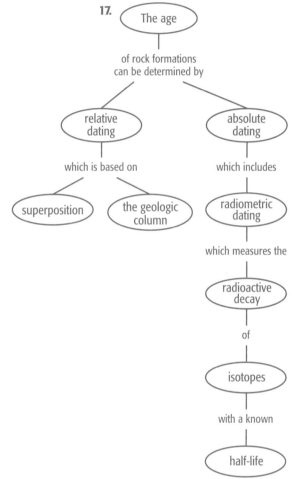

Concept Mapping Answers

CHAPTER 4 Plate Tectonics

21.

Tectonic plates

can be destroyed at a → convergent boundary → which is often a → subduction zone

are neither destroyed nor created at a → transform boundary

can be created at a → divergent boundary → which can be marked by → sea-floor spreading

CHAPTER 5 Earthquakes

15.

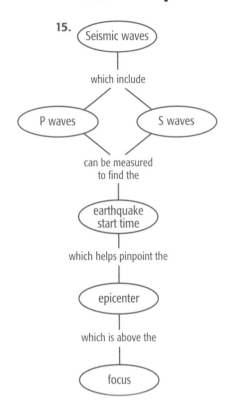

Seismic waves

which include → P waves / S waves

can be measured to find the → earthquake start time

which helps pinpoint the → epicenter

which is above the → focus

CHAPTER 6 Volcanoes

17.

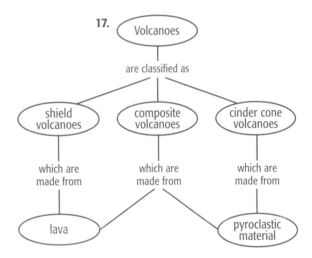

Volcanoes

are classified as → shield volcanoes / composite volcanoes / cinder cone volcanoes

which are made from → lava

which are made from → lava / pyroclastic material

which are made from → pyroclastic material

Concept Mapping Answers

T29

To the Student

This book was created to make your science experience interesting, exciting, and fun!

Go for It!

Science is a process of discovery, a trek into the unknown. The skills you develop using *Holt Science & Technology*— such as observing, experimenting, and explaining observations and ideas— are the skills you will need for the future. There is a universe of exploration and discovery awaiting those who accept the challenges of science.

Science & Technology

You see the interaction between science and technology every day. Science makes technology possible. On the other hand, some of the products of technology, such as computers, are used to make further scientific discoveries. In fact, much of the scientific work that is done today has become so technically complicated and expensive that no one person can do it entirely alone. But make no mistake, the creative ideas for even the most highly technical and expensive scientific work still come from individuals.

Activities and Labs

The activities and labs in this book will allow you to make some basic but important scientific discoveries on your own. You can even do some exploring on your own at home! Here's your chance to use your imagination and curiosity as you investigate your world.

Keep a ScienceLog

In this book, you will be asked to keep a type of journal called a ScienceLog to record your thoughts, observations, experiments, and conclusions. As you develop your ScienceLog, you will see your own ideas taking shape over time. You'll have a written record of how your ideas have changed as you learn about and explore interesting topics in science.

Know "What You'll Do"

The "What You'll Do" list at the beginning of each section is your built-in guide to what you need to learn in each chapter. When you can answer the questions in the Section Review and Chapter Review, you know you are ready for a test.

Check Out the Internet

You will see this 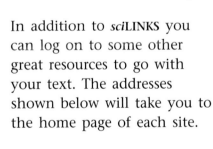 logo throughout the book. You'll be using *sci*LINKS as your gateway to the Internet. Once you log on to *sci*LINKS using your computer's Internet link, type in the *sci*LINKS address. When asked for the keyword code, type in the keyword for that topic. A wealth of resources is now at your disposal to help you learn more about that topic.

In addition to *sci*LINKS you can log on to some other great resources to go with your text. The addresses shown below will take you to the home page of each site.

---

internet**connect**

This textbook contains the following on-line resources to help you make the most of your science experience.

Visit **go.hrw.com** for extra help and study aids matched to your textbook. Just type in the keyword HR2 HOME.

Visit **www.scilinks.org** to find resources specific to topics in your textbook. Keywords appear throughout your book to take you further.

 Smithsonian Institution®
Internet Connections

Visit **www.si.edu/hrw** for specifically chosen on-line materials from one of our nation's premier science museums.

Visit **www.cnnfyi.com** for late-breaking news and current events stories selected just for you.

Chapter Organizer

CHAPTER ORGANIZATION	TIME MINUTES	OBJECTIVES	LABS, INVESTIGATIONS, AND DEMONSTRATIONS
Chapter Opener pp. 2–3	45	National Standards: UCP 5, SAI 1	**Start-Up Activity,** Riding a Mineral?, p. 3
Section 1 **What Is a Mineral?**	90	▶ Explain the four characteristics of a mineral. ▶ Classify minerals according to the two major compositional groups. UCP 1, 5	
Section 2 **Identifying Minerals**	90	▶ Classify minerals using common mineral-identification techniques. ▶ Explain special properties of minerals. ▶ Describe what makes a mineral crystal a gem. UCP 1, 5, SAI 1; Labs SAI 1	**QuickLab,** Scratch Test, p. 10 **Skill Builder,** Mysterious Minerals, p. 16 **Datasheets for LabBook,** Mysterious Minerals **Skill Builder,** Is It Fool's Gold?–A Dense Situation, p. 176 **Datasheets for LabBook,** Is It Fool's Gold?–A Dense Situation
Section 3 **The Formation and Mining of Minerals**	90	▶ Describe the environments in which minerals are formed. ▶ Compare and contrast the different types of mining. UCP 5, SAI 1, SPSP 2, 4	**Long-Term Projects & Research Ideas,** What's Yours Is Mined

See page **T23** for a complete correlation of this book with the

NATIONAL SCIENCE EDUCATION STANDARDS.

TECHNOLOGY RESOURCES

 Guided Reading Audio CD English or Spanish, Chapter 1

 One-Stop Planner CD-ROM with Test Generator

 CNN. **Eye on the Environment,** Greening Sudbury, Segment 12

 Earth Science Videodisc Composition of the Earth: 32233–44060 Chemical Elements: 32234–37845 Minerals of the Earth's Crust: 37846–44060

CLASSROOM WORKSHEETS, TRANSPARENCIES, AND RESOURCES	SCIENCE INTEGRATION AND CONNECTIONS	REVIEW AND ASSESSMENT
Directed Reading Worksheet **Science Puzzlers, Twisters & Teasers**		
Directed Reading Worksheet, Section 1 **Transparency 107,** Gold Crystal Structure	**Connect to Life Science,** p. 4 in ATE **Biology Connection,** p. 6 **Connect to Chemistry,** p. 6 in ATE **Multicultural Connection,** p. 6 in ATE **Holt Anthology of Science Fiction,** *The Metal Man*	**Homework,** p. 6 in ATE **Section Review,** p. 7 **Quiz,** p. 7 in ATE **Alternative Assessment,** p. 7 in ATE
Directed Reading Worksheet, Section 2 **Reinforcement Worksheet,** Mystery Mineral **Transparency 108,** Mohs' Hardness Scale **Transparency 109,** Special Properties of Some Minerals **Reinforcement Worksheet,** The Mineral Quiz Show	**Multicultural Connection,** p. 10 in ATE **Real-World Connection,** p. 11 in ATE	**Section Review,** p. 11 **Quiz,** p. 11 in ATE **Alternative Assessment,** p. 11 in ATE
Directed Reading Worksheet, Section 3 **Transparency 210,** The Three Major Categories of Elements **Math Skills for Science Worksheet,** Percentages, Fractions, and Decimals **Critical Thinking Worksheet,** Mineral Hunt	**Connect to Life Science,** p. 13 in ATE **Cross-Disciplinary Focus,** p. 13 in ATE **Multicultural Connection,** p. 13 in ATE **MathBreak,** How Pure is Pure? p. 14 **Math and More,** p. 14 in ATE **Connect to Physical Science,** p. 14 in ATE **Multicultural Connection,** p. 14 in ATE **Weird Science:** Lightning Leftovers, p. 22	**Self-Check,** p. 13 **Section Review,** p. 15 **Quiz,** p. 15 in ATE **Alternative Assessment,** p. 15 in ATE

 **internet connect**

 go. hrw .com **Holt, Rinehart and Winston On-line Resources**

go.hrw.com

For worksheets and other teaching aids related to this chapter, visit the HRW Web site and type in the keyword: **HSTMIN**

 SCiLINKS **NSTA** **National Science Teachers Association**

www.scilinks.org

Encourage students to use the *sci*LINKS numbers listed in the internet connect boxes to access information and resources on the **NSTA** Web site.

END-OF-CHAPTER REVIEW AND ASSESSMENT

Chapter Review in Study Guide
Vocabulary and Notes in Study Guide
Chapter Tests with Performance-Based Assessment, Chapter 1 Test
Chapter Tests with Performance-Based Assessment, Performance-Based Assessment 1
Concept Mapping Transparency 3

Chapter Resources & Worksheets

Visual Resources

TEACHING TRANSPARENCIES

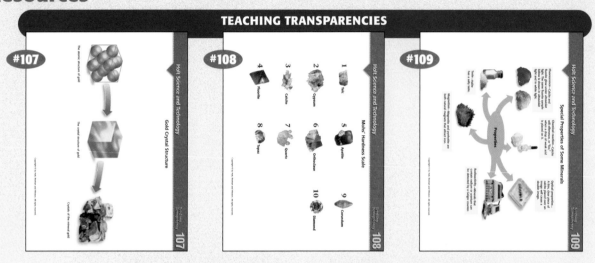

#107 — Gold Crystal Structure

#108 — Mohs' Hardness Scale

#109 — Special Properties of Some Minerals

TEACHING TRANSPARENCIES

#210 — The Three Major Categories of Elements

LINK TO PHYSICAL SCIENCE

CONCEPT MAPPING TRANSPARENCY

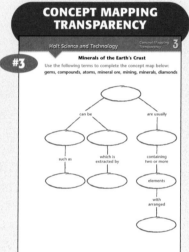

#3 — Minerals of the Earth's Crust
Use the following terms to complete the concept map below:
gems, compounds, atoms, mineral ore, mining, minerals, diamonds

Meeting Individual Needs

DIRECTED READING

#1 — DIRECTED READING WORKSHEET
Minerals of the Earth's Crust

REINFORCEMENT & VOCABULARY REVIEW

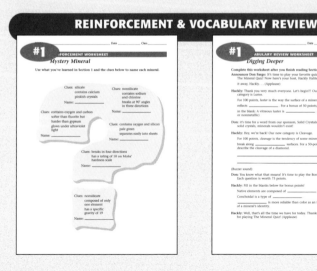

#1 — REINFORCEMENT WORKSHEET
Mystery Mineral

#1 — VOCABULARY REVIEW WORKSHEET
Digging Deeper

SCIENCE PUZZLERS, TWISTERS & TEASERS

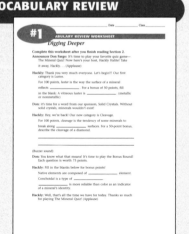

#1 — SCIENCE PUZZLERS, TWISTERS & TEASERS
Minerals of the Earth's Crust

Chapter 1 • Minerals of the Earth's Crust

Review & Assessment

STUDY GUIDE

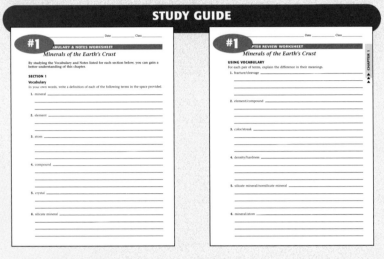

CHAPTER TESTS WITH PERFORMANCE-BASED ASSESSMENT

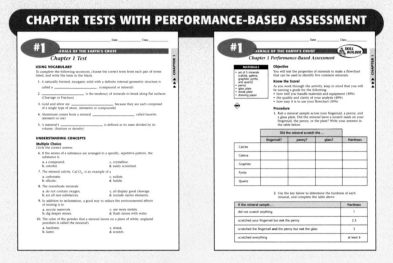

Lab Worksheets

LONG-TERM PROJECTS & RESEARCH IDEAS

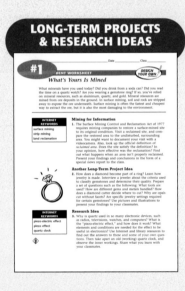

DATASHEETS FOR LABBOOK

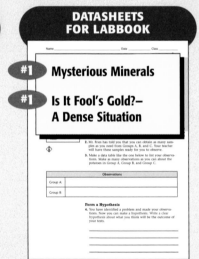

Applications & Extensions

CRITICAL THINKING & PROBLEM SOLVING

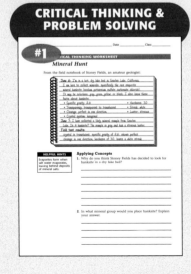

EYE ON THE ENVIRONMENT

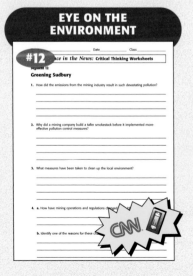

SECTION 1

What Is a Mineral?

▶ Crystal Structures

Minerals are composed of atoms that are arranged in repeating three-dimensional patterns. The basic building block of a mineral crystal is called a unit cell. A unit cell is the smallest three-dimensional arrangement of atoms that displays the basic form, or symmetry, of the crystal. Many unit cells stacked together form a crystal. For example, a crystal of halite is composed of unit cells of sodium and chlorine atoms arranged in a unique three-dimensional structure.

▶ The Origins of Mineralogy

The founder of mineralogy is considered to be Georgius Agricola. His treatise on minerals, *De Re Metallica* (1556), recorded most of what was known about minerals at that time. The science of mineralogy advanced greatly when Rome de l'Isle, a French scientist, proposed the concept of the unit cell in 1772. He argued that the characteristics of mineral crystals could be explained only if they were composed of identical unit cells organized in a predictable way. Crystals are composed of unit cells much like a wall might be composed of bricks. After that discovery, the composition of mineral crystals was actively studied by many scientists.

▶ Industrial Uses of Crystals

The properties of crystals make them useful in countless ways. The electronics industry uses quartz in the manufacture of radios, watches, microphones, and sonar transducers. Rubies are used in lasers and as ball bearings in record players and watches, while diamonds are used in industrial drills and saws.

IS THAT A FACT!

- ➤ Currently about 3,600 minerals have been identified, and about 50 new minerals are discovered each year.

SECTION 2

Identifying Minerals

▶ Methods of Identifying Minerals

Scientists usually identify minerals using one of the following three methods.

- The *hand-specimen* method involves determining the color, luster, streak, cleavage, hardness, fluorescence, density, and magnetic qualities of a mineral.

- When geologists take samples back to the lab, they often use *petrographic microscopes* to identify minerals. These microscopes make it easier to identify minerals by the optical properties of their crystals. The image below is a photograph taken with a petrographic microscope of a metamorphic rock called *schist*. The clear mineral grains are quartz, and the more textured, colorful ones are muscovite mica.

- Geologists can analyze minerals at the atomic level by using *X-ray diffraction,* which measures the way crystal structures diffract X rays.

▶ Mohs' Hardness Scale

Friedrich Mohs (1773–1839) was a mineralogist who lived in Vienna, Austria. In 1812, Mohs developed a method for identifying minerals based on their relative hardness. He proposed that a mineral's identity can be determined by comparing the mineral with several minerals of known hardness. A mineral can scratch another mineral of equal or lesser hardness, but it cannot scratch a mineral of greater hardness.

▶ Gemstones

Of the 3,600 known minerals, only about 100 can be cut and polished to become gemstones. The definition of a gemstone is any naturally occurring mineral, rock, or organic material that, when cut and polished, is suitable for use as jewelry. Diamonds, emeralds, rubies, and topazes are usually referred to as precious stones. Amethysts, garnets, and jades are considered semiprecious. Materials such as coral, pearls, and amber are also considered gemstones, even though they form by organic processes.

- Many gems used in jewelry are imitations. For example, glass can be colored green to look like an emerald. Scientists also create some gems artificially. Synthetic rubies, for example, have the same chemical structure as natural rubies. However, a gemologist can identify synthetic rubies by the presence of curved growth striations and air pockets, which do not occur in natural rubies.

IS THAT A FACT!

- ➤ The largest gold nugget ever found had a mass of 71 kg! It was found in Australia on February 5, 1869.

- ➤ One of the world's largest rubies has a mass of 8,500 carats and is cut to resemble the Liberty Bell.

SECTION 3

The Formation and Mining of Minerals

▶ Ancient Mines

The earliest evidence of mining dates to a 43,000-year-old iron mine in South Africa. Early iron miners were probably interested in the pigments associated with iron ores. The earliest metals used by neolithic people were gold and copper. Archaeological evidence indicates that the Egyptians mined copper and turquoise around

3400 B.C. Although most of the earliest mining was conducted on the surface, underground mining did occur by 1300 B.C. in Africa.

▶ Intrusions and Mineral Formation

Plutons are bodies of igneous rock that cooled beneath the Earth's surface. They are composed of coarse-grained, interlocking crystals. A large area of exposed intrusive rock (greater than 100 km²) is called a batholith. Large batholiths occur in British Columbia, Alaska, and in the Sierra Nevada.

- A pegmatite is a very coarse-grained intrusive rock formed from the fluid-rich magma that remains after the rest of a pluton has solidified. Pegmatites may contain minerals such as tourmaline, topaz, or beryl.

▶ The Hope Diamond

The Hope diamond is a 45.5 carat blue diamond owned by the Smithsonian Institution since 1958. The gem was thought to be cursed because it was allegedly stolen from a statue of the Hindu goddess Sita. Misfortune and tragedy seemed to befall those who came in contact with the stone. The fabled gem was originally 112 carats. It was sold to King Louis XIV in 1668, and named the French Blue. The French Blue was stolen in 1792 from Louis XVI and may have been depicted in an 1800 portrait of a Spanish queen. In 1830, a 45.5 carat cut diamond surfaced in London. Experts declared that it was the French Blue recut to hide its identity. The American Henry Hope bought it, and it has since been called the Hope diamond.

IS THAT A FACT!

- ➤ The Wieliczka Salt Mine, in Poland, has more than 200 km of tunnels and is carved entirely out of halite (rock salt). Rock salt has been mined there since the late thirteenth century. The mine contains a number of sculptures, statues, altars, and even a chapel—all carved from salt!

For background information about teaching strategies and issues, refer to the *Professional Reference for Teachers.*

Minerals of the Earth's Crust

Pre-Reading Questions

Students may not know the answers to these questions before reading the chapter, so accept any reasonable response.

Suggested Answers

1. A mineral is a naturally occurring inorganic solid that has a crystalline structure.

2. Minerals form when salt water evaporates; they can crystallize out of a solution; and they form when magma solidifies.

CHAPTER 1

Minerals of the Earth's Crust

Sections

Pre-Reading
Questions

1. What is a mineral?
2. How do minerals form?

2

Cave Curtains

Look at the lacy hanging mineral formations in this photo of a limestone cavern. These *stalactites* were formed from dripping water that contained a dissolved mineral, calcium bicarbonate. The mineral reacted with air and hardened into another mineral compound, calcium carbonate. Sometimes called dripstone, such mineral formations may have many colors caused by the presence of yet other minerals in the dripping water. In this chapter, you will learn how mineral compounds form and how they are classified.

---

internet connect

**HRW
On-line
Resources**

go.hrw.com
For worksheets and other teaching aids, visit the HRW Web site and type in the keyword: **HSTMIN**

NSTA

www.scilinks.com
Use the *sci*LINKS numbers at the end of each chapter for additional resources on the **NSTA** Web site.

Smithsonian
Institution®

www.si.edu/hrw
Visit the Smithsonian Institution Web site for related on-line resources.

CNNfyi.com.

www.cnnfyi.com
Visit the CNN Web site for current events coverage and classroom resources.

RIDING A MINERAL?

More than 3,000 different minerals occur naturally on Earth. What is a mineral? Do the following activity, and see if you can figure it out.

Procedure

1. In your ScienceLog, make two columns—one for minerals and one for nonminerals.

2. Ask your classmates what ideas they have about the materials that make up a motorcycle. Take notes as you gather information.

3. Based on what you already know about minerals, classify the materials in a motorcycle into things that come from minerals and things that come from nonminerals.

Analysis

4. Based on your list, is most of a motorcycle made of minerals or nonminerals?

5. Where do you think the minerals that make a motorcycle come from?

RIDING A MINERAL
Teacher's Notes

Display some photos of different types of motorcycles from magazines or books to help students make their classifications. Encourage them to take notes.

Materials that are minerals or are derived from minerals include glass headlights and any metal objects. Plastic and rubber objects are not minerals.

Answers to START-UP Activity

4. Most of the materials are metals, which come from minerals.

5. Answers will vary. Metals come from metal ore minerals, such as hematite, magnetite, beryl, and cuprite.

3

Focus

What Is a Mineral?

This section explores the nature of minerals by describing their four characteristics. Students learn that mineral crystals are generated by atomic structures, and they learn how to classify minerals in two major compositional groups—silicates and nonsilicates.

Bellringer

Display a piece of pencil lead (graphite) and a photograph of a diamond. Explain that both substances are composed of carbon. Ask students to brainstorm about how two substances with such different properties can form from atoms of the same element.

1 Motivate

GROUP ACTIVITY

Identifying Minerals Place an assortment of objects on a table. Possibilities include a piece of wood, a fossil, a piece of bone, a piece of granite, and a quartz crystal. Divide the class into groups of two or three students. Tell the students to examine the objects and to determine which ones are minerals by using the four questions on this page. Sheltered English

Directed Reading
Worksheet Section 1

Terms to Learn

mineral   crystal
element   silicate mineral
atom   nonsilicate mineral
compound

What You'll Do

◆ Explain the four characteristics of a mineral.
◆ Classify minerals according to the two major compositional groups.

What Is a Mineral?

Not all minerals look like gems. In fact, most of them look more like rocks. But are minerals the same as rocks? Well, not really. So what's the difference? For one thing, rocks are made of minerals, but minerals are not made of rocks. Then what exactly is a mineral? By asking the following four questions, you can tell whether something is a mineral:

Is it a solid?
Minerals can't be gases or liquids.

Is it formed in nature?
Crystalline materials made by people aren't classified as minerals.

Does it have a crystalline structure?
Minerals are crystals, which have a repeating inner structure that is often reflected in the shape of the crystal. Minerals generally have the same chemical composition throughout.

Is it nonliving material?
A mineral is inorganic, meaning it isn't made of living things.

How many elements does it take to "set" the periodic table? Find out by turning to page 202.

A **mineral** is a naturally formed, inorganic solid with a crystalline structure. If you cannot answer "yes" to all four questions above, you don't have a mineral.

Minerals: From the Inside Out

Three of the four questions might be easy to answer. The one about crystalline structure may be more difficult. In order to understand what crystalline structure is, you need to know a little about the elements that make up a mineral. **Elements** are pure substances that cannot be broken down into simpler substances by ordinary chemical means. All minerals contain one or more of the 92 elements present in the Earth's crust.

CONNECT TO
LIFE SCIENCE

Guide students in a discussion of the importance minerals have to life on Earth. Display a bone, a bottle of mineral supplements, and a plant. Ask students to brainstorm about how these objects are related to minerals. Explain to students that minerals, which are inorganic, provide essential nutrients to living things and are the building blocks of organisms.

• Bones are largely made of microscopic apatite crystals.

• Diatoms, which are microscopic organisms, have silica crystals in their cell walls.

Atoms and Compounds Each element is made of only one kind of atom. An **atom,** as you may recall, is the smallest part of an element that has all the properties of that element. Like all other substances, minerals are made up of atoms of one or more elements.

Most minerals are made of compounds of several different elements. A **compound** is a substance made of two or more elements that have been chemically joined, or bonded together. Halite, for example, is a compound of sodium and chlorine, as shown in **Figure 1.** A few minerals, such as gold and silver, are composed of only one element. For example, pure gold is made up of only one kind of atom—gold.

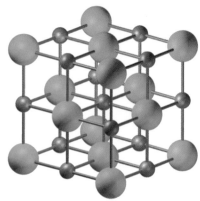

Figure 1 *Atoms of sodium and chlorine are joined together in a compound commonly known as rock salt, or the mineral halite.*

Crystals A mineral is also made up of one or more crystals. **Crystals** are solid, geometric forms of minerals produced by a repeating pattern of atoms that is present throughout the mineral. A crystal's shape is determined by the arrangement of the atoms within the crystal. The arrangement of atoms in turn is determined by the kinds of atoms that make up the mineral. Each mineral has a definite crystalline structure. All minerals can be grouped into crystal classes according to the kinds of crystals they form. **Figure 2** shows how the atomic structure of gold gives rise to cubic crystals.

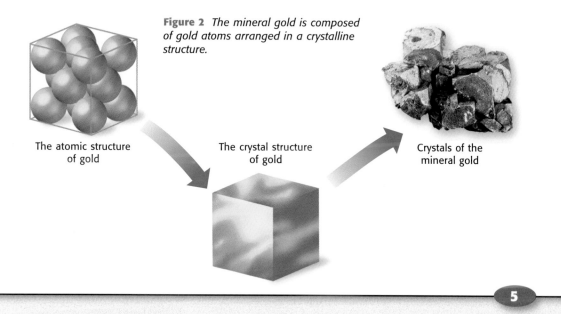

Figure 2 *The mineral gold is composed of gold atoms arranged in a crystalline structure.*

The atomic structure of gold

The crystal structure of gold

Crystals of the mineral gold

In much the same way that color is a deceptive guide to identifying minerals, crystal form is often a misleading physical property. The crystal structures of halite and gold shown on this page are atomic structures. When different unit cells are combined, however, they can generate crystal forms that look nothing like their atomic structure. A large variety of complex crystal shapes can be generated by starting with a simple polyhedron, such as a cube. For example, the mineral fluorite belongs in the isometric (cubic) class but commonly forms octahedral-shaped crystals.

DISCUSSION

Rocks and Minerals Students may benefit from a discussion of the differences between rocks and minerals. Stress that rocks are composed of minerals, but minerals are not composed of rock. It is possible for a rock to be made of just one mineral or many. Minerals should also not be confused with mineraloids. Mineraloids are similar to minerals, but they have no crystalline structure. Some common mineraloids are obsidian, limonite, flint, and opal. Sheltered English

USING SCIENCE FICTION

Have students read "The Metal Man" by Jack Williamson in *The Holt Anthology of Science Fiction*. As you discuss the story in class, tell students that the story was written in the 1920s when the phenomenon of radioactivity was poorly understood. Have students consider how our knowledge of radioactivity has increased since that time.

GROUP ACTIVITY

Writing At the beginning of this section, give pairs of students an unknown mineral. Tell students that their goal will be to identify the mineral by the end of the chapter and to present a short report on it. Their reports should include the chemical formula of the mineral, detail the mineral's uses and properties, and explain what type of rock the mineral occurs in.

Teaching Transparency 107
"Gold Crystal Structure"

ACTIVITY

Microscope Work
Sand forms from the breakdown of rock over many years. Most sand is composed of the mineral quartz. Distribute magnifying lenses or microscopes to student groups, and invite them to examine samples of sand, rock salt, granulated salt, and sugar to compare the crystalline structure of each. Have students record what they see in their ScienceLog.

USING THE FIGURE

After students study the examples shown in **Figure 3,** distribute samples of granite, feldspar, quartz, and mica to students for close examination. Encourage students to record their observations in their ScienceLog and to note differences and similarities.
Sheltered English

CONNECT TO CHEMISTRY

The way atoms bond together gives a mineral its properties. For example, carbon atoms that are bonded in one way form graphite, which is commonly used for pencil lead, while carbon atoms that are bonded in another way form diamonds. Have students research the chemical composition and structure of different minerals and find out how the minerals are used. Ask students to make a model that shows the atomic structure of a unit cell of a simple mineral, such as halite, pyrite, galena, or quartz.

Biology CONNECTION

Several species of animals have a brain that contains the mineral magnetite. Magnetite has a special property—it is magnetic. Scientists have shown that certain fish can sense magnetic fields because they have magnetite in their brain. The magnetite gives the fish a sense of direction.

Types of Minerals

Minerals can be classified by a number of different characteristics. The most common classification of minerals is based on chemical composition. Minerals are divided into two groups based on the elements they are composed of. These groups are the silicate minerals and the nonsilicate minerals.

Silicate Minerals   Silicon and oxygen are the two most common elements in the Earth's crust. Minerals that contain a combination of these two elements are called **silicate minerals.** Silicate minerals make up more than 90 percent of the Earth's crust—the rest is made up of nonsilicate minerals. Silicon and oxygen usually combine with other elements, such as aluminum, iron, magnesium, and potassium, to make up silicate minerals. Some of the more common silicate minerals are shown in **Figure 3.**

Feldspar Feldspar minerals make up about half the Earth's crust, and they are the main component of most rocks on the Earth's surface. They contain the elements silicon and oxygen along with aluminum, potassium, sodium, and calcium.

Biotite Mica Mica minerals are shiny and soft, and they separate easily into sheets when they break. Biotite is but one of several varieties of mica.

Quartz Quartz (silicon dioxide, SiO_2) is the basic building block of many rocks. If you look closely at the piece of granite, you can see the quartz crystals.

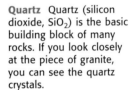

Figure 3 *Granite is a rock composed of various minerals, including feldspar, mica, and quartz.*

Multicultural CONNECTION

The first recorded use of sandpaper dates to thirteenth-century China, when crushed seashells were bound to parchment with a natural adhesive from trees. Today sandpaper is commonly made from aluminum oxide, garnet, or quartz. Interested students can make their own sandpaper at home and share it with the class.

Homework

At Home With Minerals Ask students to find four items in their home that are derived from minerals. Have them share their findings with the class on the following day. (Examples include table salt, composed of halite; pencil lead, composed of graphite; cooking pots, composed of iron, copper, or aluminum; and jewelry.)

Nonsilicate Minerals Minerals that do not contain a combination of the elements silicon and oxygen form a group called the **nonsilicate minerals.** Some of these minerals are made up of elements such as carbon, oxygen, iron, and sulfur. Below are several categories of nonsilicate minerals.

Classes of Nonsilicate Minerals

Native elements are minerals that are composed of only one element. About 20 minerals are native elements. Some examples are gold (Au), platinum (Pt), diamond (C), copper (Cu), sulfur (S), and silver (Ag).

Native copper

Carbonates are minerals that contain combinations of carbon and oxygen in their chemical structure. Calcite ($CaCO_3$) is an example of a carbonate mineral. We use carbonate minerals in cement, building stones, and fireworks.

Calcite

Halides are compounds that form when atoms of the elements fluorine, chlorine, iodine, or bromine combine with sodium, potassium, or calcium. Halite (NaCl) is better known as rock salt. Fluorite (CaF_2) can have many different colors. Halide minerals are often used to make fertilizer.

Fluorite

Oxides are compounds that form when an element, such as aluminum or iron, combines chemically with oxygen. Corundum (Al_2O_3) and magnetite (Fe_3O_4) are important oxide minerals. Oxide minerals are used to make abrasives and aircraft parts.

Corundum

Sulfates contain sulfur and oxygen (SO_4). The mineral gypsum ($CaSO_4 \cdot 2H_2O$) is a common sulfate. It makes up the white sand at White Sands National Monument, in New Mexico. Sulfates are used in cosmetics, toothpaste, and paint.

Gypsum

Sulfides are minerals that contain one or more elements, such as lead, iron, or nickel, combined with sulfur. Galena (PbS) is a sulfide. Sulfide minerals are used to make batteries, medicines, and electronic parts.

Galena

SECTION REVIEW

1. What are the differences between atoms, compounds, and minerals?

2. Which two elements are most common in minerals?

3. How are silicate minerals different from nonsilicate minerals?

4. **Making Inferences** Explain why each of the following is not considered a mineral: a cupcake, water, teeth, oxygen.

internet**connect**

SCILINKS
NSTA

TOPIC: Gems
GO TO: www.scilinks.org
sciLINKS NUMBER: HSTE055

7

---

3) Extend

RESEARCH

Writing From about 200 B.C. to A.D. 1700, alchemists explored the boundaries of chemistry and philosophy. They dedicated their lives to discovering a chemical reaction that would change common metals into precious gold and silver. Despite their unscientific methods, alchemists contributed a great deal to the development of the science we now call chemistry. Even Sir Isaac Newton devoted much of his life to pursuing alchemy. Challenge interested students to research the history of alchemy and to present a report to the class.

4) Close

Quiz

1. What is a mineral? (a naturally formed, inorganic solid with a crystalline structure)

2. What does a crystal's shape depend on? (the arrangement of the atoms within the crystal)

ALTERNATIVE ASSESSMENT

Write the following mineral-group names on the board: silicates, native elements, carbonates, halides, oxides, sulfates, and sulfides. Have students match the following items with the mineral group from which they are derived: a copper penny (native elements); cement (carbonates); rock salt (halides); oxide sandpaper (oxides); toothpaste (sulfates); batteries (sulfides); sand (silicates).

SECTION 2
READING WARM-UP

Focus

Identifying Minerals

In this lesson, students will learn some of the common techniques used to identify minerals. The section also examines some of the interesting properties of minerals, such as fluorescence, radioactivity, and magnetism.

Bellringer

Ask students to consider the question posed at the beginning of this section. Students should list as many phrases as they can to describe each mineral shown. Have students organize these phrases into different categories, such as *color, shape,* and *luster.* Students can use these comparisons to determine whether or not the samples are actually the same mineral. (The mineral on the left is a yellow variety of garnet. The mineral on the right is a "diamond in the rough.")

1 Motivate

COOPERATIVE LEARNING

Ask students to work in small groups to determine a classification system for minerals based on observable physical properties. Give groups a number of minerals or photographs of a variety of minerals. Students should create a classification system based on observable differences and similarities among the samples. After groups have developed a classification system, give them several new samples, and have them place the samples in their classification scheme.

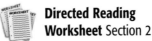
Directed Reading Worksheet Section 2

Terms to Learn

luster   fracture
streak   hardness
cleavage   density

What You'll Do

◆ Classify minerals using common mineral-identification techniques.
◆ Explain special properties of minerals.
◆ Describe what makes a mineral crystal a gem.

Luster Chart

Metallic	Submetallic

Nonmetallic

Vitreous glassy, brilliant	**Silky** swirly, fibrous
Resinous plastic	**Waxy** greasy, oily
Pearly creamy	**Earthy** rough, dull

8

Identifying Minerals

If you found the two mineral samples below, how would you know if they were the same mineral?

By looking at these minerals, you can easily see physical similarities. But how can you tell whether they are the same mineral? Moreover, how can you determine the identity of a mineral? In this section you will learn about the different properties that can help you identify minerals.

Color

Minerals come in many different colors and shades. The same mineral can come in a variety of colors. For example, in its purest state quartz is clear. Quartz that contains small amounts of impurities, however, can be a variety of colors. Rose quartz gets its color from certain kinds of impurities. Amethyst, another variety of quartz, is purple because it contains other kinds of impurities.

Besides impurities, other factors can change the appearance of minerals. The mineral pyrite, often called fool's gold, normally has a golden color. But if pyrite is exposed to weather for a long period, it turns black. Because of factors such as weathering and impurities, color usually is not a reliable indicator of a mineral's identity.

Luster

The way a surface reflects light is called **luster.** When you say an object is shiny or dull, you are describing its luster. Minerals have metallic, submetallic, or nonmetallic luster. If a mineral is shiny, it may have either a glassy or a metallic luster. If the mineral is dull, its luster is either submetallic or nonmetallic. The different types of lusters are shown in the chart at left.

How can you tell a real diamond from a fake? A gem specialist uses specialized tools to distinguish real diamonds from impostors. But there are some tests that even an untrained person can conduct.

One of the simplest is to try to pick up the stone in question with a moistened fingertip. Diamonds can be picked up this way; most other stones cannot.

Streak

The color of a mineral in powdered form is called the mineral's **streak.** To find a mineral's streak, the mineral is rubbed against a piece of unglazed porcelain called a streak plate. The mark left on the streak plate is the streak. The color of a mineral's streak is not always the same as the color of the mineral sample, as shown in **Figure 4.** Unlike the surface of a mineral sample, the streak is not affected by weathering. For this reason, streak is more reliable than color as an indicator of a mineral's identity.

Cleavage and Fracture

Different types of minerals break in different ways. The way a mineral breaks is determined by the arrangement of its atoms. **Cleavage** is the tendency of some minerals to break along flat surfaces. Gem cutters take advantage of natural cleavage to remove flaws from certain minerals, such as diamonds and rubies, and to shape them into beautiful gemstones. **Figure 5** shows minerals with different cleavage patterns.

Fracture is the tendency of some minerals to break unevenly along curved or irregular surfaces. One type of fracture is shown in **Figure 6.**

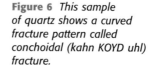

Figure 4 *The color of the mineral hematite may vary, but its streak is always red-brown.*

Figure 5 *Cleavage varies with mineral type. Mica breaks easily into distinct sheets. Halite breaks at 90° angles in three directions. Diamond breaks in four different directions.*

Diamond

Halite

Mica

Figure 6 *This sample of quartz shows a curved fracture pattern called conchoidal (kahn KOYD uhl) fracture.*

9

IS THAT A FACT!

During the black plague of the fourteenth century, opals developed a reputation for being unlucky gems. People thought that opals became brilliant when the wearer caught the plague and dulled when the person died!

internetconnect

SCILINKS
NSTA

TOPIC: Identifying Minerals
GO TO: www.scilinks.org
*sci*LINKS NUMBER: HSTE065

3 Extend

QuickLab

MATERIALS

FOR EACH STUDENT:
• penny
• pencil

Answer to QuickLab

3. The penny is the hardest material of the three, followed by the fingernail and then the mineral graphite.

READING STRATEGY

Mnemonics Have students create a mnemonic device that will help them learn Mohs' hardness scale. One example is **T**errible **G**iants **C**an **F**ind **A**lligators **O**r **Q**uaint **T**igers **C**onveniently **D**igestible. This will help students remember the minerals in order of hardness: **t**alc, **g**ypsum, **c**alcite, **f**luorite, **a**patite, **o**rthoclase feldspar, **q**uartz, **t**opaz, **c**orundum, and **d**iamond. Ask students to brainstorm for several mnemonic devices and share them with the class. Sheltered English

Multicultural CONNECTION

Jade is a mineral that has great importance in China. According to Chinese mythology, jade is a symbol of life and it possesses protective powers. Jade is actually the name given to two minerals—jadeite and nephrite—that rank between 6.5 and 7 on Mohs' hardness scale. Have students find out about the cultural significance of jade and how it was carved without metal tools.

QuickLab

Scratch Test

1. You will need a **penny,** a **pencil,** and your **fingernail.** Which one of these three materials is the hardest?
2. Use your fingernail to try to scratch the graphite at the tip of a pencil.
3. Now try to scratch the penny with your fingernail. Which is the hardest of the three?

TRY at HOME

Hardness

Hardness refers to a mineral's resistance to being scratched. If you try to scratch a diamond, you will have a tough time because diamond is the hardest mineral. Talc, on the other hand, is one of the softest minerals. You can scratch it with your fingernail. To determine the hardness of minerals, scientists use *Mohs' hardness scale,* shown below. Notice that talc has a rating of 1 and diamond has a rating of 10. Between these two extremes are other minerals with progressively greater hardness.

To identify a mineral using Mohs' scale, try to scratch the surface of a mineral with the edge of one of the 10 reference minerals. If the reference mineral scratches your mineral, it is harder than your mineral. Continue trying to scratch the mineral until you find a reference mineral that cannot scratch your mineral.

Mohs' Hardness Scale

1 Talc 2 Gypsum 3 Calcite

4 Fluorite 5 Apatite 6 Orthoclase 7 Quartz

8 Topaz 9 Corundum 10 Diamond

Density

Figure 7 *Because a golf ball has a greater density than a table-tennis ball, more table-tennis balls are needed to balance the scale.*

If you pick up a golf ball and a table-tennis ball, which will feel heavier? Although the balls are of similar size, the golf ball will feel heavier because it is denser, as shown in **Figure 7.** **Density** is the measure of how much matter there is in a given amount of space. In other words, density is a ratio of an object's mass to its volume. Density is usually measured in grams per cubic centimeter. Because water has a density of 1 g/cm^3, it is used as a reference point for other substances. The ratio of an object's density to the density of water is called the object's *specific gravity.* The specific gravity of gold, for example, is 19. This means that gold has a density of 19 g/cm^3. In other words, there is 19 times more matter in 1 cm^3 of gold than in 1 cm^3 of water.

 Teaching Transparency 108 "Mohs' Hardness Scale"

 Teaching Transparency 109 "Special Properties of Some Minerals"

Comparative Hardness Scale

Hardness	Common material
Less than 2.5	mineral that marks paper
2.5	fingernail
3	copper penny
5	steel knife blade
6.5	steel file

Special Properties

Some properties are particular to only a few types of minerals. The properties below can quickly help you identify the minerals shown. To identify some properties, however, you will need specialized equipment.

Fluorescence—Calcite and fluorite glow under ultraviolet light. The same fluorite sample below is shown in ultraviolet light and in white light.

Chemical reaction—Calcite will effervesce, or "fizz," when a drop of weak acid is placed on it.

Optical properties—A thin, clear piece of calcite placed over an image will cause a double image.

Special Properties of Some Minerals

Taste—Halite has a salty taste.

Magnetism—Magnetite and pyrrhotite are both natural magnets that attract iron.

Radioactivity—Minerals that contain radium or uranium can be detected by a Geiger counter.

SECTION REVIEW

1. How do you determine a mineral's streak?

2. What is the difference between cleavage and fracture?

3. How would you determine the hardness of an unidentified mineral sample?

4. **Applying Concepts** Suppose you have two minerals that have the same hardness. Which other mineral properties would you use to determine whether the samples are the same mineral?

For a list of minerals and their properties, see page 206.

11

Is It Fool's Gold?—A Dense Situation

REAL-WORLD CONNECTION

Invite a jeweler to visit the class, and ask the jeweler to explain how gemstones are made into jewelry. The jeweler could bring in visual aids to help students understand how gems are located, mined, and prepared for commercial use.

4 Close

Quiz

1. Why is color not always a reliable way of identifying a mineral? (Factors such as weathering and the inclusion of impurities can affect the mineral's color.)

2. What property do minerals that glow under ultraviolet light display? (fluorescence)

ALTERNATIVE ASSESSMENT

Have students prepare mineral identification cards for some of the most common minerals. They can list the words *color, luster, hardness, streak, cleavage and fracture,* and *density* on each card. For each card, ask them to fill in the properties of a common mineral. Students should write the name of the mineral on the back of the card and use the cards as study aids or assessment tools. **Sheltered English**

Reinforcement Worksheet
"The Mineral Quiz Show"

▼ Answers to Section Review

1. Scrape the mineral across a ceramic streak plate. The color of the material that rubs off the mineral sample is the mineral's streak.

2. If a mineral has cleavage, it breaks along flat surfaces. Fracture is the way a mineral breaks along curved or irregular surfaces.

3. To determine the hardness of an unknown mineral sample, take a material of known hardness and try to scratch the unknown mineral with it. If the unknown mineral is scratched, try to scratch it with a material that has a lower hardness. Continue with this process until you know which materials are harder and which are softer than the unknown mineral sample. The hardness of the unknown mineral is between these two.

4. Answers will vary but should not include color.

Focus

The Formation and Mining of Minerals

This section discusses how minerals form deep within Earth's crust as well as close to the surface. Students will learn about different techniques used to mine minerals. This section concludes with a discussion of the value of mineral resources and the importance of ecologically responsible mining and reclamation.

 **Bellringer**

Ask students to write briefly on this statement:

"The meek shall inherit the Earth but not the mineral rights."

Discuss students' responses, and ask them what they would do if valuable minerals were discovered on property they owned.

1 Motivate

DISCUSSION

Simulate the Gold Rush To simulate the excitement of the gold rush of 1849, make up a flyer that tells of a rich gold deposit found in a nearby area. Make copies and pass them out to students to read. Discuss with students what their reactions are to such an announcement. Then discuss the chaotic enthusiasm of the gold rush: from 1848 to 1860, the population in California grew from 14,000 to 380,000!

 Directed Reading Worksheet Section 3

Terms to Learn

ore
reclamation

What You'll Do

- Describe the environments in which minerals are formed.
- Compare and contrast the different types of mining.

The Formation and Mining of Minerals

Almost all known minerals can be found in the Earth's crust. They form in a large variety of environments under a variety of physical and chemical conditions. The environment in which a mineral forms determines the mineral's properties. Minerals form both deep beneath the Earth's surface and on or near the Earth's surface.

Evaporating Saltwater When a body of salt water dries up, minerals such as gypsum and halite are left behind. As the salt water evaporates, these minerals crystallize.

Limestones Surface water and ground water carry dissolved materials into lakes and seas, where they crystallize on the bottom. Minerals that form in this environment include calcite and dolomite.

Metamorphic Rocks When changes in pressure, temperature, or chemical makeup alter a rock, *metamorphism* takes place. Minerals that form in metamorphic rock include calcite, garnet, graphite, hematite, magnetite, mica, and talc.

Heat and Pressure

12

WEIRD SCIENCE

Some of the greatest untapped sources of minerals are hydrothermal vents deep under the sea. These hydrothermal vents are called black smokers because they spew out hot, mineral-rich water that is almost black. As the hot water mixes with the cool ocean water, minerals crystallize and form nodules on the ocean floor. These mineral deposits contain significant amounts of manganese, copper, zinc, gold, and silver, but no one has figured out an economical way to mine them yet.

Hot-water Solutions Ground water works its way downward and is heated by magma. It then reacts with minerals to form a hot liquid solution. Dissolved metals and other elements crystallize out of the hot fluid to form new minerals. Gold, copper, sulfur, pyrite, and galena form in such hot-water environments.

Pegmatites As magma moves upward it can form teardrop-shaped bodies called *pegmatites.* The presence of hot fluids causes the mineral crystals to become extremely large, sometimes growing to several meters across! Many gems, such as topaz and tourmaline, form in pegmatites.

Plutons As magma rises upward through the crust, it sometimes stops moving before it reaches the surface and cools slowly, forming millions of mineral crystals. Eventually, the entire magma body solidifies to form a *pluton.* Mica, feldspar, magnetite, and quartz are some of the minerals that form from magma.

Magma

13

✔ Self-Check

Where do minerals such as gypsum and halite form? *(See page 216 to check your answer.)*

 Multicultural
C O N N E C T I O N

Halite, or rock salt, is perhaps the most important mineral to human civilization. The word *salt* is derived from the Latin word *sal.* Instead of money, Roman soldiers were paid their salary, or *salarium,* in salt. Have students research the Tibetan salt trade or the use of iodized salt to correct thyroid deficiencies.

 internet**connect**

 SCI**LINKS**
NSTA

TOPIC: Mining Minerals
GO TO: www.scilinks.org
*sci***LINKS NUMBER:** HSTE070

② Teach

Answer to Self-Check

These minerals form wherever salt water has evaporated.

CONNECT TO
LIFE SCIENCE

The Surface Environment and Mining (SEAM) program was established by the U.S. Forest Service in 1973 to address the issue of land reclamation in the wake of mining operations. Since then, this highly successful program has returned vast areas of land formerly used for mining to its original condition. The most recent SEAM projects can be researched on the Internet. To research local reclamation efforts, students could contact local conservation groups listed in the phone directory.

CROSS-DISCIPLINARY FOCUS

History Encourage students to learn more about the social and environmental effects of mining by having each student create a scrapbook detailing the history of a mining community. Students should research the history of a community from the discovery of ore to the present. Students' scrapbooks should include drawings and photographs showing changes in the community as well as text describing the history of the area. Have students focus on the types of ore extracted, the use and value of the ore in the world market, and the impact mining has had on the people and environment of the area. Possible communities include: Leadville, Colorado; Butte, Montana; and the Yanomami Indian tribes of Brazil and Venezuela. Have students share their scrapbooks with the class.

MATH and MORE

To produce 1 metric ton of coal, up to 30 metric tons of earth must first be removed or stripped. Some strip mines produce up to 50,000 metric tons of coal a day. How many metric tons of earth could be removed in order to mine 50,000 metric tons of coal?
(1,500,000 metric tons)

Answer to MATHBREAK

$\frac{18}{24} = \frac{3}{4} = 75\%$ pure

CONNECT TO
PHYSICAL SCIENCE

Referring to the chart on the following page, discuss with students that minerals are valuable because of the properties of the elements that are in them. Elements can be divided into three major groups: *metals, nonmetals,* and *metalloids.* Use the Teaching Transparency below to discuss how the characteristics of each element group make the minerals they are found in useful to human cultures.

 Teaching Transparency 210 "The Three Major Categories of Elements" *LINK TO PHYSICAL SCIENCE*

 Math Skills Worksheet "Percentages, Fractions, and Decimals"

MATH BREAK

$\div$ 5 $\div$ Ω $\leq$ ∞ $+$ Ω $\sqrt{}$ 9 ∞ $\leq$ Σ 2

How Pure Is Pure?

Gold classified as 24-karat is 100 percent gold. Gold classified as 18-karat is 18 parts gold and 6 parts another, similar metal. It is therefore $18/24$ or $3/4$ pure. What is the percentage of pure gold in 18-karat gold?

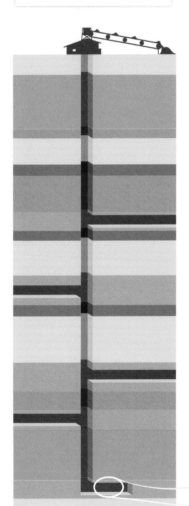

Mining

Many kinds of rocks and minerals must be mined in order to extract the valuable elements they contain. Geologists use the term **ore** to describe a mineral deposit large enough and pure enough to be mined for a profit. Rocks and minerals are removed from the ground by one of two methods—surface mining or deep mining. The method miners choose depends on how far down in the Earth the mineral is located and how valuable the ore is. The two types of mining are illustrated below.

Surface mining is the removal of minerals or other materials at or near the Earth's surface. Types of surface mines include open pits, strip mines, and quarries. Materials mined in this way include copper ores and bauxite, a mixture of minerals rich in aluminum.

Deep mining is the removal of minerals or other materials from deep within the Earth. Passageways must be dug underground to reach the ore. The retrieval of diamonds and coal commonly requires deep mining.

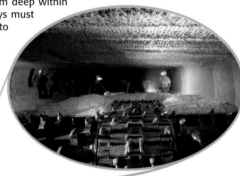

14

MISCONCEPTION
///ALERT\\\\

The mass of gems is measured using a unit called the *carat.* This should not be confused with the *karat* used to measure the purity of gold. A 1-carat diamond crystal has a mass of 200 mg. This is approximately the same as the mass of one children's aspirin. A one karat gold nugget is one twenty-fourth pure gold.

🌐 Multicultural
CONNECTION

The mining of gold, copper, and iron in southeastern Africa helped build the empire of Great Zimbabwe, which arose during the mid-thirteenth century and lasted until about the middle of the fifteenth century. Invite students to find out more about mining techniques in Great Zimbabwe and about the Karanga people who ruled then.

The Value of Minerals

Many of the metals you are familiar with originally came from mineral ores. You may not be familiar with the minerals, but you will probably recognize the metals extracted from the minerals. The table at right lists some mineral ores and some of the familiar metals that come from them.

As you have seen, some minerals are highly valued for their beauty rather than for their usefulness. Mineral crystals that are attractive and rare are called gems, or gemstones. An example of a gem is shown in **Figure 8**. Gems must be hard enough to be cut and polished.

Common Uses of Minerals		
Mineral	**Metal**	**Uses**
Chalcopyrite	copper	coins, electrical wire
Galena	lead	batteries, paints
Beryl	beryllium	bicycle frames, airplanes
Chromite	chromium	stainless steel, cast iron, leather tanners

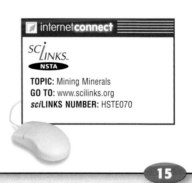

Figure 8 *The Cullinan diamond, at the center of this scepter, is part of the largest diamond ever found.*

Responsible Mining

Mining gives us the minerals we need, but it also creates problems. Mining can destroy or disturb the habitats of plants and animals. The waste products from a mine can get into water sources, polluting both surface water and ground water.

One way to reduce the harmful effects of mining is to return the land to its original state after the mining is completed. This process is called **reclamation.** Reclamation of mined public land has been required by law since the mid-1970s. But reclamation is an expensive and time-consuming process. Another way to reduce the effects of mining is to reduce our need for minerals. We do this by recycling many of the mineral products we currently use, such as aluminum and iron. Mineral ores are *nonrenewable resources;* therefore, the more we recycle, the more we will have in the future.

SECTION REVIEW

1. Describe how minerals form underground.

2. What are the two main types of mining?

3. **Analyzing Ideas** How does reclamation protect the environment around a mine?

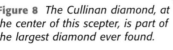

internet**connect**

SC*LINKS*
NSTA

TOPIC: Mining Minerals
GO TO: www.scilinks.org
*sci*LINKS NUMBER: HSTE070

15

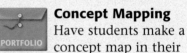

Mysterious Minerals
Teacher's Notes

Time Required

One 45-minute class period

Lab Ratings

EASY ———————————→ HARD

TEACHER PREP 🧪🧪
STUDENT SET-UP 🧪🧪
CONCEPT LEVEL 🧪🧪
CLEAN UP 🧪

MATERIALS

The materials listed on the student page are sufficient for each student. Students may also work in groups of 3–4. A class should be able to share 3–5 streak plates.

Safety Caution

Remind students to review all safety cautions and icons before beginning this lab activity. Students need to be careful with glass microscope slides. Broken slides are likely to have sharp edges. Caution students not to taste the mineral samples.

Preparation Notes

Explain to students that they are not determining the absolute hardness of the mineral samples. Instead they are comparing the hardness of the samples with that of glass.

Your sample minerals should include pyrite, galena, hematite, magnetite, orthoclase (feldspar), quartz, muscovite, gypsum, hornblende (amphibole), garnet, biotite, and graphite.

Mysterious Minerals

Imagine sitting on a rocky hilltop, gazing at the ground below you. You can see dozens of different types of rocks. How can scientists possibly identify the countless variations? It's a mystery! In this activity you'll use your powers of observation and a few simple tests to determine the identities of rocks and minerals.

MATERIALS

• several sample minerals
• glass microscope slides
• streak plate
• safety gloves
• iron filings

Procedure

1. In your ScienceLog, create a data chart like the one below. Choose one mineral sample. Follow the Mineral Identification Key to find the identity of your sample. When you are finished, record the mineral's name and primary characteristics in the appropriate column in your data chart.
Caution: Put on your gloves when scratching the glass slide.

2. Select another mineral sample, and repeat the process until your data table is complete.

Mineral Summary Chart						
Characteristics	1	2	3	4	5	6
Mineral name						
Luster						
Color						
Streak						
Hardness						
Cleavage						
Special properties						

DO NOT WRITE IN BOOK

16

Lab Notes

Each test in this lab tells the student more about the sample and narrows the possibilities. For example, the fact that a particular mineral sample does not have a streak eliminates hematite as a possibility but indicates that quartz is a possibility.

It is possible for minerals that are softer than glass to leave a mark on glass. If the glass wipes clean and no scratch remains, then students will know that the mineral is softer than glass.

Garnet is typically red but it can also be pale green.

Analysis

3 Were some minerals easier to identify than others? Explain.

4 A streak test is a better indicator of a mineral's true color than visual observation. Why isn't a streak test used to help identify every mineral?

5 In your ScienceLog, summarize what you learned about the various characteristics of each mineral sample you identified.

Mineral Identification Key

1. **a.** If your mineral has a metallic luster, **GO TO STEP 2.**
   b. If your mineral has a nonmetallic luster, **GO TO STEP 3.**

2. **a.** If your mineral is black, **GO TO STEP 4.**
   b. If your mineral is yellow, it is **PYRITE.**
   c. If your mineral is silver, it is **GALENA.**

3. **a.** If your mineral is light in color, **GO TO STEP 5.**
   b. If your mineral is dark in color, **GO TO STEP 6.**

4. **a.** If your mineral leaves a red-brown line on the streak plate, it is **HEMATITE.**
   b. If your mineral leaves a black line on the streak plate, it is **MAGNETITE.** Test your sample for its magnetic properties by holding it near some iron filings.

5. **a.** If your mineral scratches the glass slide, **GO TO STEP 7.**
   b. If your mineral does not scratch the glass slide, **GO TO STEP 8.**

6. **a.** If your mineral scratches the glass slide, **GO TO STEP 9.**
   b. If your mineral does not scratch the glass slide, **GO TO STEP 10.**

7. **a.** If your mineral shows signs of cleavage, it is **ORTHOCLASE FELDSPAR.**
   b. If your mineral does not show signs of cleavage, it is **QUARTZ.**

8. **a.** If your mineral shows signs of cleavage, it is **MUSCOVITE.** Examine this sample for twin sheets.
   b. If your mineral does not show signs of cleavage, it is **GYPSUM.**

9. **a.** If your mineral shows signs of cleavage, it is **HORNBLENDE.**
   b. If your mineral does not show signs of cleavage, it is **GARNET.**

10. **a.** If your mineral shows signs of cleavage, it is **BIOTITE.** Examine this sample for twin sheets.
    b. If your mineral does not show signs of cleavage, it is **GRAPHITE.**

Going Further

Using your textbook and other reference books, research other methods of identifying different types of minerals. Based on your findings, create a new identification key. Give it to a friend along with a few sample minerals, and see if your friend can unravel the mystery!

Answers

3. Students will find that some minerals required fewer steps to identify than others. For example, pyrite and galena are identified in two steps. Students may also find that they recognize some of the minerals and that the identification key is there merely to verify the identity.

4. For a mineral to leave a streak on the streak plate, the plate must be harder than the mineral. Therefore, extremely hard minerals do not leave a streak. Alternatively, some minerals that are softer than a streak plate leave behind a colorless streak.

5. Answers will vary.

Going Further

Scientists test minerals for their density, crystal form, reaction to acids, optical properties, fluorescence, and radio-activity. Students should create an identification key that is very similar to the one provided in the lab, but their key should include different characteristics.

 Datasheets for LabBook

David Jones
Andrew Jackson Middle School
Cross Lanes, West Virginia

CLASSROOM TESTED & APPROVED

17

Chapter Highlights

Chapter Highlights

VOCABULARY DEFINITIONS

SECTION 1

mineral a naturally formed, inorganic solid with a crystalline structure

element a pure substance that cannot be separated or broken down into simpler substances by ordinary chemical means

atom the smallest part of an element that has all of the properties of that element

compound a pure substance made of two or more elements that have been chemically joined, or bonded together

crystal the solid, geometric form of a mineral produced by a repeating pattern of atoms

silicate mineral a mineral that contains a combination of the elements silicon and oxygen

nonsilicate mineral a mineral that does not contain compounds of silicon and oxygen

SECTION 2

luster the way the surface of a mineral reflects light

streak the color of a mineral in powdered form

cleavage the tendency of a mineral to break along flat surfaces

fracture the tendency of a mineral to break along curved or irregular surfaces

hardness the resistance of a mineral to being scratched

density the amount of matter in a given space; mass per unit volume

---

SECTION 1

Vocabulary

- **mineral** (p. 4)
- **element** (p. 4)
- **atom** (p. 5)
- **compound** (p. 5)
- **crystal** (p. 5)
- **silicate mineral** (p. 6)
- **nonsilicate mineral** (p. 7)

Section Notes

- A mineral is a naturally formed, inorganic solid with a definite crystalline structure.

- An atom is the smallest unit of an element that retains the properties of the element.

- A compound forms when atoms of two or more elements bond together chemically.

- Every mineral has a unique crystalline structure. The crystal class a mineral belongs to is directly related to the mineral's chemical composition.

- Minerals are classified as either silicates or nonsilicates. Each group includes different types of minerals.

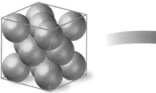 

SECTION 2

Vocabulary

- **luster** (p. 8)
- **streak** (p. 9)
- **cleavage** (p. 9)
- **fracture** (p. 9)
- **hardness** (p. 10)
- **density** (p. 10)

Section Notes

- Color is not a reliable indicator for identifying minerals.

- The luster of a mineral can be metallic, submetallic, or nonmetallic.

- A mineral's streak does not necessarily match its surface color.

- The way a mineral breaks can be used to determine its identity. Cleavage and fracture are two ways that minerals break.

☑ Skills Check

Math Concepts

THE PURITY OF GOLD The karat is a measure of the purity of gold. Gold that is 24 karats is 100 percent gold. But gold that is less than 24 karats is mixed with other elements, so it is less than 100 percent gold. If you have a gold nugget that is 16 karats, then 16 parts out of 24 are pure gold—the other 8 parts are composed of other elements.

> 24 karats = 100% gold
> 16 karats = 24 karats − 8 karats
> $\frac{16}{24} = \frac{2}{3} = 0.67 = 67\%$ gold

Visual Understanding

ATOMIC STRUCTURE This illustration of the atomic structure of the mineral halite shows that halite is made of two elements—sodium and chlorine. The large spheres represent atoms of chlorine, and the small spheres represent atoms of sodium. The bars between the atoms represent the chemical bonds that hold them together.

18

Lab and Activity Highlights

Mysterious Minerals `PG 16`

Is It Fool's Gold?— A Dense Situation `PG 176`

 Datasheets for LabBook (blackline masters for these labs)

SECTION 2

- Mohs' hardness scale provides a numerical rating for the hardness of minerals.

- The density of a mineral can be used to identify it.

- Some minerals have special properties that can be used to quickly identify them.

Labs

Is It Fool's Gold?—A Dense Situation (p. 176)

SECTION 3

Vocabulary

ore (p. 14)

reclamation (p. 15)

Section Notes

- Minerals form in both underground environments and surface environments.

- Two main types of mining are surface mining and deep mining.

- Minerals are valuable because metals can be extracted from them and because some of them can be cut to form gems.

- Reclamation is the process of returning mined land to its original state.

---

internet**connect**

 GO TO: go.hrw.com

Visit the **HRW** Web site for a variety of learning tools related to this chapter. Just type in the keyword:

KEYWORD: HSTMIN

  GO TO: www.scilinks.org

Visit the **National Science Teachers Association** on-line Web site for Internet resources related to this chapter. Just type in the *sci*LINKS number for more information about the topic:

TOPIC:		*sci*LINKS NUMBER:
Gems		HSTE055
Birthstones		HSTE060
Identifying Minerals		HSTE065
Mining Minerals		HSTE070

19

Lab and Activity Highlights

LabBank

Long-Term Projects & Research Ideas,
What's Yours Is Mined

Chapter Review
Answers

USING VOCABULARY

1. If a mineral breaks along a curved or irregular surface, it has fracture. If a mineral breaks along flat surfaces, it has cleavage.
2. Elements are made of only one kind of atom, while compounds are made of two or more elements that are chemically bonded.
3. Streak is the color of a mineral in powdered form. The color of a mineral may change, but the mineral's streak is always the same.
4. The hardness of a mineral is its resistance to being scratched, while the density of a mineral is a measure of the amount of matter in a given space.
5. Silicate minerals are made of silicon and oxygen compounds, while nonsilicate minerals are made of other compounds.
6. A mineral is made up of a particular arrangement of different kinds of atoms.

UNDERSTANDING CONCEPTS

Multiple Choice

7. d
8. a
9. d
10. d
11. d
12. b
13. b

Chapter Review

USING VOCABULARY

For each pair of terms, explain the difference in their meaning.

1. fracture/cleavage
2. element/compound
3. color/streak
4. density/hardness
5. silicate mineral/nonsilicate mineral
6. mineral/atom

UNDERSTANDING CONCEPTS

Multiple Choice

7. On Mohs' hardness scale, which of the following minerals is harder than quartz?
   a. talc
   b. apatite
   c. gypsum
   d. topaz

8. A mineral's streak
   a. is more reliable than color in identifying a mineral.
   b. reveals the mineral's specific gravity.
   c. is the same as a luster test.
   d. reveals the mineral's crystal structure.

9. Which of the following factors is **not** important in the formation of minerals?
   a. heat
   b. volcanic activity
   c. presence of ground water
   d. wind

10. Which of the following terms is **not** used to describe a mineral's luster?
    a. pearly
    b. waxy
    c. dull
    d. hexagonal

11. Which of the following is considered a special property that applies to only a few minerals?
    a. color
    b. luster
    c. streak
    d. magnetism

12. Which of the following physical properties can be expressed in numbers?
    a. luster
    b. hardness
    c. color
    d. reaction to acid

13. Which of the following minerals would scratch fluorite?
    a. talc
    b. quartz
    c. gypsum
    d. calcite

Short Answer

14. Using no more than 25 words, define the term *mineral*.

15. In one sentence, describe how density is used to identify a mineral.

16. What methods of mineral identification are the most reliable? Explain.

Concept Mapping

17. Use the following terms to create a concept map: minerals, oxides, nonsilicates, carbonates, silicates, hematite, calcite, quartz.

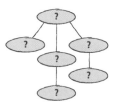

Short Answer

14. A mineral is a naturally occurring inorganic solid with a crystalline structure.
15. Each mineral has its own unique density.
16. Answers will vary. Cleavage, hardness, and density are very reliable because they can be measured and do not change. Color and fracture are less reliable.

Concept Mapping

17. An answer to this exercise can be found at the front of this book.

CRITICAL THINKING AND PROBLEM SOLVING

Write one or two sentences to answer the following questions:

18. Suppose you have three rings, each with a different gem. One has a diamond, one has an amethyst (purple quartz), and one has a topaz. You mail the rings in a small box to your friend who lives five states away. When the box arrives at its destination, two of the gems are damaged. One gem, however, is damaged much worse than the other. What scientific reason can you give for the difference in damage?

19. While trying to determine the identity of a mineral, you decide to do a streak test. You rub the mineral across the plate, but it does not leave a streak. Does this mean your test failed? Explain your answer.

20. Imagine that you work at a jeweler's shop and someone brings in some "gold nuggets" that they want to sell. The person claims that an old prospector found the gold nuggets during the California gold rush. You are not sure if the nuggets are real gold. How would you decide whether to buy the nuggets? Which identification tests would help you decide the nuggets' identity?

21. Suppose that you find a mineral crystal that is as tall as you are. What kinds of environmental factors would cause such a crystal to form?

MATH IN SCIENCE

22. Gold has a specific gravity of 19. Pyrite's specific gravity is 5. How much denser is gold than pyrite?

23. In a quartz crystal there is one silicon atom for every two oxygen atoms. That means that the ratio of silicon atoms to oxygen atoms is 1:2. If there were 8 million oxygen atoms in a sample of quartz, how many silicon atoms would there be?

INTERPRETING GRAPHICS

Imagine that you had a sample of feldspar and analyzed it to find out what it is made of. The results of your analysis are shown below.

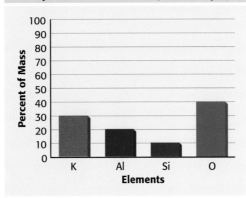

Composition of Orthoclase (Pink Feldspar)

24. Your sample consists of four elements. What percentage of each one is your sample made of?

25. If your mineral sample has a mass of 10 g, how many grams of oxygen does it contain?

26. Make a circle graph showing how much of each of the four elements the feldspar contains. (You will find help on making circle graphs in the Appendix of this book.)

Reading Check-up

Take a minute to review your answers to the Pre-Reading Questions found at the bottom of page 2. Have your answers changed? If necessary, revise your answers based on what you have learned since you began this chapter.

CRITICAL THINKING AND PROBLEM SOLVING

18. Each mineral has a different hardness. The hardest mineral was damaged the least. (The diamond will not be damaged, the topaz will be slightly damaged, and the amethyst will sustain the most damage.)

19. No; the test was actually successful. You learned that the unknown mineral has no streak and that it is harder than the streak plate. This clue will help you classify the mineral.

20. Students should suggest performing several tests to see whether the mineral is gold or not. Gold is very dense and soft, so one would start with density and hardness tests.

21. Answers will vary. When magma contains a lot of hot fluids and cools slowly, very large crystals can grow.

MATH IN SCIENCE

22. Gold is $\frac{19}{5} = 3\frac{4}{5}$, or 3.8 times as dense as pyrite.

23. $\frac{8 \text{ million}}{2} = 4$ million silicon atoms

INTERPRETING GRAPHICS

24. K: 30 percent
    Al: 20 percent
    Si: 10 percent
    O: 40 percent

25. 4 g

26. Answers will vary.

Concept Mapping Transparency 3

Blackline masters of this Chapter Review can be found in the **Study Guide.**

LIGHTNING LEFTOVERS

Background

Silica, also known as silicon dioxide, SiO_2, is a compound of the two most common elements in the Earth's crust, silicon and oxygen. Silica can take a variety of forms. Crystalline forms include quartz, agate, and amethyst. Noncrystalline forms include obsidian, flint, and opal. Silica is the primary ingredient of most commercial glasses and ceramics and is also used in cements and mortars.

Without warning, a bolt of lightning lashes out from a storm cloud and strikes a sandy shoreline with a crash. Almost instantly, the sky is dark again—the lightning has disappeared without a trace. Or has it?

Nature's Glass Factory

Fulgurites are a rare type of natural glass formed when lightning strikes silica-rich minerals that occur commonly in sand, soil, and some rocks. *Tubular fulgurites* are found in areas with a lot of silica, such as beaches or deserts. Lightning creates a tubular fulgurite when a bolt penetrates the sand and melts silica into a liquid. The liquid silica cools and hardens quickly, leaving behind a thin glassy tube, usually with a rough outer surface and a smooth inner surface. Underground, a fulgurite may be shaped like the roots of a tree. It branches out with many arms that trace the zigzag path of the lightning bolt. Some fulgurites are as short as your little finger, while others stretch 20 m into the ground.

Underground Puzzles

So should you expect to run across a fulgurite on your next trip to the beach? Don't count on it. Scientists and collectors search long and hard for the dark glass formations, which often form with little or no surface evidence pointing to their underground location. Even when a fulgurite is located, removing it in one piece is difficult. They are quite delicate, with walls no thicker than 1–2 mm. Some of the largest fulgurites are removed from the ground in many pieces then glued back into their original shape.

Rock Fulgurites

Rock fulgurites are extremely rare, usually occurring only on high mountains. These oddities are created when lightning strikes the surface of a silica-rich rock. A rock fulgurite often looks like a bubbly glass case 1–3 mm thick around the rock. Lightning travels around the outside of the rock, fusing silica-rich minerals on its surface. Depending on which minerals melt, a rock fulgurite's color can range from glassy black to light gray or even bright yellow.

Find Out More

▶ Investigate how scientists studying the formation of fulgurites try to make lightning bolts strike a precise location to create a new fulgurite. You may also want to do some research to find out about companies that will *create* a fulgurite just for you!

◀ *A Tubular Fulgurite*

22

Sample Answer to Find Out More

To learn more about how fulgurites form, scientists have to get lightning to strike where they can observe it. To attract lightning, scientists attach long metal wires to a rocket that is then shot into storm clouds, triggering a huge electrical spark. The bolt of lightning travels down the wire and into the ground. There, it comes in contact with silica, forming a fulgurite, which scientists then study. But scientific study is not the only reason to create a fulgurite: some companies sell custom-made fulgurites as natural works of art. You provide the sand, and they will fire the rocket and reel in a bolt of lightning, forming a fulgurite made just for you!

Science Fiction

"The Metal Man"

by Jack Williamson

In a dark, dusty corner of Tyburn College Museum stands a life-sized statue of a man. Except for its strange greenish color, the statue looks pretty ordinary. But if you look closely, you will marvel at the perfect detail of the hair and skin. You will also see a strange mark on the statue's chest, a dark crimson shape with six sides.

No one knows how the statue ended up in the dark corner. Everyone believes that the Metal Man is, or once was, Professor Thomas Kelvin of the Geology Department. Professor Kelvin had for many years spent his summer vacations along the Pacific coast of Mexico, prospecting for radium. Then at the end of one summer, Kelvin did not return to Tyburn. He had been more successful than he ever dreamed, and he had become very rich. But high in the mountains, he had also found something else . . .

Now there is only one person who knows what really happened to Professor Kelvin, and he tells the professor's story in "The Metal Man," by Jack Williamson. The tale involves Kelvin's expedition to search for the source of El Rio de la Sangre, the River of Blood, and the radium that makes the river radioactive. Did he find it? Is that what made Kelvin so rich? And what else did Professor Kelvin find there in the remote mountain valley?

Read for yourself the strange story of Professor Kelvin and the Metal Man in the *Holt Anthology of Science Fiction.*

23

Further Reading

Wonder's Child: My Life in Science Fiction, Bluejay, 1985

The Best of Jack Williamson, Ballantine, 1978

The Pandora Effect, Ace Books, 1969

SCIENCE FICTION
"The Metal Man"
by Jack Williamson

The Metal Man stands tall in the Tyburn College Museum, but it is no ordinary statue . . .

Teaching Strategy

Reading Level This compelling story will be a challenge for many students, but with some vocabulary help, they will enjoy this inventive work.

Background

About the Author Few people have had as long-lasting an impact on science fiction as Jack Williamson (1908–). This story, "The Metal Man," was first published in 1928—over 70 years ago! Although it was his very first short story, it is still a classic. Since then, Williamson has written dozens of science fiction novels, short-stories, other novels, and books about writing.

The term *science fiction* was not even around when Williamson began writing. Known as one of the great pioneers of science fiction, Williamson was the first to write about antimatter. In addition, he coined the terms *terraform* (in 1941) and *genetic engineering* (in 1951).

Williamson is also credited for legitimizing science fiction as a field worthy of literary attention. For this accomplishment, Williamson has received several awards. In 1976, he became the second person to win the Grand Master Nebula Award. In 1994, Williamson earned a lifetime achievement award from World Fantasy.

Chapter Organizer

CHAPTER ORGANIZATION	TIME MINUTES	OBJECTIVES	LABS, INVESTIGATIONS, AND DEMONSTRATIONS
Chapter Opener pp. 24–25	45	National Standards: SAI 1, ES 1d	**Start-Up Activity,** Classifying Objects, p. 25
Section 1 Understanding Rock	135	▶ Describe two ways rocks were used by early humans, and describe two ways they are used today. ▶ Describe how each type of rock changes into another as it moves through the rock cycle. ▶ List two characteristics of rock that are used to help classify it. UCP 1, SAI 1, ST 2, HNS 1, SPSP 5, ES 1d, 1k, 2b	**Labs You Can Eat,** Famous Rock Groups **Making Models,** Round and Round in Circles, p. 46 **Datasheets for LabBook,** Round and Round in Circles
Section 2 Igneous Rock	90	▶ Explain how the cooling rate of magma affects the properties of igneous rocks. ▶ Distinguish between igneous rock that cools deep within the crust and igneous rock that cools at the surface. ▶ Identify common igneous rock formations. UCP 1, ES 1c, 1d; Labs UCP 2, SAI 1	**Skill Builder,** Crystal Growth, p. 178 **Datasheets for LabBook,** Crystal Growth
Section 3 Sedimentary Rock	90	▶ Describe how the two types of sedimentary rock form. ▶ Explain how sedimentary rocks record Earth's history. UCP 1, ES 1c, 1d, 1k, 2b; Labs UCP 2, SAI 1	**Demonstration,** Dissolution of Minerals, p. 37 in ATE **Skill Builder,** Let's Get Sedimental, p. 182 **Datasheets for LabBook,** Let's Get Sedimental **Whiz-Bang Demonstrations,** Settling Down
Section 4 Metamorphic Rock	90	▶ Describe two ways a rock can undergo metamorphism. ▶ Explain how the mineral composition of rocks changes as they undergo metamorphism. ▶ Describe the difference between foliated and non-foliated metamorphic rock. UCP 1, 2, SAI 1, ST 2, HNS 3, ES 1d; Labs UCP 2, SAI 1	**QuickLab,** Stretching Out, p. 42 **Interactive Explorations CD-ROM,** Rock On! *A **Worksheet** is also available in the **Interactive Explorations Teacher's Edition.*** **Making Models,** Metamorphic Mash, p. 181 **Datasheets for LabBook,** Metamorphic Mash **Long-Term Projects & Research Ideas,** Home-Grown Crystals

*See page **T23** for a complete correlation of this book with the*

NATIONAL SCIENCE EDUCATION STANDARDS.

TECHNOLOGY RESOURCES

 Guided Reading Audio CD English or Spanish, Chapter 2

 One-Stop Planner CD-ROM with Test Generator

 Interactive Explorations CD-ROM CD 2, Exploration 6, Rock On!

 CNN. **Scientists in Action,** Meteor Collision Geologist, Segment 6

 Earth Science Videodisc Determining Relative Age: 331–6305 Field Trip—Understanding Rock Layers: 6306–22647

CLASSROOM WORKSHEETS, TRANSPARENCIES, AND RESOURCES	SCIENCE INTEGRATION AND CONNECTIONS	REVIEW AND ASSESSMENT
Directed Reading Worksheet **Science Puzzlers, Twisters & Teasers**	**Cross-Disciplinary Focus,** p. 25 in ATE	
Directed Reading Worksheet, Section 1 **Transparency 110,** The Rock Cycle **Math Skills for Science Worksheet,** Parts of 100: Calculating Percentages **Transparency 63,** The Digestive System of a Bird	**Cross-Disciplinary Focus,** pp. 27, 29 in ATE **Connect to Life Science,** pp. 27, 29, 31 in ATE **Multicultural Connection,** p. 28 in ATE **Real-World Connection,** p. 29 in ATE **Apply,** p. 30 **Math and More,** p. 31 in ATE **MathBreak,** What's in It? p. 31 **Science, Technology, and Society:** Rock City, p. 52	**Homework,** p. 31 in ATE **Section Review,** p. 32 **Quiz,** p. 32 in ATE **Alternative Assessment,** p. 32 in ATE
Directed Reading Worksheet, Section 2 **Transparency 111,** The Cooling Rate of Magma and the Texture of Igneous Rock **Transparency 112,** Intrusive Igneous Rock Formations	**Connect to Life Science,** p. 34 in ATE **Multicultural Connection,** p. 34 in ATE	**Self-Check,** p. 34 **Section Review,** p. 36 **Quiz,** p. 36 in ATE **Alternative Assessment,** p. 36 in ATE
Transparency 113, A Sedimentary Rock Cycle **Directed Reading Worksheet,** Section 3	**Connect to Life Science,** p. 38 in ATE **Real-World Connection,** p. 39 in ATE **Cross-Disciplinary Focus,** p. 39 in ATE	**Section Review,** p. 40 **Quiz,** p. 40 in ATE **Alternative Assessment,** p. 40 in ATE
Directed Reading Worksheet, Section 4 **Transparency 114,** Regional and Contact Metamorphism **Math Skills for Science Worksheet,** The Unit Factor and Dimensional Analysis **Reinforcement Worksheet,** What Is It? **Critical Thinking Worksheet,** Between a Rock and a Hard Place	**Cross-Disciplinary Focus,** p. 42 in ATE **Real-World Connection,** p. 43 in ATE **Math and More,** p. 44 in ATE **Biology Connection,** p. 45 **Health Watch:** Glass Scalpels, p. 53	**Self-Check,** p. 42 **Homework,** pp. 43, 44 in ATE **Section Review,** p. 45 **Quiz,** p. 45 in ATE **Alternative Assessment,** p. 45 in ATE

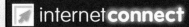 **internet connect**

 Holt, Rinehart and Winston On-line Resources

go.hrw.com

For worksheets and other teaching aids related to this chapter, visit the HRW Web site and type in the keyword: **HSTRCK**

 National Science Teachers Association

www.scilinks.org

Encourage students to use the *sci*LINKS numbers listed in the internet connect boxes to access information and resources on the **NSTA** Web site.

END-OF-CHAPTER REVIEW AND ASSESSMENT

Chapter Review in Study Guide
Vocabulary and Notes in Study Guide
Chapter Tests with Performance-Based Assessment, Chapter 2 Test
Chapter Tests with Performance-Based Assessment, Performance-Based Assessment 2
Concept Mapping Transparency 4

Chapter Resources & Worksheets

Visual Resources

TEACHING TRANSPARENCIES

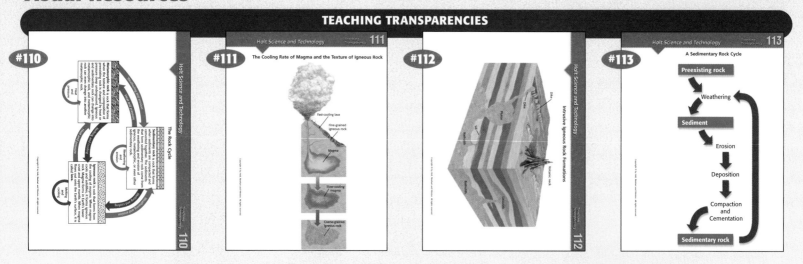

TEACHING TRANSPARENCIES

CONCEPT MAPPING TRANSPARENCY

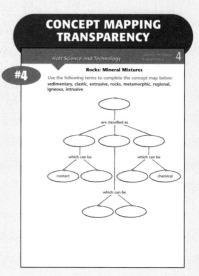

Meeting Individual Needs

DIRECTED READING

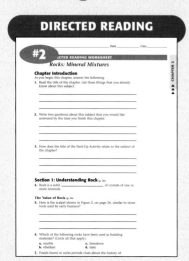

REINFORCEMENT & VOCABULARY REVIEW

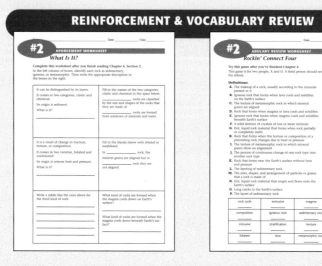

SCIENCE PUZZLERS, TWISTERS & TEASERS

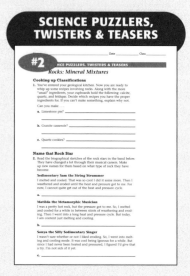

Chapter 2 • Rocks: Mineral Mixtures

Review & Assessment

STUDY GUIDE

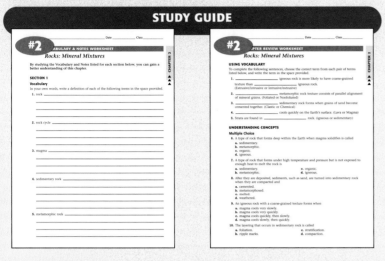

CHAPTER TESTS WITH PERFORMANCE-BASED ASSESSMENT

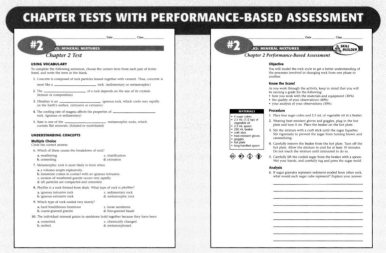

Lab Worksheets

LABS YOU CAN EAT

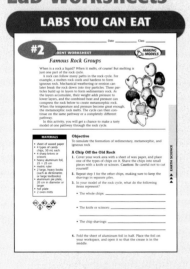

WHIZ-BANG DEMONSTRATIONS

LONG-TERM PROJECTS & RESEARCH IDEAS

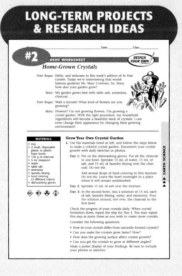

DATASHEETS FOR LABBOOK

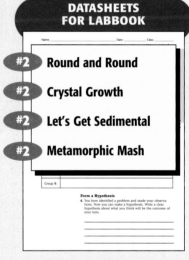

Applications & Extensions

CRITICAL THINKING & PROBLEM SOLVING

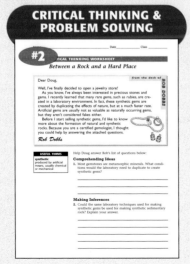

SCIENTISTS IN ACTION

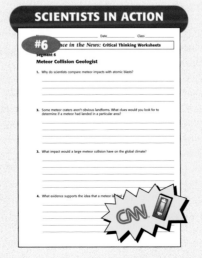

INTERACTIVE EXPLORATIONS

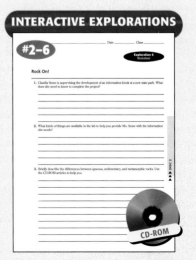

SECTION 1

Understanding Rock

▶ Rock Composition

This chapter focuses on the mineral composition of rock, not its bulk composition. These are two very different means of measuring rock composition.

- The *mineral composition* of a rock refers to the proportions of the different *minerals* in the rock and is usually expressed in percentages by volume. But not all rocks consist of minerals. For example, coal consists of organic matter and does not contain any minerals.

- The *bulk composition* of a rock is the sum of the different *elements* that make up the rock and is usually expressed in percentages by weight. Mineral composition is affected by bulk composition.

IS THAT A FACT!

- ▶ Although rocks contain many elements, the rocks in Earth's crust are nearly 94 percent oxygen by volume.

- ▶ Ninety-five percent of the outer 10 km of Earth is igneous and metamorphic rock.

- ▶ Although sedimentary rock makes up less than 5 percent of the Earth's crust, it is spread thinly over much of the planet's surface. Sedimentary rock covers 75 percent of the Earth's continental surfaces!

SECTION 2

Igneous Rock

▶ The Great Dike of Rhodesia

Dikes can range in width from a few millimeters to thousands of meters. The Great Dike of Rhodesia, in Africa, is the largest known dike on Earth. It has an average width of 10 km and extends for almost 600 km.

IS THAT A FACT!

- ▶ A common name for quartz is rock crystal. Its name comes from the Greek word *krystallos,* meaning "ice."

▶ Pumice

Some magmas contain dissolved gases such as carbon dioxide. When these gases come out of magma in the form of small bubbles, the magma greatly increases its volume, causing an enormous buildup of pressure. This results in a violent volcanic eruption. The result is a frothy-looking rock called pumice. Pumice is full of small holes called vesicles, where the trapped gases used to be. Depending on how much space is taken up by vesicles, some types of pumice can float in water!

- Pumice has a variety of industrial and household uses. Its abrasive qualities make it perfect for use in scouring and cleaning products. People use chunks of pumice in the bathtub to remove callouses from their feet.

IS THAT A FACT!

- ▶ Igneous rocks that form deep underground are called plutonic rocks, after Pluto, the god of the underworld in Roman mythology. Volcanic rocks are named after Vulcan, the Roman god of metalworking and fire.

- ▶ Although many people think of lava as a thin and runny liquid, lava flows are often quite viscous. Usually the temperature has cooled enough for crystals to begin forming, which can give lava a consistency similar to that of thick oatmeal.

SECTION 3

Sedimentary Rock

▶ **Working with Clay**

Clay is composed primarily of silicate minerals. Clays are easy to work with when they are wet because the tiny plate-shaped silicate crystals are trapped between water molecules. As the water evaporates, the silicates are cemented into place and the clay becomes brittle and difficult to work with.

IS THAT A FACT!

- Bentonite, a form of clay composed of very fine silicate crystals, has a wide variety of industrial applications. Some forms of bentonite can expand as much as 300 percent when mixed with water. Bentonite is used to make cat litter, to line artificial ponds, to remove impurities from wines and juices, to treat waste water, and in a variety of applications for oil drilling.

- The Mississippi River carries sediment from land as far away as the Appalachians and the Rocky Mountains. The Mississippi Delta, at the Gulf of Mexico, covers about 33,700 km². The delta has been forming for the last 2 million years.

SECTION 4

Metamorphic Rock

▶ **Foliated Rocks**

Foliated rocks develop during regional metamorphism. In slate, tiny flakes of mica line up into sheets. In some schists, mica forms dark or light layers, and the crystals are large enough to see. Gneiss has a coarse texture, and alternating layers are dominated by different minerals.

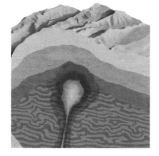

▶ **Metamorphosis in a Lab**

How do scientists determine the geologic history of a metamorphic rock? Geologists can estimate the temperature and pressure that metamorphosed a rock by simulating the process in a laboratory. When geologists know the chemical composition of certain minerals within a rock, they can subject a similar compound to a range of temperatures and pressures. By observing the laboratory results, they can make predictions about how similar materials behave in nature. Geologists can determine the temperature at which metamorphosis occurred within 20°C and the pressure within a fraction of a kilobar.

▶ **Carrara Marble**

In the mountains around Carrara, Italy, a marble prized for its purity has been quarried for at least 2,000 years. Its whiteness is due to the lack of organic materials in the limestone from which it recrystallized. Carrara marble was used in the interior of the Pantheon, in Rome. It is also found in the Leaning Tower of Pisa, in the pavement of Saint Peter's Basilica, in Vatican City, and in the Kennedy Center, in Washington, D.C.

IS THAT A FACT!

- Metamorphic rocks are a challenge to study because they form within a wide range of heat and pressure. Scientists must distinguish between the geologic history of the metamorphic rock and the history of the igneous, sedimentary, or previously metamorphosed rocks it formed from. For the same reason, however, metamorphic rocks offer many important clues about tectonic activity in the Earth's past.

- Metamorphism occurs quickly at high temperatures, but it also occurs at temperatures that are surprisingly low. For example, clay minerals in mudstone and shale can begin to metamorphose at temperatures as low as 50°C! This reaction, however, takes many millions of years to occur.

For background information about teaching strategies and issues, refer to the *Professional Reference for Teachers.*

 Pre-Reading Questions

Students may not know the answers to
these questions before reading the chapter, so accept any reasonable response.

Suggested Answers

1. A mineral is an inorganic crystalline solid with a definite chemical composition. A rock is a solid
   mixture of one or more minerals
   or organic materials like coal.

2. Answers will vary. Rocks are used
   as surgical blades and building
   materials and are studied to learn
   about the history of Earth and
   other planets.

3. There are many ways a rock can
   form: when magma cools and
   solidifies, when sediments or the
   remains of organisms are
   deposited and cemented
   together, when minerals crystallize out of sea water, or when the
   composition or texture of a preexisting rock changes due to heat
   or pressure.

Sections

 Pre-Reading
Questions

1. What is the difference
   between a rock and a
   mineral?

2. What are some modern
   uses of rocks?

3. How does rock form?

⟐ internet**connect**

 **HRW
On-line
Resources**

go.hrw.com

For worksheets and other
teaching aids, visit the HRW
Web site and type in the
keyword: **HSTRCK**

SCILINKS™
NSTA

www.scilinks.com

Use the *sci*LINKS numbers
at the end of each chapter
for additional resources
on the **NSTA** Web site.

Smithsonian
Institution®

www.si.edu/hrw

Visit the Smithsonian
Institution Web site for
related on-line resources.

CNN**fyi**.com.

www.cnnfyi.com

Visit the CNN Web site for
current events coverage
and classroom resources.

STEPS FOR A GIANT?

Irish legend claims that the mythical hero Finn MacCool built the Giant's Causeway, shown here. According to legend, these stepping stones were used to cross the sea in order to invade a neighboring island. Actually, this rock formation is the result of the cooling of huge amounts of molten rock. As the molten rock cooled, it formed tall, hexagonal pillars called *columnar joints*. Columnar joints can be seen in basalt rocks around the world. In this chapter, you will learn more about how rocks form.

START-UP Activity

CLASSIFYING OBJECTS

Scientists use the physical and chemical properties of rocks to classify them. Classifying objects such as rocks requires close attention to many properties. Do this exercise to get some classifying practice.

Procedure

1. Your teacher will give you a **bag containing several objects**. Examine the objects and note features such as size, color, shape, texture, smell, and any unique properties.

2. Invent three different ways to sort these objects. You may have only one group or as many as 14.

3. Create an identification key explaining how you organized the objects into each group.

Analysis

4. What properties did you use to sort the items?

5. Were there any objects that could fit into more than one group? How did you solve this problem?

6. Which properties might you use to classify rocks? Explain your answer.

START-UP Activity

CLASSIFYING OBJECTS

MATERIALS
FOR EACH GROUP: • bag of objects, such as an apple, a lemon, a green ball, a sugar cube, a pair of sunglasses, a piece of chalk, a paper clip, a plastic spoon, a pencil, a pen, a ruler, a rock, a twig, a tissue, an eraser, a screw, and a nail.

Answers to START-UP Activity

4. Answers will vary. Sample answer: I sorted the objects by color, size, and what they are made of.

5. Answers will vary. Sample answer: Yes, there were objects that could fit into more than one group. I solved this problem by deciding which characteristics were more important and sorting the object into a matching group.

6. Answers will vary. Accept all reasonable responses. Students may mention color, texture, luster, and hardness.

25

Focus

Understanding Rock

In this section students learn about the variety of ways rocks are used in human civilization. The section explains the rock cycle and introduces the three types of rock: igneous, sedimentary, and metamorphic. Students learn how each type of rock forms and that rocks are classified by texture and mineral composition.

📻 Bellringer

Ask students to make a list of the ways rock is used in their life. Encourage them to think of imaginative answers.

(People use rock to sharpen knives; make gardens or borders in yards; produce fertilizer; carve statues; create jewelry; and construct buildings, roads, and sidewalks.)

Sheltered English

1 Motivate

ACTIVITY

Have students examine samples of various types of rock and take notes on their characteristics, such as texture, color, weight, and composition. Then divide the class into groups of four. Groups should hypothesize about how each rock formed and suggest three different uses for each type of rock.

Directed Reading Worksheet Section 1

Terms to Learn

rock   texture
rock cycle   igneous rock
magma   sedimentary rock
composition   metamorphic rock

What You'll Do

◆ Describe two ways rocks were used by early humans, and describe two ways they are used today.
◆ Describe how each type of rock changes into another as it moves through the rock cycle.
◆ List two characteristics of rock that are used to help classify it.

Understanding Rock

The Earth's crust is made up mostly of rock. But what exactly is rock? **Rock** is simply a solid mixture of crystals of one or more minerals. However, some types of rock, such as coal, are made of organic materials. Rocks come in all sizes—from pebbles to formations thousands of kilometers long!

The Value of Rock

Rock has been an important natural resource as long as humans have existed. Early humans used rocks as hammers to make other tools. They discovered that they could make arrowheads, spear points, knives, and scrapers by carefully hammering flint, chert, and obsidian rocks. See **Figure 1**. These rocks were shaped to form extremely sharp edges and points. Even today, obsidian is used to form special scalpels, as shown in **Figure 2**.

Rock has also been used for centuries to make buildings, roads, and monuments. **Figure 3** shows some inventive uses of rock by both ancient and modern civilizations. Buildings have been made out of marble, granite, sandstone, limestone, and slate. Modern buildings also use concrete, in which rock is an important ingredient. Concrete is one of the most common building materials used today.

Figure 1 *This stone tool was made and used more than 5,000 years ago.*

Figure 2 *This stone tool was made recently. It is an obsidian scalpel used in delicate operations.*

Figure 3 *These photos show a few samples of structures built with rock. On this page are structures built by ancient civilizations. On the facing page are some more-modern examples.*

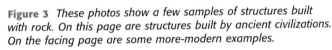

Pyramids at Giza, Egypt (3000 B.C.)

Machu Picchu, Peru (A.D. 600)

SCIENCE HUMOR

In 1976, Gary Dahl of California began marketing Pet Rocks. They came in a carrying case with a training manual and a pedigree that certified that they came from a California beach. In no time at all, more than 1 ton of the stones were sold. People held Pet Rock beauty contests and bought specialized foods and beds for them. There were even Pet Rock cemeteries!

Humans have a long history with rock. Certain types of rock have helped us to survive and to develop both our ancient and modern civilizations. Rock is also very important to scientists. The study of rocks helps answer questions about the history of the Earth and our solar system. Rocks provide a record of what the Earth and other planets were like before recorded history.

The fossils some rocks contain also provide clues about life-forms that lived billions of years ago, long before dinosaurs walked the Earth. **Figure 4** shows how rocks can capture evidence of life that became extinct long ago. Without such fossils, scientists would know very little about the history of life on Earth. The answers we get from studying rocks often cause us to ask even more questions!

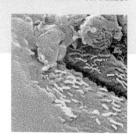

Figure 4 *These fossils were found on a mountaintop. Their presence indicates that what is now a mountaintop was once the bottom of a shallow sea.*

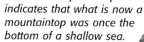

Exeter Cathedral, Exeter, England (A.D. 1120–1520)

LBJ Library, Austin, Texas (1972)

27

CONNECT TO LIFE SCIENCE

European songbirds and jackdaws break the shells of snails by hammering them against rocks. Egyptian vultures break open ostrich eggs by grasping a pebble in their beak and pounding on the shell until it breaks. Have students research other animals that also use stones as tools, such as sea otters. Students can then demonstrate for the class how these tools are used.

2) Teach

MISCONCEPTION //ALERT\\\\

The terms *rocks* and *rock formations* refer to the same material, but rock formations are large-scale bodies of rock, such as plutons, batholiths, and sedimentary strata, while rocks can be any size.

CROSS-DISCIPLINARY FOCUS

Writing **History** Between A.D. 900 and 1400 the Anasazi Indians of the American Southwest carved small towns in cliff sides. In what is now Cambodia, a vast temple complex called Angkor was carved from brick, sandstone, and laterite in the twelfth century. In the 1300s, African traders built the Great Zimbabwe, an elaborate walled city guarded by huge monoliths. Have students write a report or build a model of one of these ancient sites.

USING THE FIGURE

Ask students to use the information in the rock-cycle illustration to draw a diagram of the rock cycle in their ScienceLog. The first step in the textbook illustration is the formation of sedimentary rock; ask students to begin their rock cycle with a different step. Encourage them to write a descriptive caption for every stage of the rock cycle.

MEETING INDIVIDUAL NEEDS

Learners Having Difficulty

Have students prepare a *Rock Dictionary.* Ask them to list the three types of rock and the processes that occur in the rock cycle. Ask students to record the dictionary definition for each rock type or process and then define it in their own words. Encourage students to make up mnemonic devices, such as jokes or rhymes, to help them remember the meaning of each term.
Sheltered English

MISCONCEPTION ///ALERT\\\\

Rocks rarely undergo the complete process shown in the rock-cycle diagram. Sedimentary rocks can become igneous rocks, and metamorphic rocks can become sedimentary rocks. Some students may not realize the length of time it takes for changes to occur in the rock cycle. The process shown in the diagram can take billions of years.

Teaching Transparency 110
"The Rock Cycle"

The Rock Cycle

The rocks in the Earth's crust are constantly changing. Rock changes its shape and composition in a variety of ways. The way rock forms determines what type of rock it is. The three main types of rock are *igneous, sedimentary,* and *metamorphic.* Each type of rock is a part of the *rock cycle.* The **rock cycle** is the process by which one rock type changes into another. Follow this diagram to see one way sand grains can change as they travel through the rock cycle.

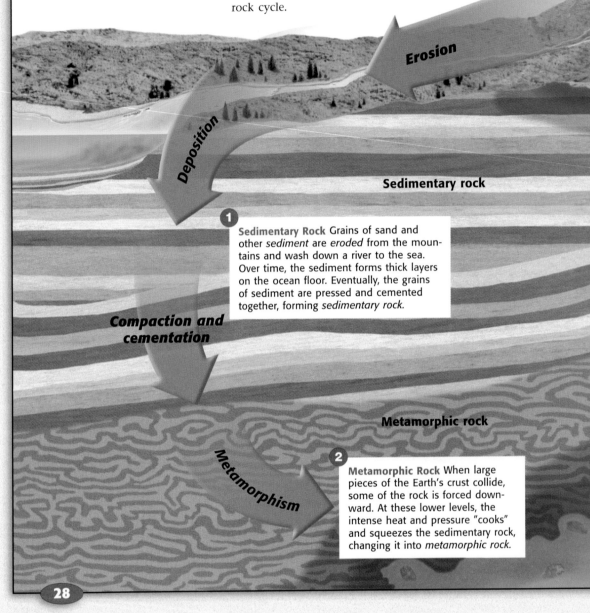

Erosion

Deposition

Sedimentary rock

1 **Sedimentary Rock** Grains of sand and other *sediment* are *eroded* from the mountains and wash down a river to the sea. Over time, the sediment forms thick layers on the ocean floor. Eventually, the grains of sediment are pressed and cemented together, forming *sedimentary rock.*

Compaction and cementation

Metamorphic rock

Metamorphism

2 **Metamorphic Rock** When large pieces of the Earth's crust collide, some of the rock is forced downward. At these lower levels, the intense heat and pressure "cooks" and squeezes the sedimentary rock, changing it into *metamorphic rock.*

28

Multicultural CONNECTION

The Islamic scholar Avicenna (980–1037) contributed immensely to our knowledge of medicine, astronomy, mathematics, and geology. In the *Book of Minerals* he described how rivers and seas laid down sediment that eventually became rock.

Avicenna's theories contributed to the foundations of Western geology. Many of his controversial ideas did not gain acceptance in Europe until the 1600s. Encourage interested students to learn more about the life and work of Avicenna.

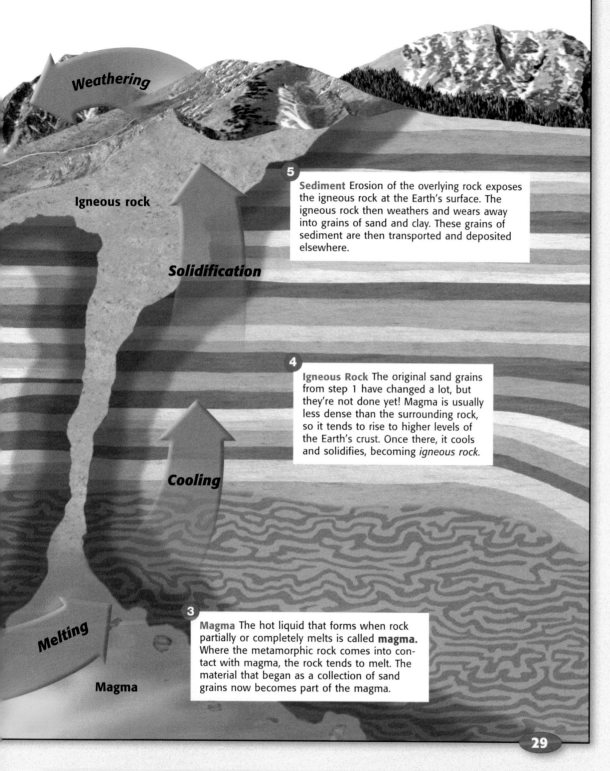

Weathering

Igneous rock

Solidification

5 **Sediment** Erosion of the overlying rock exposes the igneous rock at the Earth's surface. The igneous rock then weathers and wears away into grains of sand and clay. These grains of sediment are then transported and deposited elsewhere.

4 **Igneous Rock** The original sand grains from step 1 have changed a lot, but they're not done yet! Magma is usually less dense than the surrounding rock, so it tends to rise to higher levels of the Earth's crust. Once there, it cools and solidifies, becoming *igneous rock.*

Cooling

3 **Magma** The hot liquid that forms when rock partially or completely melts is called **magma.** Where the metamorphic rock comes into contact with magma, the rock tends to melt. The material that began as a collection of sand grains now becomes part of the magma.

Melting

Magma

29

IS THAT A FACT!

The space probes *Viking 1* and *Viking 2* provided detailed images of a gigantic volcano on Mars called Olympus Mons. The volcano is 25 km high, three times as high as Mount Everest. NASA scientists believe Olympus Mons is the largest volcano in the solar system.

Science Bloopers

In the Middle Ages, people believed that some rocks, called *eagle stones,* could reproduce. Scholars reported that the rocks crack like eggs and small stones pour out. Today, scientists call them *atetites,* or *clay-ironstone concretions.* Atetites have a shell of iron-rich clay that encloses smaller clay pebbles.

Many important substances on Earth follow cycles. Examples include water, nitrogen, sulfur, carbon, and phosphorous. Have students make a poster depicting the rock cycle and one other cycle in nature. Ask them to consider the ways that these cycles interact with each other.

CROSS-DISCIPLINARY FOCUS

Writing **Language Arts** Ask students to imagine being an ancient grain of sand on a beach. Have them write a letter to a young igneous rock describing their lifetime in the rock cycle. Students can share their letters with the class.

REAL-WORLD CONNECTION

Invite a local rock collector to address the class, and share his or her collection with the class. Tell the students to collect some rocks from their neighborhood for the collector to identify.

MISCONCEPTION ALERT

In some areas of the United States, especially in regions that experience long, cold winters, some people speak of rocks "growing." In the fall, farm fields are cleared of large rocks. The following spring, large rocks are found again in the fields and people say that the rocks have "grown" over the winter. In fact, when the ground freezes, it shifts and heaves, pushing buried rocks toward the surface.

GROUP ACTIVITY

Divide the class into small groups. Give each group samples of sandstone, limestone, and conglomerate. Number the samples. Provide a magnifying glass, a small dental pick, and paper towels to capture any pieces of rock that break off during the activity. Write the following instructions on the board:

1. Describe the color and texture of the specimen.

2. Using your unaided eye, examine the particles that make up the rock. Describe what you see.

3. Using the magnifying glass, try to identify the mineral composition of the specimen.

4. Use the dental pick to test the cohesiveness of the rocks, and record what you discover.

5. Try to classify each rock as fine-grained, medium-grained, or coarse-grained.

After groups have analyzed the rocks, discuss their findings.
Sheltered English

internetconnect

SCiLINKS
NSTA

TOPIC: Rock Formations
GO TO: www.scilinks.org
*sci***LINKS NUMBER:** HSTE100

Now that you know something about the natural processes that make the three major rock types, you can see that each type of rock can become any other type of rock. This is why it is called a cycle—there is no beginning or end. All rocks are at some stage of the rock cycle and can change into a different rock type. **Figure 5** shows how the three types of rock change form.

Figure 5 The Rock Cycle

Sedimentary rock is rock that forms when sediments are compacted and cemented together. The sediments that form sedimentary rock come from the weathering and erosion of igneous, metamorphic, or even other sedimentary rock.

Weathering and erosion

Heat and pressure

Weathering and erosion

Melting and cooling

Weathering and erosion

Metamorphic rock is rock that forms when the texture and composition of a preexisting rock is changed by heat or pressure deep underground. Igneous and sedimentary rock can change into metamorphic rock, and metamorphic rock can even change into another metamorphic rock.

Melting and cooling

Heat and pressure

Heat and pressure

Igneous rock is rock that forms from the cooling of *magma*. When magma cools and solidifies, it forms igneous rock. Magma forms in Earth's lower crust and upper mantle. When magma flows out onto the Earth's surface, it is called **lava**.

Heat and pressure

Melting and cooling

APPLY

Classifying Objects

Geologists sometimes use food examples to describe geologic processes. For example, when you tap a block of gelatin, it shakes much like the ground shakes during an earthquake. Melting and solidifying chocolate chips models the formation of magma and igneous rocks. Think of a way that food can be used to describe the formation of sedimentary and metamorphic rocks. What do you think are the strengths and weaknesses of using food to describe geologic processes? Explain.

30

Answers to APPLY

Answers will vary. (These questions are intended to get the students to anticipate the content in the next two pages.)

Q: What happens to a small stone when it works up its courage?

A: It becomes a little boulder.

The Nitty-Gritty on Rock Classification

You now know that scientists classify all rock into three main types based on how they formed. But did you know that each type of rock is divided into even smaller groups? These smaller groups are also based on differences in the way rocks form. For example, all igneous rock forms when hot liquid cools and solidifies. But some igneous rocks form when lava cools on the Earth's surface, while others form when magma cools deep beneath the surface. Therefore, igneous rock is divided into two smaller groups, depending on how and where it forms. In the same way, sedimentary and metamorphic rocks are also divided into smaller groups. How do Earth scientists know how to classify different rocks? They study them in detail using two important criteria—*composition* and *texture*.

Composition The minerals a rock is made of determine the **composition** of the rock. For example, a rock that is made up mostly of the mineral quartz will have a composition very similar to quartz. A rock that is made of 50 percent quartz and 50 percent feldspar will have a very different overall composition. Use this idea to compare the examples given in **Figure 6**.

÷ 5 ÷ Ω ≤ ∞ +Ω √ 9 ∞ ≤ Σ 2

MATH BREAK

What's in It?

Assume that a granite rock you are studying is made of 30 percent quartz, 55 percent feldspar, and the rest biotite mica. What percentage of the rock is biotite mica?

MATH and MORE

A percentage is a ratio that is expressed in terms of hundredths. When analyzing pure substances, percentage composition remains the same at any mass. For example, in terms of atomic mass, the percentage of oxygen atoms in water is 88.8 percent whether you are describing a single raindrop or an entire ocean.

Math Skills Worksheet "Parts of 100: Calculating Percentages"

Answer to MATHBREAK

100 percent of rock − (30 percent quartz + 55 percent feldspar) = 15 percent biotite mica

Figure 6 *The overall composition of a rock depends on the minerals it contains.*

Limestone

Granite

10% Biotite mica

35% Quartz

55% Feldspar

95% Calcite

5% Aragonite

CONNECT TO
LIFE SCIENCE

Some birds swallow stones to help with digestion. The stones settle in a specialized stomach compartment called the gizzard. As seeds, stems, and leaves enter the gizzard, its strong muscles contract, and the stones grind up the tough cellulose fibers into pieces that are small enough to digest. To see how a gizzard functions, have students fill a small cloth bag with different-sized pebbles. Add some breakfast cereal and birdseed to the bag. Knead the bag to see what happens to the food. Tell students that some dinosaurs had gizzards as well.

31

Homework

Illustration Have students make a poster that illustrates the rock cycle. Encourage them to cut out pictures from magazines of the different types of rock and processes in the rock cycle. For example, marble is a metamorphic rock that could be represented by a picture of a marble statue.
Sheltered English

internetconnect

SCiLINKS
NSTA

TOPIC: Composition of Rock
GO TO: www.scilinks.org
*sci*LINKS NUMBER: HSTE090

Teaching Transparency 63 "The Digestive System of a Bird"

LINK TO LIFE SCIENCE

RESEARCH

Investigate Your Area Students can search the Internet to learn about nearby places that are good for rock hunting. Ask students to report their findings to the class.

4 **Close**

Quiz

1. Name four processes that change rock from one type to another. (weathering, changes in pressure, melting, and cooling)

2. Explain how making glass is similar to the formation of igneous rock. (Glass is made by melting quartz sand grains.)

3. Explain how mixing concrete and allowing it to harden is similar to the formation of sedimentary rock. (Concrete is a mixture of different compounds and rock particles. After it is poured, it hardens much like sedimentary rock.)

4. Explain how baking bricks in a kiln is similar to the formation of metamorphic rock. (Bricks are made from clay and are baked to make them strong and resistant to weathering. Bricks are "metamorphosed" because they have different properties than dried clay.)

ALTERNATIVE ASSESSMENT

Have students write a skit portraying the rock cycle. Roles can include the minerals that make up rock and the forces that affect them. To represent the forces— heat, pressure, erosion, and weathering—suggest that students create special costumes.

Texture The **texture** of a rock is determined by the sizes, shapes, and positions of the grains of which it is made. Rocks that are made entirely of small grains, such as silt or clay particles, are said to have a *fine-grained* texture. Rocks that are made of large grains, such as pebbles, are said to have a *coarse-grained* texture. Rocks that have a texture between fine- and coarse-grained are said to have a *medium-grained* texture. Examples of these textures are shown in **Figure 7**.

Figure 7 *These three sedimentary rocks are made up of grains of different sizes. Can you see the differences in their textures?*

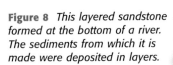

| Fine-grained | Medium-grained | Coarse-grained |
| Siltstone | Sandstone | Conglomerate |

Each rock type has a different kind of texture that can provide good clues to how and where the rock formed. For example, the rock shown in **Figure 8** has a texture that reflects how it formed. Both texture and composition are important characteristics that scientists use to understand the origin and history of rocks. Keep these characteristics in mind as you continue reading through this chapter.

Figure 8 *This layered sandstone formed at the bottom of a river. The sediments from which it is made were deposited in layers.*

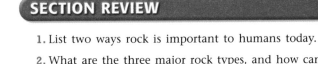

internetconnect

SC*i*LINKS.
NSTA

TOPIC: Composition of Rock
GO TO: www.scilinks.org
*sci*Links Number: HSTE090

SECTION REVIEW

1. List two ways rock is important to humans today.

2. What are the three major rock types, and how can they change from one type to another type?

3. How is lava different from magma?

4. **Comparing Concepts** Explain the difference between texture and composition.

Answers to Section Review

1. Answers will vary.

2. Igneous rock forms when magma cools and solidifies. Sedimentary rock forms when sediments are cemented and compacted together or when minerals crystallize out of sea water. Metamorphic rock forms when the texture or mineral composition of a preexisting rock is changed by heat or pressure.

3. Magma is a hot liquid that exists underground. Lava is magma that erupts and flows onto the Earth's surface.

4. The texture of a rock is determined by the sizes, shapes, and positions of the grains that make it up. The composition of a rock is determined by the kinds of minerals the rock is made of.

Terms to Learn

intrusive
extrusive

What You'll Do

- Explain how the cooling rate of magma affects the properties of igneous rock.
- Distinguish between igneous rock that cools deep within the crust and igneous rock that cools at the surface.
- Identify common igneous rock formations.

Igneous Rock

The word *igneous* comes from the Latin word for "fire." Magma cools into various types of igneous rock depending on the composition of the magma and the amount of time it takes the magma to cool and solidify. Like all other rock, igneous rock is classified according to its composition and texture.

Origins of Igneous Rock

Magma and lava solidify in the same way that water freezes. When magma or lava cools down enough, it solidifies, or "freezes," to form igneous rock. The only difference between water freezing and magma freezing is that water freezes at 0°C and magma and lava freeze at between 700°C and 1,250°C.

There are three ways magma can form: when rock is heated, when pressure is released, or when rock changes composition. To see how this can happen, follow along with **Figure 9**.

Figure 9 *There are three ways a rock can melt.*

Temperature An increase in temperature deep within the Earth's crust can cause the minerals in a rock to melt. Different minerals melt at different temperatures. So depending on how hot a rock gets, some of the minerals can melt while other minerals remain solid.

Pressure The high pressure deep within the Earth forces minerals to stay in the solid state, when otherwise they would melt from the intense heat. When hot rocks rise to shallow depths, the pressure is finally released and the minerals can melt.

Composition Sometimes fluids like water and carbon dioxide enter a rock that is close to its melting point. When these fluids combine with the rock, they can lower the melting point of the rock enough for it to melt and form magma.

33

WEIRD SCIENCE

Surtsey is a volcanic island south of Iceland that people actually saw being born! In 1963, fishermen far out at sea saw jets of spray, steam, and lava shooting more than 30 m out of the ocean. One month later the volcano broke through the surface to form an island.

By the time the eruptions ended, Surtsey covered an area of approximately 2.8 km². Seabirds started visiting, and tough grasses began to sprout. Today scientists think Surtsey may erode completely if the volcano doesn't erupt again.

Focus

Igneous Rock

This section examines the relationship between magma and rock. It discusses how temperature, pressure, and composition affect the melting point of rock. Changes in all three of these conditions can occur simultaneously, interacting in complex ways. Students learn about the difference between felsic and mafic igneous rock as well as the difference between intrusive and extrusive igneous rock.

Bellringer

Pose the following question to students:

Do you think rocks that cooled and solidified from lava on Earth's surface would look different from those that cooled and solidified from magma inside the Earth? Why?

1 Motivate

DISCUSSION

Ask students to talk about how volcanoes affect people and places. Discuss eruptions, lava flows, and ash clouds before asking students about the positive effects of volcanoes, such as land formation. Explain that lava and magma form land, and point out volcanic islands such as Hawaii and Iceland on a world map. Explain that volcanic soil is some of the most fertile soil in the world, which is why many populations are willing to live alongside potentially dangerous volcanoes.

Directed Reading Worksheet Section 2

2 Teach

CONNECT TO
LIFE SCIENCE

Until 1977, biologists thought few life-forms lived at ocean depths where sunlight does not reach. When scientists in the submersible *Alvin* explored the bottom of a deep ocean trench called the Galápagos Rift, they discovered structures called black smokers that release dissolved mineral compounds and heat the water. Scientists were amazed to discover an entire ecosystem that did not depend on photosynthesis for energy. This discovery has led many scientists to speculate that life may also have evolved in the outer solar system—particularly in the oceans that may exist under the surface of Europa, one of Jupiter's moons. Have students research the bizarre life-forms that scientists found living around black smokers.

Multicultural
CONNECTION

In the Tule Lake region of northern California, volcanic eruptions created a rugged landscape of broken lava beds with glassy, splintery edges, deep trenches, and small lava caves where people can live—and hide.

In 1872, the United States and the Modoc Indians went to war. The Modocs set up a stronghold for 50 people in the jagged lava beds. The terrain was so hard to negotiate that the Modocs held off more than 1,000 federal troops for more than 5 months. Today, this area is part of Lava Beds National Monument.

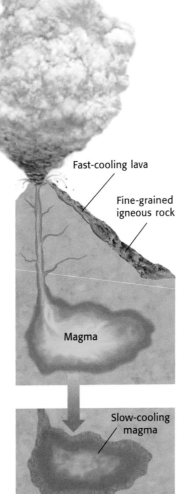

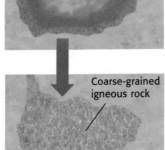

Figure 11 *The amount of time it takes for magma or lava to cool determines the texture of igneous rock.*

Fast-cooling lava

Fine-grained igneous rock

Magma

Slow-cooling magma

Coarse-grained igneous rock

34

Teaching Transparency 111
"The Cooling Rate of Magma and the Texture of Igneous Rock"

Composition and Texture of Igneous Rock

Look at the rocks in **Figure 10.** All of these are igneous rocks, even though they look very different from one another. These rocks differ from one another in what they are made of and how fast they cooled.

The light-colored rocks are not only lighter in color but also less dense. They are rich in elements such as silicon, aluminum, sodium, and potassium. These lightweight rocks are called *felsic*. The darker rocks are denser than the felsic rocks. These rocks are rich in iron, magnesium, and calcium and are called *mafic*.

Figure 10 *Light-colored igneous rock generally has a felsic composition. Dark-colored igneous rock generally has a mafic composition.*

	Coarse-grained	Fine-grained
Felsic	Granite	Rhyolite
Mafic	Gabbro	Basalt

Now look at **Figure 11.** This illustration shows what happens to magma when it cools at different rates. The longer it takes for the magma or lava to cool, the more time mineral crystals have to grow. And the more time the crystals have to grow, the coarser the texture of the resulting igneous rock.

✓ Self-Check

Rank the rocks shown in Figure 10 by how fast they cooled. Hint: Pay attention to their texture. (*See page 216 to check your answer.*)

Answers to Self-Check

From fastest-cooled to slowest-cooled, the rocks in **Figure 10** are: basalt, rhyolite, gabbro, and granite.

Igneous Rock Formations

You have probably seen igneous rock formations that were caused by lava cooling on the Earth's surface. But not all magma reaches the surface. Some magma cools and solidifies deep within the Earth's crust.

Intrusive Igneous Rock When magma cools beneath the Earth's surface, the resulting rock is called **intrusive.** Intrusive rock usually has a coarse-grained texture. This is because it is well insulated by the surrounding rock and thus cools very slowly.

Intrusive rock formations are named for their size and the way in which they intrude, or push into, the surrounding rock. *Plutons* are large, balloon-shaped intrusive formations that result when magma cools at great depths. Because plutons are some of the most common intrusions, intrusive rocks are often called *plutonic rocks.* **Figure 12** shows an example of an intrusive formation that has been exposed on the Earth's surface. Some common intrusive rock formations are shown in **Figure 13.**

Figure 12 *Enchanted Rock, near Llano, Texas, is an exposed pluton made of granite.*

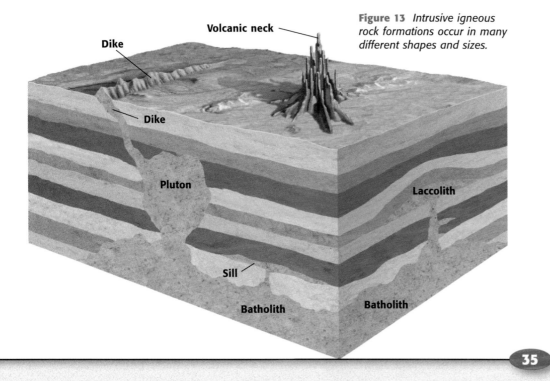

Figure 13 *Intrusive igneous rock formations occur in many different shapes and sizes.*

Volcanic neck

Dike

Dike

Pluton

Laccolith

Sill

Batholith

Batholith

3) Close

Quiz

1. Describe felsic and mafic rocks, and name three elements that occur in each type. (Felsic rock is lighter in color and weight; it is rich in aluminum, silicon, sodium, and potassium. Mafic rock is darker and heavier; it is rich in iron, magnesium, and calcium.)

2. What is the difference between intrusive and extrusive rock? (Intrusive rock forms from magma that solidifies while still underground, while extrusive rock forms from magma that solidifies after it has reached the surface.)

ALTERNATIVE ASSESSMENT

Have students create a model cross section that shows the formation of both intrusive and extrusive igneous rock. Supply students with several different colors of clay so they can color-code different formations, such as the magma source, dikes, sills, plutons, and the lava that forms extrusive rock. **Sheltered English**

PG 178

Crystal Growth

BRAIN FOOD

Violent volcanic eruptions sometimes produce a porous rock called pumice. Pumice is full of small holes once filled with trapped gases. Depending on how much space is taken up by these holes, some types of pumice can even float!

internet connect

SCI*LINKS*
NSTA

TOPIC: Igneous Rock
GO TO: www.scilinks.org
*sci*LINKS NUMBER: HSTE093

Extrusive Igneous Rock   Igneous rock that forms on the Earth's surface is called **extrusive**. Most volcanic rock is extrusive. Extrusive rock cools quickly on the surface and contains either very small crystals or none at all.

When lava erupts from a volcano, a formation called a *lava flow* is made. You can see an active lava flow in **Figure 14**. But lava does not always come from volcanoes. Sometimes lava erupts from long cracks in the Earth's surface called *fissures*. When a large amount of lava flows out of a fissure, it can cover a vast area, forming a plain called a *lava plateau*. Pre-existing landforms are often buried by extrusive igneous rock formations.

Figure 14 *Below is an active lava flow. When exposed to surface conditions, lava quickly cools and solidifies, forming a fine-grained igneous rock.*

SECTION REVIEW

1. What two properties are used to classify igneous rock?

2. How does the cooling rate of lava or magma affect the texture of an igneous rock?

3. **Interpreting Illustrations**   Use the diagram in Figure 13 to compare a sill with a dike. What makes them different from each other?

▼ *Answers to Section Review*

1. texture and color (mineral composition)

2. When magma cools slowly, crystals have a long time to grow, so the igneous rock that forms is coarse-grained. When magma cools quickly, crystals have a short time to grow, so the igneous rock that forms is fine-grained.

3. Both a sill and a dike are sheetlike bodies of igneous rock. A sill intrudes rock parallel to the surrounding rock layers. A dike cuts across the surrounding rock layers.

Terms to Learn

strata
stratification

What You'll Do

- Describe how the two types of sedimentary rock form.
- Explain how sedimentary rocks record Earth's history.

Figure 15 A Sedimentary Rock Cycle

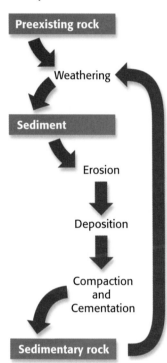

Preexisting rock

Weathering

Sediment

Erosion

Deposition

Compaction and Cementation

Sedimentary rock

Sedimentary Rock

Wind, water, ice, sunlight, and gravity all cause rock to *weather* into fragments. **Figure 15** shows how some sedimentary rocks form. Through the process of erosion, rock fragments, called sediment, are transported from one place to another. Eventually the sediment is deposited in layers. Sedimentary rock then forms as sediments become compacted and cemented together.

Origins of Sedimentary Rock

As new layers of sediment are deposited, the layers eventually become compressed, or compacted. Dissolved minerals separate out of the water to form a natural glue that binds the sediments together into sedimentary rock. Sedimentary rock forms at or near the Earth's surface, without the heat and pressure involved in the formation of igneous and metamorphic rocks. The physical features of sedimentary rock tell part of its history. The most noticeable feature of sedimentary rock is its layers, or **strata.** Road cuts and construction zones are good places to observe sedimentary rock formations, and as you can see in **Figure 16,** canyons carved by rivers provide some spectacular views.

Figure 16 *Millions of years of erosion by the Colorado River have revealed the rock strata in the walls of the Grand Canyon.*

37

SECTION **3**

Focus

Sedimentary Rock

This section explores how sedimentary rock forms and how it accumulates in layers, or strata. Students distinguish between clastic and chemical sedimentary rock and learn how each forms.

🔔 Bellringer

Ask students to write about how layers in sedimentary rock are like the rings in a tree. How are they different? What information can geologists infer by examining sedimentary layers?

1) Motivate

DEMONSTRATION

Dissolution of Minerals
Limestone forms when calcium carbonate crystallizes out of ocean water. Students may not believe that water contains the chemical components of dissolved minerals. If you live in an area with hard water, have students observe ice melting in warm water. After the ice melts, there is a layer of fluffy calcium carbonate that forms at the bottom of the glass. If you live in an area with soft water, make hard water by dissolving a little baking soda (sodium bicarbonate) and calcium chloride in water. Then freeze it into ice cubes. Use these ice cubes for the demonstration.

SCIENCE HUMOR

Q: What did the limestone rock say to the geologist?

A: Don't take me for granite.

Teaching Transparency 113
"A Sedimentary Rock Cycle"

Directed Reading Worksheet Section 3

internet**connect**

SCI**LINKS**
NSTA

TOPIC: Sedimentary Rock
GO TO: www.scilinks.org
*sci*LINKS NUMBER: HSTE095

USING THE FIGURE

Point out that **Figure 18** illustrates part of a cyclical process. First rain falls to Earth, drenching the soil. Calcium and carbonate dissolve in the rainwater and are washed out to sea. As some of the sea water evaporates and returns to the atmosphere, the calcium and carbonate accumulate in the ocean. When the concentration of these two substances becomes high enough, the substances combine, forming crystals of calcium carbonate, $CaCO_3$. The calcium carbonate settles on the sea floor, where it begins to accumulate as a limestone deposit. If this limestone deposit is uplifted and becomes part of a continental landmass, the cycle will continue as erosion contributes calcium and carbonate to the ocean again.
Sheltered English

CONNECT TO
LIFE SCIENCE

Calcium carbonate is an important compound for many different animals. Many mollusks remove calcium and carbonate from the sea water and combine them in special tissues that then harden to form a calcium carbonate shell. When the mollusk dies, its shell either dissolves back into the water or becomes part of the sediment on the bottom of the ocean. If the shell is part of deposited sediment, it may become a fossil. Have students research the Mazon Creek deposits, in Kansas, to learn more about these kinds of fossil beds.

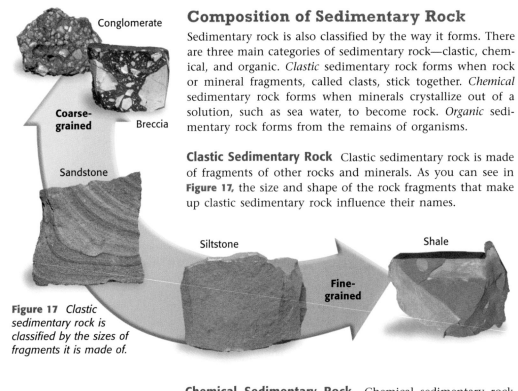

Figure 17 *Clastic sedimentary rock is classified by the sizes of fragments it is made of.*

Composition of Sedimentary Rock

Sedimentary rock is also classified by the way it forms. There are three main categories of sedimentary rock—clastic, chemical, and organic. *Clastic* sedimentary rock forms when rock or mineral fragments, called clasts, stick together. *Chemical* sedimentary rock forms when minerals crystallize out of a solution, such as sea water, to become rock. *Organic* sedimentary rock forms from the remains of organisms.

Clastic Sedimentary Rock Clastic sedimentary rock is made of fragments of other rocks and minerals. As you can see in **Figure 17,** the size and shape of the rock fragments that make up clastic sedimentary rock influence their names.

Chemical Sedimentary Rock Chemical sedimentary rock forms from *solutions* of minerals and water. As rainwater slowly makes its way to the ocean, it dissolves some of the rock material it passes through. Some of this dissolved material eventually forms the minerals that make up chemical sedimentary rock. One type of chemical sedimentary rock, chemical limestone, is made of calcium carbonate ($CaCO_3$), or the mineral calcite. It forms when calcium and carbonate become so concentrated in the sea water that calcite crystallizes out of the sea water solution, as shown in **Figure 18.**

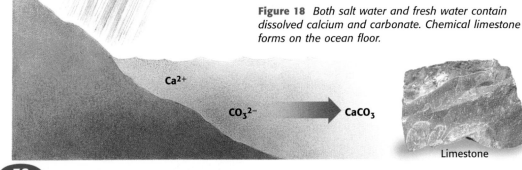

Figure 18 *Both salt water and fresh water contain dissolved calcium and carbonate. Chemical limestone forms on the ocean floor.*

SCIENTISTS AT ODDS

In the 1700s, the Neptunists and the Plutonists disagreed vehemently about how rocks form. Neptunists believed that all rocks developed from sediment laid down by a vast primordial ocean. The Plutonists believed rock formation was caused by heat from Earth's core. James Hutton's colleague, Sir James Hall, demonstrated the Plutonists' theories by melting rock in a furnace and letting it cool, showing how it changed from one form to another. This demonstration was a major victory for the Plutonists' arguments, but the debate raged for years until Charles Lyell synthesized both arguments in 1830 with *Principles of Geology*.

Organic Sedimentary Rock

Most limestone forms from the remains of animals that once lived in the ocean. This organic material consists of shells or skeletons, which are made of calcium carbonate that the animals get from sea water.

For example, some limestone is made of the skeletons of tiny organisms called coral. Coral are very small, but they live in huge colonies, as shown in **Figure 19.** Over time, the remains of these sea animals accumulate on the ocean floor. These animal remains eventually become cemented together to form *fossiliferous* (FAHS uhl IF uhr uhs) *limestone.*

Fossils are the remains or traces of plants and animals that have been preserved in sedimentary rock. Fossils have given us enormous amounts of information about ancient life-forms and how they lived. Most fossils come from animals that lived in the oceans. Another type of organic limestone, shown in **Figure 20,** forms from organisms that leave their shells in the mud on the ocean floor.

Figure 19 *Sea animals called coral create huge deposits of limestone. As they die, their skeletons accumulate on the ocean floor.*

Figure 20 *Shellfish, such as clams (above right), get the calcium for their shells from sea water. When these organisms die, their shells collect on the ocean floor, eventually becoming rock (below). In time, huge rock formations result (right).*

IS THAT A FACT!

The Great Barrier Reef, a long coral reef that lies off the northeastern coast of Australia, is the most massive structure ever built by living creatures. It is more than 2,000 km long and covers an area of 207,000 km².

WEIRD SCIENCE

The Bonneville Salt Flats, in Utah, are the remnants of a vast lake. After the last ice age, most of the lake drained quickly, but the remaining water slowly evaporated, leaving behind the salt flats. The Great Salt Lake is the largest of the few lakes left after Lake Bonneville evaporated.

RETEACHING

Now that students have learned about both chemical and clastic sedimentary rock, have them refer back to **Figure 15.** It is a diagram of the clastic sedimentary rock cycle. Have students explain the steps of the cycle and then create a diagram that shows the chemical sedimentary rock cycle.

REAL-WORLD CONNECTION

The most abundant material in toothpaste is water and the second-most abundant is chalk. Chalk is a sedimentary rock which often contains the shells of ancient diatoms, and it is used as an abrasive to clean teeth.

DISCUSSION

Chemical sedimentary rock can be divided into two categories: chemical and biochemical. Some rare forms of limestone are purely the result of a chemical process by which calcium carbonate precipitates out of sea water. But most limestones are biochemical because they form from the skeletons of marine organisms that extracted calcium and carbonate from sea water. Coal is also a biochemical sedimentary rock.

CROSS-DISCIPLINARY FOCUS

Fine Arts One type of printing used to reproduce fine art is called lithography. Lithography uses a flat piece of fine-grained, porous limestone. Interestingly, many important fossil beds were discovered while people quarried for lithographic limestone. The same qualities that make some limestone good for lithography also allow the preservation of extremely detailed fossils. Ask students to find out more about lithography and lithographic limestone beds around the world.

3 Extend

GROUP ACTIVITY

Divide students into two groups to investigate sandstone, shale, and limestone. The first group should work together to learn how the rocks form. The second group should investigate how the rocks are used in industry, architecture, or the arts. Both could investigate rock formations that have become tourist attractions. Members of each group should prepare exhibits, posters, or models to demonstrate what they have learned.

4 Close

Quiz

1. How does chemical limestone form? (It forms when calcium carbonate crystallizes out of sea water.)

2. What is stratification, and why is it important to Earth scientists? (Stratification is the layering of rock. It is important because it records many events in Earth's history as well as erosion and deposition rates.)

ALTERNATIVE ASSESSMENT

To review sedimentary rock formation, have students draw a picture of an environment that shows the source of sediments and where they are deposited. A second drawing should show what the environment will look like millions of years later after sedimentary rock has formed.

LabBook **PG 182**
Let's Get Sedimental

Figure 21 *Strata are not always parallel like the layers in a cake. Some strata are slanted. Wind caused these slanted deposits, called* cross-beds, *but water can also cause them.*

Sedimentary Rock Structures

Many sedimentary rock features can tell you about the way the rock formed. The most characteristic feature of sedimentary rock is **stratification,** or layering. Strata differ from one another depending on the kind, size, and color of their sediment. The rate of deposition can also affect the thickness of the layers. Sedimentary rocks sometimes record the motion of wind and water waves on lakes, seas, rivers, and sand dunes. Some of these features are shown in **Figures 21** and **22.**

Figure 22 *These* ripple marks *were made by flowing water and were preserved when the sediments became sedimentary rock. Ripple marks can also form from the action of wind.*

internet**connect**

SC/LINKS.
NSTA

TOPIC: Sedimentary Rock
GO TO: www.scilinks.org
*sci*LINKS **NUMBER:** HSTE095

SECTION REVIEW

1. Describe the process by which clastic sedimentary rock forms.

2. List three sedimentary rock structures, and explain how they record geologic processes.

3. **Analyzing Relationships** Both clastic and chemical sedimentary rocks are classified according to texture and composition. Which property is more important for each sedimentary rock type? Explain.

40

▼ *Answers to Section Review*

1. Clastic sedimentary rock forms when sediments become compacted and cemented together.

2. Three sedimentary structures are strata, ripple patterns, and fossils. Strata form when layers of sediment are deposited on top of each other. Ripple patterns form when sediments are shaped by flowing water before they turn into rock. Fossils

form from the remains of organisms in sedimentary rock.

3. Texture is more important in classifying clastic sedimentary rock because clastic sedimentary rock is made of different sizes of sediments. Composition is more important in classifying chemical sedimentary rock because chemical sedimentary rock forms from different materials that crystallize out of solution.

Terms to Learn

foliated
nonfoliated

What You'll Do

- Describe two ways a rock can undergo metamorphism.
- Explain how the mineral composition of rocks changes as they undergo metamorphism.
- Describe the difference between foliated and nonfoliated metamorphic rock.

Metamorphic Rock

The word *metamorphic* comes from *meta,* meaning "changed," and *morphos,* meaning "shape." Remember, metamorphic rocks are those in which the structure, texture, or composition of the rock has changed. Rock can undergo metamorphism by heat or pressure acting alone or by a combination of the two. All three types of rock—igneous, sedimentary, and even metamorphic—can change into metamorphic rock.

Origins of Metamorphic Rock

The texture or mineral composition of a rock can change when its surroundings change. If the temperature or pressure of the new environment is different from the one the rock formed in, the rock will undergo metamorphism.

Most metamorphic change is caused by increased pressure that takes place at depths greater than 2 km. At depths greater than 16 km, the pressure can be more than 4,000 times the pressure of the atmosphere! Look at **Figure 23.** This rock, called garnet schist, formed at a depth of about 30 km. At this depth, some of the crystals the rock is made of change as a result of the extreme pressure. Other types of schist form at much shallower depths.

The temperature at which metamorphism occurs ranges from 50°C to 1,000°C. At temperatures higher than 1,000°C, most rocks will melt. Metamorphism does not melt rock—when rock melts, it becomes magma and then igneous rock. In **Figure 24** you can see that this rock was deformed by intense pressure.

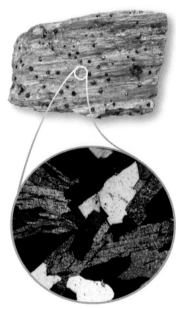

Figure 23 *At top is a metamorphic rock called garnet schist. At bottom is a microscopic view of a thin slice of a garnet schist.*

Figure 24 *In this outcrop, you can see an example of how sedimentary rock was deformed as it underwent metamorphism.*

41

Focus

Metamorphic Rock

This section examines what happens when a rock metamorphoses. Changes in heat or pressure can alter a rock's chemical nature and physical structure. Students will learn how different types of metamorphism cause changes in a rock's texture and mineral composition.

🔔 Bellringer

Ask students to write a brief description of how cookies are made. Ask them to consider how the mixture of raw ingredients is like sedimentary rock. Ask them to describe how cookie dough metamorphoses when it is baked in an oven.

1) Motivate

ACTIVITY

Provide each student with pieces of red, yellow, green, and purple modeling clay. Have them flatten each piece, pile the pieces on top of each other, and press down on them firmly. Then have the students push inward on opposite sides of the stack or pull it gently so that the clay doesn't break apart. Explain that they will be learning how intense pressure and heat can cause rock to behave in similar ways.

 Directed Reading Worksheet Section 4

BRAIN FOOD

This rock in **Figure 23** is called garnet schist because it includes the mineral garnet. In the microscopic view, the brightly colored shapes are crystals of the mineral biotite mica, the black and white crystals are quartz, and the speckled grain in the upper right part of the circle is garnet. Have students compare the garnet schist with siltstone and shale, discussed in the sedimentary rock section. What is different? (Under high temperature and pressure conditions, both of these sedimentary rocks can become garnet schist.)

QuickLab

MATERIALS

- paper
- black-ink pen
- plastic play putty

Answer to QuickLab

3. The "crystals" became stretched and deformed. The "granite" changed its shape because of the force applied to it.

CROSS-DISCIPLINARY FOCUS

Art Invite a potter to talk to the class about the processes involved in firing clay. Then have the class explore the different types of clay products that potters create (earthenware, stoneware, and ceramics) and the composition of the clays and glazes potters use.

GUIDED PRACTICE

 As you discuss **Figure 25,** be sure students understand that a metamorphic rock's composition and the heat and pressure it receives determine how much it deforms. Students should understand that the bulk composition of rock does not change during metamorphism unless fluids are introduced to the rock. However, the mineral composition of the rock may change as heat and pressure change. Ask students to think of some analogies for contact metamorphism (for example, an egg frying in a skillet). Have students draw rocks undergoing contact metamorphism. Have the class think of some analogies for regional metamorphism (for example, making toast). Then have students draw rocks undergoing regional metamorphism.

QuickLab

Stretching Out

1. Draw your version of a granite rock on a **piece of paper** with a **black-ink pen.** Be sure to include the outline of the rock, and fill it in with different crystal shapes.

2. Mash some **plastic play putty** over the "granite," and slowly peel it off.

3. After making sure that the outline of your "granite" has been transferred to the putty, push and pull on the putty. What happened to the "crystals"? What happened to the "granite"?

TRY at HOME

Contact Metamorphism One way rock can undergo metamorphism is by coming into contact with magma. When magma moves through the crust, it heats the surrounding rock and "cooks" it. As a result, the magma changes some of the minerals in the surrounding rock into other minerals. The greatest change takes place where magma comes into direct contact with the surrounding rock. The effect of heat gradually lessens with distance from the magma. As you can see in **Figure 25,** *contact metamorphism* only happens next to igneous intrusions.

Regional Metamorphism When enormous pressure builds up in rock that is deeply buried under other rock formations, or when large pieces of the Earth's crust collide with each other, *regional metamorphism* occurs. The pressure and increased temperature that exist under these conditions cause rock to become deformed and chemically changed. This kind of metamorphic rock is underneath most continental rock formations.

✓ Self-Check

How could a rock undergo both contact and regional metamorphism? *(See page 216 to check your answer.)*

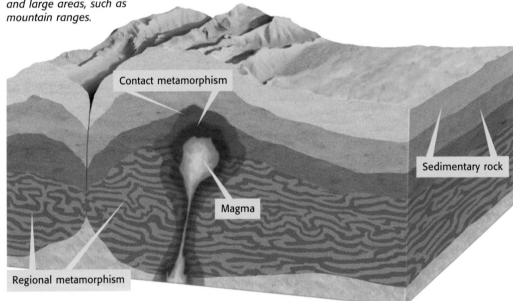

Figure 25 *Metamorphism occurs over small areas, such as next to bodies of magma, and large areas, such as mountain ranges.*

Labels: Contact metamorphism; Sedimentary rock; Magma; Regional metamorphism

Answer to Self-Check

Answers will vary. A rock can come into contact with magma and also be subjected to pressure underground.

IS THAT A FACT!

The largest expanse of exposed metamorphic rock in the world is the Canadian Shield, a huge horseshoe-shaped region encircling Hudson Bay. Covering about half of Canada, it is about 4,586,900 km² and is the source of more than 70 percent of the minerals mined in Canada.

Composition of Metamorphic Rock

When conditions within the Earth's crust change because of collisions between continents or the intrusion of magma, the temperature and pressure of the existing rock change. Minerals that were present in the rock when it formed may no longer be stable in the new environment. The original minerals change into minerals that are more stable in the new temperature and pressure conditions. Look at **Figure 26** to see an example of how this happens.

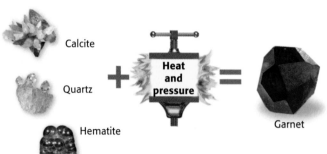

Calcite

Quartz

Hematite

Heat and pressure

Garnet

Figure 26 *The minerals calcite, quartz, and hematite combine and recrystallize to form the metamorphic mineral garnet.*

Many of these new minerals occur only in metamorphic rock. As shown in **Figure 27,** some metamorphic minerals form only within a specific range of temperature and pressure conditions. When scientists observe these metamorphic minerals in a rock, they can estimate the temperature and depth (pressure) at which recently exposed rock underwent metamorphism.

Figure 27 *Scientists can understand a metamorphic rock's history by observing the minerals it contains. For example, metamorphic rock containing garnet formed at a greater depth than one that contains only chlorite.*

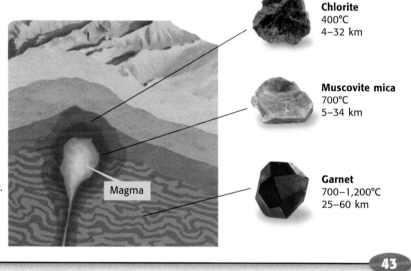

Magma

Chlorite
400°C
4–32 km

Muscovite mica
700°C
5–34 km

Garnet
700–1,200°C
25–60 km

Homework

Making Models Have students make a model cross section of the Earth's crust. The model should include materials that represent magma, contact and regional metamorphic rocks, and sedimentary strata. Sheltered English

Teaching Transparency 114 "Regional and Contact Metamorphism"

MISCONCEPTION ///ALERT

Heat and temperature are not the same thing. *Heat* is the amount of thermal energy that is transferred from one object to another. *Temperature* is a measure of how hot something is. Temperature is not a form of energy. When a rock comes into contact with magma, thermal energy is transferred from the magma to the rock because the magma is at a higher temperature than the rock. As a result, the temperature of the rock increases while the temperature of the magma decreases. But heating a rock does not always raise its temperature. If the rock is already so hot that it is on the verge of melting, additional heat will cause the rock to melt (change state) but will not change the rock's temperature.

REAL-WORLD CONNECTION

Asbestos Removal Asbestos is an informal name for a group of fibrous minerals usually found in regionally metamorphosed rock. Manufacturers value these minerals because they resist burning and don't readily conduct thermal energy or electrical current. However, some kinds of asbestos fracture into tiny needles that can become airborne. This dust is linked to a lung disease called asbestosis. As a result, asbestos has been removed from many public places at great expense. Have students find out about the many uses for asbestos and any cleanup projects that are occurring in your area.

Activity

Did you know that you have a birthstone? Birthstones are gemstones, or mineral crystals. For each month of the year, there are one or two different birthstones. Find out which birthstone or birthstones you have by doing research in your school library or on the Internet. The names of birthstones are not usually the same as their actual mineral names. In what kind of rock would you likely find your birthstone? Why?

3 Extend

DISCUSSION

Display metamorphic rocks in groups of foliated rocks (slate, schist, phyllite, gneiss) and nonfoliated rocks (quartzite, marble, hornfels, soapstone). Have students compare the rocks according to color, appearance, and composition. Explain that regional metamorphism tends to produce *foliated rocks,* while contact metamorphism tends to produce *nonfoliated rocks.* Ask students to predict what the terms mean then read this page to see if they were correct.

MATH and MORE

Metamorphic rock usually forms at depths greater than 16 km. To convert kilometers to miles, multiply the number of kilometers by 0.6. For example, 16 km multiplied by 0.6 is equal to 9.6 mi. Tell students that the continental crust can be up to 100 km thick. How many miles is that? (60 mi)

The crust under the ocean is about 5 km thick. How many miles is that? (3 mi)

Students might be interested in comparing these distances with the distance to a nearby town or landmark.

Math Skills Worksheet
"The Unit Factor and Dimensional Analysis"

 **PG 181**
Metamorphic Mash

Reinforcement Worksheet
"What Is It?"

Textures of Metamorphic Rock

As you know, texture helps to classify igneous and sedimentary rock. The same is true of metamorphic rock. All metamorphic rock has one of two textures—*foliated* or *nonfoliated.* **Foliated** metamorphic rock consists of minerals that are aligned and look almost like pages in a book. **Nonfoliated** metamorphic rock does not appear to have any regular pattern. Let's take a closer look at each of these types of metamorphic rock to find out how they form.

Foliated Metamorphic Rock Foliated metamorphic rock contains mineral grains that are aligned by pressure. Strongly foliated rocks usually contain flat minerals, like biotite mica. Look at **Figure 28.** Shale consists of layers of clay minerals. When first subjected to heat and pressure, the clay minerals change into mica minerals and the shale becomes a fine-grained, foliated metamorphic rock called slate.

Metamorphic rocks can become other metamorphic rocks if the environment changes again. With additional heat and pressure, slate can change into phyllite, another metamorphic rock. When phyllite is exposed to additional heat and pressure, it can change into a metamorphic rock called schist.

As the degree of metamorphism increases, the arrangement of minerals in the rock changes. With additional heat and pressure, coarse-grained minerals separate into bands in a metamorphic rock called *gneiss* (pronounced "nice").

Sedimentary shale

Slate

Phyllite

Figure 28 The effects of metamorphism depend on the heat and pressure applied to the rock. Here you can see what happens to shale when it is exposed to more and more heat and pressure.

Schist

Gneiss

Wouldn't it be "gneiss" to make your own foliated rock? Turn to page 181 in your LabBook to find out how.

44

Homework

Investigate Your Area Have students look at stone buildings and houses around their town. Ask students to identify the rock used in construction as igneous, sedimentary, or metamorphic. Which rock type was most commonly used? Which was used least? Encourage students to find out the origin of rock used in buildings in your community.

WEIRD SCIENCE

When rocks metamorphose under high temperature and pressure, they become plastic and can be easily deformed. It is not unusual for spherical pebbles in a conglomerate to be stretched into ellipses more than 30 times their original diameter!

Nonfoliated Metamorphic Rock Nonfoliated metamorphic rocks are shown in **Figure 29.** Do you notice anything missing? The lack of aligned mineral grains makes them nonfoliated. They are rocks commonly made of only one, or just a few, minerals.

Sandstone is a sedimentary rock made of distinct quartz sand grains. But when sandstone is subjected to the heat and pressure of metamorphism, the spaces between the sand grains disappear as they recrystallize, forming quartzite. Quartzite has a shiny, glittery appearance. It is still made of quartz, but the mineral grains are larger. When limestone undergoes metamorphism, the same process happens to the mineral calcite, and the limestone becomes marble. Marble has larger calcite crystals than limestone. You have probably seen marble in buildings and statues.

Biology
CONNECTION

The term *metamorphosis* means "change in form." When certain animals undergo a dramatic change in the shape of their body, they are said to have undergone a metamorphosis. As part of their natural life cycle, moths and butterflies go through four stages of life. After they hatch from an egg, they are in the larval stage in the form of a caterpillar. In the next stage they build a cocoon or become a chrysalis. This is called the pupal stage. They finally emerge into the adult stage of their life, complete with wings, antennae, and legs!

Marble

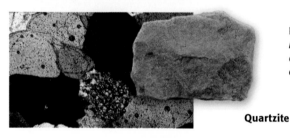

Quartzite

Figure 29 *Marble and quartzite are nonfoliated metamorphic rocks. As you can see in the microscopic views, none of the mineral crystals are aligned.*

SECTION REVIEW

1. What environmental factors cause rock to undergo metamorphism?

2. What is the difference between foliated and nonfoliated metamorphic rock?

3. **Making Inferences** If you had two metamorphic rocks, one with garnet crystals and the other with chlorite crystals, which one would have formed at a deeper level in the Earth's crust? Explain.

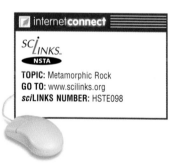

internet connect

SCILINKS
NSTA

TOPIC: Metamorphic Rock
GO TO: www.scilinks.org
***sci*LINKS NUMBER:** HSTE098

45

Round and Round in Circles
Teacher's Notes

Time Required

One or two 45-minute class periods

Lab Ratings

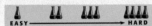

EASY ———————→ HARD

TEACHER PREP �
STUDENT SET-UP ♦
CONCEPT LEVEL ♦♦
CLEAN UP ♦♦

MATERIALS

The materials listed for this activity are enough for 4 or 5 students. Depending on the number of hot plates available, the size of groups will vary. Ask students to supply old crayons and candles.

Safety Caution

Remind students to review all safety cautions and icons before beginning this lab activity.

Lab Notes

Remind students to write their observations in their ScienceLog after every step of the activity so that they will have accurate notes on the stages of the rock cycle.

The different mineral crystals that make up igneous rock would be best represented by different colors of wax. However, the different minerals in igneous rock are not easily shown using melted and solidified wax. This lab can be modified to use modeling clay instead of wax.

Making Models Lab

Round and Round in Circles

The rocks that make up the Earth are constantly being recycled. One form of rock is often broken down and changed into another form of rock. Do this activity to learn what happens to rocks as they change from one rock type to another.

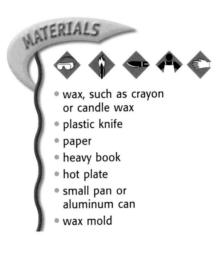

MATERIALS

- wax, such as crayon or candle wax
- plastic knife
- paper
- heavy book
- hot plate
- small pan or aluminum can
- wax mold

Procedure

1. Take several pieces of wax of different colors. Carefully scrape off some wax of each color with the edge of a plastic knife. These shavings will represent tiny grains of rock or sand.

2. When you have made a large pile of wax shavings, cover it with a piece of paper and a heavy book. Gently press down on the book until the wax shavings stick together. This mixture of mineral grains will represent sedimentary rock. Write a description of the "rock" in your ScienceLog. How is the rock different from the tiny shavings you started with?

3. Now take your wax "sedimentary rock" and warm it in your hands for a while. Place the paper and the book on top of the warm wax. Press down on the wax a little harder than you did in the first step. Fold the warmed wax in half, and press down some more. This second type of "rock" represents metamorphic rock. Describe this new "rock" in your ScienceLog.

4. Place the wax in the pan. Turn on the hot plate, and place the pan on the hot plate. Observe the wax as it melts. In this state, what does the wax represent?

Answers

2. The shavings are stuck together in the "rock."
4. The melted wax represents magma.

Bert Sherwood
Socorro Middle School
El Paso, Texas

5 Turn off the hot plate. Carefully pour the melted wax into a mold. Observe the wax as it cools and hardens. Carefully touch the wax with the eraser end of your pencil. Record your observations. The newly cooled wax represents igneous rock. Describe how this "rock" is different from the first two.

6 Finally, take the cooled wax and scrape off bits of the "rock" to form grains of rock or sand. If you have time, repeat steps 2–5.

Analysis

7 Review your descriptions of each type of "rock." Which "rock" do you think resembles the rock that forms from erupting volcanoes?

8 Which "rock" is formed from pieces of broken-down rock? How do these rock fragments harden into rock?

9 In step 6 you were asked to go back to step 2. Explain how this activity can be described as a rock cycle.

10 Does this model of the rock cycle have any limitations? Explain your answer.

Answers

5. Sample answer: The igneous rock is a solid mass of mixed chemicals, while the other two rocks contain grains of distinctly different minerals.

7. The igneous rock formed in step 5 is most like the igneous rock formed by volcanoes.

8. The sedimentary rock formed from pieces of broken-down rock when the grains were squeezed together.

9. This activity is a cycle because the wax can be used over and over to create new rocks.

10. The explanation should say that this model of the rock cycle does not include cementation of sedimentary rock or exactly recreate the temperatures and pressures of the rock cycle; the rock cycle takes millions of years; and the rock cycle can take many paths, not just the one in this exercise.

Chapter Highlights

Chapter Highlights

VOCABULARY DEFINITIONS

SECTION 1

rock a solid mixture of crystals of one or more minerals or other materials

rock cycle the process by which one rock type changes into another rock type

magma the hot liquid that forms when rock partially or completely melts; may include mineral crystals

sedimentary rock rock that forms when sediments are compacted and cemented together

metamorphic rock rock that forms when the texture and composition of preexisting rock changes due to heat or pressure

igneous rock rock that forms from the cooling of magma

composition the makeup of a rock; describes either the minerals or elements present in it

texture the sizes, shapes, and positions of the grains that a rock is made of

SECTION 2

intrusive the type of igneous rock that forms when magma cools and solidifies beneath Earth's surface

extrusive the type of igneous rock that forms when lava or pyroclastic material cools and solidifies on the Earth's surface

SECTION 1

Vocabulary

rock (p. 26)

rock cycle (p. 28)

magma (p. 29)

sedimentary rock (p. 30)

metamorphic rock (p. 30)

igneous rock (p. 30)

composition (p. 31)

texture (p. 32)

Section Notes

- Rocks have been used by humans for thousands of years, and they are just as valuable today.

- Rocks are classified into three main types—igneous, sedimentary, and metamorphic—depending on how they formed.

- The rock cycle describes the process by which a rock can change from one rock type to another.

- Scientists further classify rocks according to two criteria—composition and texture.

- Molten igneous material creates rock formations both below and above ground.

SECTION 2

Vocabulary

intrusive (p. 35)

extrusive (p. 36)

Section Notes

- The texture of igneous rock is determined by the rate at which it cools. The slower magma cools, the larger the crystals are.

- Felsic igneous rock is light-colored and lightweight, while mafic igneous rock is dark-colored and heavy.

- Igneous material that solidifies at the Earth's surface is called extrusive, while igneous material that solidifies within the crust is called intrusive.

Lab

Crystal Growth (p. 178)

☑ Skills Check

Math Concepts

MINERAL COMPOSITION Rocks are classified not only by the minerals they contain but also by the amounts of those minerals. Suppose a particular kind of granite is made of feldspar, biotite mica, and quartz. If you know that feldspar makes up 55 percent of the rock and biotite mica makes up 15 percent of the rock, the remaining 30 percent must be made of quartz.

$$
\begin{array}{ll}
55\% \text{ feldspar} & 100\% \text{ of granite} \\
+\ 15\% \text{ biotite mica} \quad \text{or} & -\ 55\% \text{ feldspar} \\
+\ 30\% \text{ quartz} & -\ 15\% \text{ biotite mica} \\
\hline
=\ 100\% \text{ of granite} & =\ 30\% \text{ quartz}
\end{array}
$$

Visual Understanding

PIE CHARTS The pie charts on page 31 help you visualize the relative amounts of minerals in different types of rock. The circle represents the whole rock, or 100 percent. Each part, or "slice," of the circle represents a fraction of the rock.

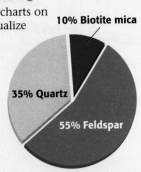

10% Biotite mica

35% Quartz

55% Feldspar

Lab and Activity Highlights

Round and Round in Circles `PG 46`

Crystal Growth `PG 178`

Metamorphic Mash `PG 181`

Let's Get Sedimental `PG 182`

Datasheets for LabBook (blackline masters for these labs)

SECTION 3

Vocabulary

strata *(p. 37)*

stratification *(p. 40)*

Section Notes

- Clastic sedimentary rock is made of rock and mineral fragments that are compacted and cemented together. Chemical sedimentary rock forms when minerals crystallize out of a solution such as sea water. Organic sedimentary rock forms from the remains of organisms.

- Sedimentary rocks record the history of their formation in their features. Some common features are strata, ripple marks, and fossils.

Lab

Let's Get Sedimental *(p. 182)*

SECTION 4

Vocabulary

foliated *(p. 44)*

nonfoliated *(p. 44)*

Section Notes

- One kind of metamorphism is the result of magma heating small areas of surrounding rock, changing its texture and composition.

- Most metamorphism is the product of heat and pressure acting on large regions of the Earth's crust.

- The mineral composition of a rock changes when the minerals it is made of recrystallize to form new minerals. These new minerals are more stable under increased temperature and pressure.

- Metamorphic rock that contains aligned mineral grains is called foliated, and metamorphic rock that does not contain aligned mineral grains is called nonfoliated.

Lab

Metamorphic Mash *(p. 181)*

VOCABULARY DEFINITIONS, *continued*

SECTION 3

strata layers of sedimentary rock that form from the deposition of sediment

stratification the layering of sedimentary rock

SECTION 4

foliated the texture of metamorphic rock in which the mineral grains are aligned like the pages of a book

nonfoliated the texture of metamorphic rock in which mineral grains show no alignment

Vocabulary Review Worksheet

Blackline masters of these Chapter Highlights can be found in the **Study Guide.**

---

internetconnect

GO TO: go.hrw.com

KEYWORD: HSTRCK

Visit the **HRW** Web site for a variety of learning tools related to this chapter. Just type in the keyword:

SCiLINKS
NSTA

GO TO: www.scilinks.org

Visit the **National Science Teachers Association** on-line Web site for Internet resources related to this chapter. Just type in the *sci*LINKS number for more information about the topic:

TOPIC: Composition of Rock   *sci***LINKS NUMBER:** HSTE090
TOPIC: Igneous Rock   *sci***LINKS NUMBER:** HSTE093
TOPIC: Sedimentary Rock   *sci***LINKS NUMBER:** HSTE095
TOPIC: Metamorphic Rock   *sci***LINKS NUMBER:** HSTE098
TOPIC: Rock Formations   *sci***LINKS NUMBER:** HSTE100

49

Lab and Activity Highlights

LabBank

Labs You Can Eat, Famous Rock Groups

Whiz-Bang Demonstrations, Settling Down

Long-Term Projects & Research Ideas, Home-Grown Crystals

Interactive Explorations CD-ROM

CD 2, Exploration 6, "Rock On!"

Chapter Review
Answers

USING VOCABULARY

1. Intrusive/extrusive
2. Foliated
3. Clastic
4. Lava
5. sedimentary

UNDERSTANDING CONCEPTS

Multiple Choice

6. d
7. b
8. a
9. a
10. c
11. b
12. c
13. b
14. c
15. b

Short Answer

16. Answers will vary. In the rock cycle, igneous, sedimentary, and metamorphic rock can change into other rock types through a variety of natural processes. Although rock material changes form, it still remains a part of the rock cycle.

17. Sandstone has a coarser-grained texture than siltstone. Both sandstone and siltstone are clastic sedimentary rocks.

Concept Mapping Transparency 4

Blackline masters of this Chapter Review can be found in the **Study Guide.**

Chapter Review

USING VOCABULARY

To complete the following sentences, choose the correct term from each pair of terms listed below:

1. __?__ igneous rock is more likely to have coarse-grained texture than __?__ igneous rock. (*Extrusive/intrusive* or *Intrusive/extrusive*)

2. __?__ metamorphic rock texture consists of parallel alignment of mineral grains. (*Foliated* or *Nonfoliated*)

3. __?__ sedimentary rock forms when grains of sand become cemented together. (*Clastic* or *Chemical*)

4. __?__ cools quickly on the Earth's surface. (*Lava* or *Magma*)

5. Strata are found in __?__ rock. (*igneous* or *sedimentary*)

UNDERSTANDING CONCEPTS

Multiple Choice

6. A type of rock that forms deep within the Earth when magma solidifies is called
   a. sedimentary.
   b. metamorphic.
   c. organic.
   d. igneous.

7. A type of rock that forms under high temperature and pressure but is not exposed to enough heat to melt the rock is
   a. sedimentary.
   b. metamorphic.
   c. organic.
   d. igneous.

8. After they are deposited, sediments, such as sand, are turned into sedimentary rock when they are compacted and
   a. cemented.
   b. metamorphosed.
   c. melted.
   d. weathered.

9. An igneous rock with a coarse-grained texture forms when
   a. magma cools very slowly.
   b. magma cools very quickly.
   c. magma cools quickly, then slowly.
   d. magma cools slowly, then quickly.

10. The layering that occurs in sedimentary rock is called
    a. foliation.
    b. ripple marks.
    c. stratification.
    d. compaction.

11. An example of a clastic sedimentary rock is
    a. obsidian.
    b. sandstone.
    c. gneiss.
    d. marble.

12. A common sedimentary rock structure is
    a. a sill.
    b. a pluton.
    c. cross-bedding.
    d. a lava flow.

13. An example of mafic igneous rock is
    a. granite.
    b. basalt.
    c. quartzite.
    d. pumice.

14. Chemical sedimentary rock forms when
    a. magma cools and solidifies.
    b. minerals are twisted into a new arrangement.
    c. minerals crystallize from a solution.
    d. sand grains are cemented together.

15. Which of the following is a foliated metamorphic rock?
    a. sandstone
    b. gneiss
    c. shale
    d. basalt

Short Answer

16. In no more than three sentences, explain the rock cycle.

17. How are sandstone and siltstone different from one another? How are they the same?

18. In one or two sentences, explain how the cooling rate of magma affects the texture of the igneous rock that forms.

Concept Mapping

19. Use the following terms to create a concept map: rocks, clastic, metamorphic, nonfoliated, igneous, intrusive, chemical, foliated, organic, extrusive, sedimentary.

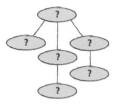

CRITICAL THINKING AND PROBLEM SOLVING

Write one or two sentences to answer the following questions:

20. The sedimentary rock coquina is made up of pieces of seashells. Which of the three kinds of sedimentary rock could it be? Explain.

21. If you were looking for fossils in the rocks around your home and the rock type that was closest to your home was metamorphic, would you find many fossils? Why or why not?

22. Suppose you are writing a book about another planet. In your book, you mention that the planet has no atmosphere or weather. Which type of rock will you not find on the planet? Explain.

23. Imagine that you want to quarry or mine granite. You have all of the equipment, but you need a place to quarry. You have two pieces of land to choose from. One piece is described as having a granite batholith under it, and the other has a granite sill. If both plutonic bodies were at the same depth, which one would be a better buy for you? Explain your answer.

MATH IN SCIENCE

24. If a 60 kg granite boulder were broken down into sand grains and if quartz made up 35 percent of the boulder's mass, how many kilograms of the resulting sand would be quartz grains?

INTERPRETING GRAPHICS

The red curve on the graph below shows how the melting point of a particular rock changes with increasing temperature and pressure. Use the graph to answer the questions below.

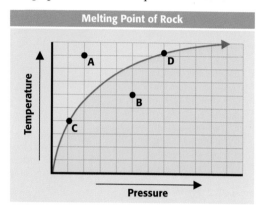
Melting Point of Rock

25. What type of material, liquid or solid, would you find at point A? Why?

26. What would you find at point B?

27. Points C and D represent different temperature and pressure conditions for a single, solid rock. Why does this rock have a higher melting temperature at point D than it does at point C?

Reading Check-up
Take a minute to review your answers to the Pre-Reading Questions found at the bottom of page 24. Have your answers changed? If necessary, revise your answers based on what you have learned since you began this chapter.

---

18. When magma cools slowly, crystals have a long time to grow, so they grow to a much larger size than they do when magma cools quickly.

Concept Mapping

19. An answer to this exercise can be found at the front of this book.

CRITICAL THINKING AND PROBLEM SOLVING

20. The seashells that make up coquina are made by shellfish, so coquina is an organic sedimentary rock. (Coquina could also be considered a clastic sedimentary rock because the shell fragments are clasts that have been deposited.)

21. You would not find many fossils where you lived because fossils are found in sedimentary rock, not metamorphic rock. (Occasionally, fossils are preserved in metamorphic rock that was once sedimentary rock.)

22. You will not find sedimentary rock because no weathering of rock can occur because there is no atmosphere.

23. The property with the batholith would be a better buy because batholiths are much bigger than sills.

MATH IN SCIENCE

24. 35% of 60 kg = $60 \times 0.35 = 21$ kg

INTERPRETING GRAPHICS

25. The material at point A is magma. It is magma because everything above the curve on the graph is liquid.

26. solid rock

27. Although at point D the rock is at a higher temperature, it has much more pressure on it, which keeps it solid.

Background

Just north of Petra is another huge temple, the magnificent El-Deir. This temple was carved from the mountainside, and it sits 1,200 m above the valley floor. Its facade is 50 m wide and 45 m tall, and its huge doorway is 8 m high.

Science, Technology, and Society

Rock City

Today when we dig into a mountainside to build a highway or make room for a building, we use heavy machinery and explosives. Can you imagine doing the same job with just a hammer and chisel? Well, between about 300 B.C. and A.D. 200, an Arab tribe called the Nabataeans (nab uh TEE uhns) did just that. In fact, they carved a whole city—homes, storage areas, monuments, administrative offices, and temples—right into the mountainsides!

▲ *Petra's most famous building, the Treasury, was shown in the movie* Indiana Jones and the Last Crusade.

Rose-Red City

This amazing city in southern Jordan is Petra (named by the Roman emperor Hadrian Petra during a visit in A.D. 131). A poet once described Petra as "the rose-red city" because all the buildings and monuments were carved from the pink sandstone mountains surrounding Petra.

Using this reddish stone, the Nabataeans lined the main street in the center of the city with tall stone columns. The street ends at what was once the foot of a mountain but is now known as the Great Temple—a two-story stone religious complex larger than a football field!

The High Place of Sacrifice, another site near the center of the city, was a mountaintop. The Nabataeans leveled the top and created a place of worship more than 1,000 m above the valley floor. Today visitors climb stairs to the top. Along the way, they pass dozens of tombs carved into the pink rock walls.

Tombs and More Tombs

There are more than 800 other tombs dug into the mountainsides in and around Petra. One of them, the Treasury (created for a Nabataean ruler), stands more than 40 m high! It is a magnificent building with an elaborate facade. Behind the massive stone front, the Nabataeans carved one large room and two smaller rooms deeper into the mountain.

Petra Declines

The Nabataeans once ruled an area extending from Petra to Damascus. They grew wealthy and powerful by controlling important trade routes near Petra. But their wealth attracted the Roman Empire, and in A.D. 106, Petra became a Roman province. Though the city prospered under Roman rule for almost another century, a gradual decline in Nabataean power began. The trade routes by land that the Nabataeans controlled for hundreds of years were abandoned in favor of a route by the Red Sea. People moved and the city faded. By the seventh century, nothing was left of Petra but empty stone structures.

Think About It!

► Petra is sometimes referred to as a city "from the rock as if by magic grown." Why might such a city seem "magic" to us today? What might have encouraged the Nabataeans to create this city? Share your thoughts with a classmate.

52

Answer to Think About It!

Answers will vary. (Students can do research to find out more about Nabataean culture.)

Glass Scalpels

Would you want your surgeon to use a scalpel that was thousands of years old? Probably not, unless it was a razor-sharp knife blade made of obsidian, a natural volcanic glass. Such blades and arrowheads were used for nearly 18,000 years by our ancestors. Recently, physicians have found a new use for these Stone Age tools. Obsidian blades, once used to hunt woolly mammoths, are now being used as scalpels in the operating room!

Obsidian or Stainless Steel?

Traditionally, physicians have used inexpensive stainless-steel scalpel blades for surgical procedures. Steel scalpels cost about $2 each, and surgeons use them just once and throw them away. Obsidian scalpels are more expensive— about $20 each—but they can be used many times before they lose their keen edge. And obsidian scalpel blades can be 100 times sharper than traditional scalpel blades!

During surgery, steel scalpels actually tear the skin apart. Obsidian scalpels divide the skin and cause much less damage. Some plastic surgeons use obsidian blades to make extremely fine incisions that leave almost no scarring. An obsidian-scalpel incision heals more quickly because the blade causes less damage to the skin and other tissues.

▲ *An obsidian scalpel can have an edge as fine as a single molecule.*

Many patients have allergic reactions to mineral components in steel blades. These patients often do not have an allergic reaction when obsidian scalpels are used. Given all of these advantages, it is not surprising that some physicians have made the change to obsidian scalpels.

A Long Tradition

Early Native Americans were among the first people to recognize that chipped obsidian has extremely sharp edges. Native Americans made obsidian arrowheads and knife blades by flaking away chips of rock by hand. Today obsidian scalpels are fashioned in much the same way by a *knapper,* a person who makes stone tools by hand. Knappers use the same basic technique that people have used for thousands of years to make obsidian blades and other stone tools.

Find Out for Yourself!

▶ Making obsidian blades and other stone tools requires a great deal of skill. Find out about the steps a knapper follows to create a stone tool. Find a piece of rock, and see if you can follow the steps to create a stone tool of your own. Be careful not to hit your fingers, and wear safety goggles.

53

HEALTH WATCH
Glass Scalpels

Background

Medical professionals use a variety of tools and treatments that rely on rocks and minerals. As students have learned in this chapter, every rock has unique properties that vary depending on its composition, its crystalline structure, and the conditions in which it formed. For example, obsidian's most prominent characteristic is the lack of a crystalline structure.

Students will know that diamonds are valuable gemstones, but they may be surprised that diamonds are frequently used in medicine. For example, dentists use drill bits coated with synthetic diamonds. Synthetic diamonds are used because they are much less expensive than their natural counterparts and are disposable. Diamonds are four times harder than the next hardest natural mineral.

Chapter Organizer

CHAPTER ORGANIZATION	TIME MINUTES	OBJECTIVES	LABS, INVESTIGATIONS, AND DEMONSTRATIONS
Chapter Opener pp. 54–55	45	National Standards: SAI 1, HNS 1, 2, ES 2b	**Start-Up Activity,** Making Fossils, p. 55
Section 1 Earth's Story and Those Who First Listened	45	▶ Identify the role of uniformitarianism in Earth science. ▶ Contrast uniformitarianism with catastrophism. ▶ Describe how the role of catastrophism in Earth science has changed. UCP 2, 4, SAI 1, HNS 1–3, ES 2a	**Inquiry Labs,** A Penny for Your Thoughts
Section 2 Relative Dating: Which Came First?	90	▶ Explain how relative dating is used in geology. ▶ Explain the principle of superposition. ▶ Demonstrate an understanding of the geologic column. ▶ Identify two events and two features that disrupt rock sequences. ▶ Explain how physical features are used to determine relative ages. UCP 1–4, SAI 1, 2, ES 2b; Labs UCP 1, 2, SAI 1	**Demonstration,** p. 59 in ATE **Discovery Lab,** How DO You Stack Up? p. 78 **Datasheets for LabBook,** How DO You Stack Up? **Labs You Can Eat,** Geopancakes
Section 3 Absolute Dating: A Measure of Time	90	▶ Explain how radioactive decay occurs. ▶ Explain how radioactive decay relates to radiometric dating. ▶ List three types of radiometric dating. ▶ Determine the best type of radiometric dating to use to date an object. UCP 1, 3, SAI 1	**Long-Term Projects and Research Ideas,** The Hard Rock Chronicles
Section 4 Looking at Fossils	90	▶ Describe how different types of fossils are formed. ▶ List the types of fossils that are not part of organisms. ▶ Demonstrate how fossils can be used to determine changes in environments and in the organisms the fossils came from. ▶ Describe index fossils, and explain how they are used. UCP 3, ST 2, SPSP 5, ES 1k, ES 2b	
Section 5 Time Marches On	90	▶ Demonstrate an understanding of the geologic time scale. ▶ Identify important dates on the geologic time scale. ▶ Identify the eon we know the most about, and explain why we know more about it than other eons. UCP 1–4, SAI 1, ES 2b	**EcoLabs And Field Activities,** Rock of Ages **QuickLab,** Make a Time Scale, p. 77

*See page **T23** for a complete correlation of this book with the*

NATIONAL SCIENCE EDUCATION STANDARDS.

TECHNOLOGY RESOURCES

 Guided Reading Audio CD English or Spanish, Chapter 3

 One-Stop Planner **CD-ROM with Test Generator**

 CNN. Scientists in Action, Dinosaur Egg Discovery, Segment 9, Creating Digital Dinos, Segment 12

Multicultural Connections, A Thailand Fossil Discovery, Segment 4 Protecting New Mexico's Petroglyphs, Segment 6

CLASSROOM WORKSHEETS, TRANSPARENCIES, AND RESOURCES	SCIENCE INTEGRATION AND CONNECTIONS	REVIEW AND ASSESSMENT
Directed Reading Worksheet **Science Puzzlers, Twisters & Teasers**	**Career: Paleontologist—Jack Horner**, p. 85	
Directed Reading Worksheet, Section 1 **Transparency 118**, Hutton and the Principle of Uniformitarianism	**Multicultural Connection**, p. 56 in ATE **Biology Connection**, p. 57 **Apply**, p. 57 **Cross-Disciplinary Focus**, p. 58 in ATE	**Section Review**, p. 58 **Quiz**, p. 58 in ATE **Alternative Assessment**, p. 58 in ATE
Directed Reading Worksheet, Section 2 **Transparency 119**, Constructing the Geologic Column **Transparency 120**, Formation of Unconformities **Reinforcement Worksheet**, A Geologic Column Sandwich	**Real-World Connection**, p. 62 in ATE	**Homework**, p. 62 in ATE **Section Review**, p. 63 **Quiz**, p. 63 in ATE **Alternative Assessment**, p. 63 in ATE
Directed Reading Worksheet, Section 3 **Transparency 263**, Radioactive Decay and Half-life	**MathBreak**, Get a Half-Life! p. 65 **Math and More**, p. 65 in ATE **Connect to Physical Science**, p. 65 in ATE **Cross-Disciplinary Focus**, p. 66 in ATE **Connect to Life Science**, p. 67 in ATE	**Section Review**, p. 67 **Quiz**, p. 67 in ATE **Alternative Assessment**, p. 67 in ATE
Directed Reading Worksheet, Section 4 **Critical Thinking Worksheet**, Adiós Alamosaurus	**Science, Technology, and Society:** CAT Scanning Fossils, p. 84	**Self-Check**, p. 70 **Homework**, p. 72 in ATE **Section Review**, p. 72 **Quiz**, p. 72 in ATE **Alternative Assessment**, p. 72 in ATE
Directed Reading Worksheet, Section 5 **Transparency 121**, The Geologic Time Scale	**Biology Connection**, p. 73 **Connect to Life Science**, p. 74 in ATE **Math and More**, p. 75 in ATE **Cross-Disciplinary Focus**, p. 75 in ATE	**Homework**, pp. 74, 76 in ATE **Section Review**, p. 77 **Quiz**, p. 77 in ATE **Alternative Assessment**, p. 77 in ATE

 internet**connect**

 Holt, Rinehart and Winston On-line Resources
go.hrw.com

For worksheets and other teaching aids related to this chapter, visit the HRW Web site and type in the keyword: **HSTFOS**

 National Science Teachers Association
www.scilinks.org

Encourage students to use the *sci*LINKS numbers listed in the internet connect boxes to access information and resources on the **NSTA** Web site.

END-OF-CHAPTER REVIEW AND ASSESSMENT

Chapter Review in Study Guide
Vocabulary and Notes in Study Guide
Chapter Tests with Performance-Based Assessment, Chapter 3 Test, Performance-Based Assessment 3
Concept Mapping Transparency 6

Chapter Resources & Worksheets

Visual Resources

TEACHING TRANSPARENCIES

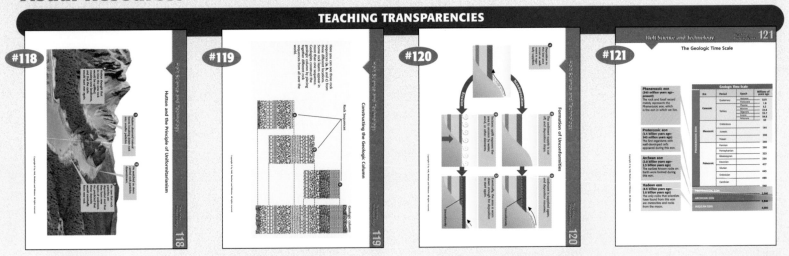

#118 — Hutton and the Principle of Uniformitarianism

#119 — Constructing the Geologic Column

#120 — Formation of Unconformities

#121 — The Geologic Time Scale

TEACHING TRANSPARENCIES

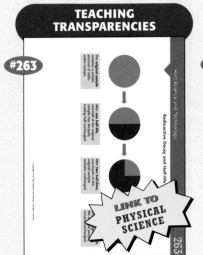

#263 — Radioactive Decay and Half-Life

LINK TO PHYSICAL SCIENCE

CONCEPT MAPPING TRANSPARENCY

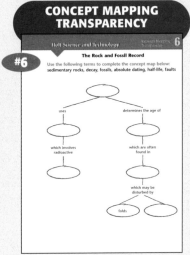

#6 — The Rock and Fossil Record

Use the following terms to complete the concept map below: sedimentary rocks, decay, fossils, absolute dating, half-life, faults

Meeting Individual Needs

DIRECTED READING

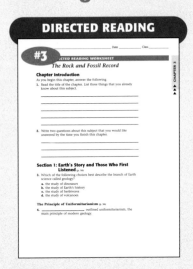

#3 — DIRECTED READING WORKSHEET
The Rock and Fossil Record

REINFORCEMENT & VOCABULARY REVIEW

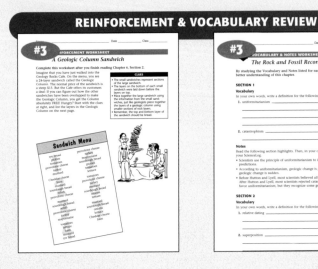

#3 — REINFORCEMENT WORKSHEET
A Geologic Column Sandwich

#3 — VOCABULARY & NOTES WORKSHEET
The Rock and Fossil Record

SCIENCE PUZZLERS, TWISTERS & TEASERS

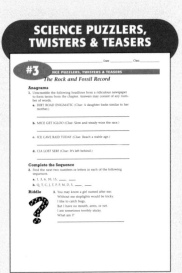

#3 — SCIENCE PUZZLERS, TWISTERS & TEASERS
The Rock and Fossil Record

Chapter 3 • The Rock and Fossil Record

Review & Assessment

STUDY GUIDE

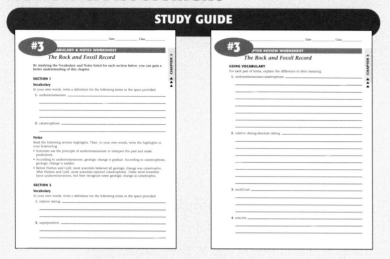

CHAPTER TESTS WITH PERFORMANCE-BASED ASSESSMENT

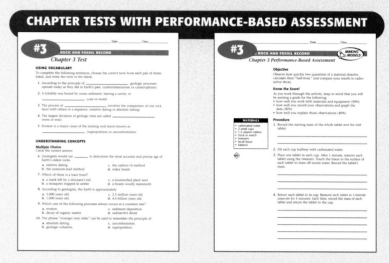

Lab Worksheets

INQUIRY LABS

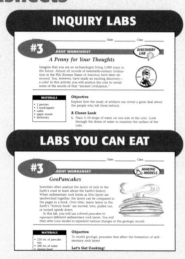

LABS YOU CAN EAT

ECOLABS & FIELD ACTIVITIES

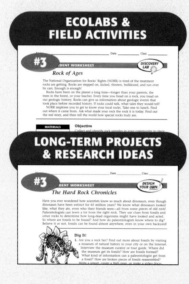

LONG-TERM PROJECTS & RESEARCH IDEAS

DATASHEETS FOR LABBOOK

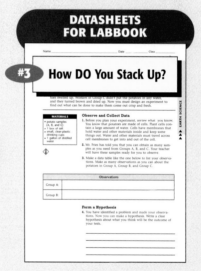

Applications & Extensions

CRITICAL THINKING & PROBLEM SOLVING

MULTICULTURAL CONNECTIONS

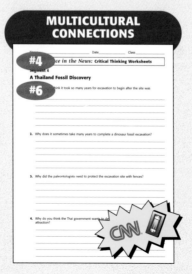

SCIENTISTS IN ACTION

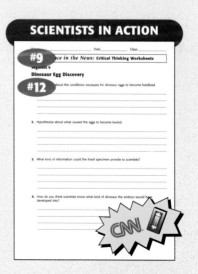

SECTION 1

Earth's Story and Those Who First Listened

▶ Baron Georges Cuvier

Baron Georges Cuvier, a French naturalist and pioneer in comparative anatomy, was the leading proponent of catastrophism. He used his skills as an anatomist to figure out what extinct animals looked like from just a few fossil bones.

▶ Evolution and Uniformitarianism

The development of geology and the theory of evolution are closely tied together. The arguments of both fields lent support and evidence for each other. The fossil record provided clear evidence of evolution, and the biological record gave a time reference to geology. The union of these two fields gave rise to paleontology and historical geology.

▶ Actualism

Although James Hutton was the first to introduce the principles of uniformitarianism, he is considered an actualist, not a strict uniformitarianist. He recognized that while many geologic processes happen slowly, some occur more abruptly. Contemporary geologists accept actualism as a more logical explanation of Earth's history.

SECTION 2

Relative Dating: Which Came First?

▶ Nicolaus Steno

Credit for discovering the principles of superposition and original horizontality is given to Niels Stensen (also known as Nicolaus Steno), born in Denmark on January 10, 1638. Though originally trained in anatomy and medicine, Steno became interested in geology while serving as the house physician to Grand Duke Ferdinand II of Tuscany. It was during this period that Steno made significant geologic discoveries. In addition to establishing the principles of superposition and original horizontality, Nicolaus Steno

was one of the first Western scientists to argue that fossils were organic in nature.

IS THAT A FACT!

➤ Despite his numerous contributions to medicine and geology, Nicolaus Steno gave up his scientific career in 1677 to become a bishop. He died 9 years later on December 6, 1686.

SECTION 3

Absolute Dating: A Measure of Time

▶ Marie and Pierre Curie

The Curies met in spring 1894 while Marie was studying mathematics and physics at the Sorbonne, in Paris. They married in 1895 and worked together in Pierre's laboratory. Marie began work on her doctoral thesis shortly after 1896, the year Henri Becquerel discovered that a strange radiation was emitted by uranium. Marie continued Becquerel's work, obtained her doctorate on radioactive substances in 1903, and won the Nobel Prize for physics with her husband and Becquerel.

• In 1906, Pierre was killed in a wagon accident in Paris. Marie, grief-stricken, dedicated the rest of her life to the work she and her husband had begun. She headed his laboratory at the Sorbonne and became the first woman lecturer at the university. In 1911, Marie Curie received her second Nobel Prize, this time in chemistry for isolating pure radium. She died on July 4, 1934, of leukemia, no doubt caused by her prolonged exposure to radiation.

▶ Radiometric Age-Dating

The work of Becquerel and the Curies eventually changed the fields of archaeology, geology, and paleontology. Before their work, geologists were restricted to using relative methods of dating when trying to determine the age of rocks and minerals. However, after it was discovered that radioactive elements decay at a constant rate, the American chemist Willard Libby developed radiocarbon dating in the late 1940s.

▶ Clock Numerals and Cancer

The carcinogenic effects of radium were discovered by accident in the 1930s. A paste of radium salts and zinc sulfide was used to paint numbers on watch faces to make them glow. Radium was discontinued after it was discovered that many of the radium painters developed mouth and throat cancer. To form a precise brush point, the painters, mostly women, used their mouth to moisten the brush tip between strokes. The element promethium, which emits less-hazardous radiation, soon replaced radium.

SECTION 4

Looking at Fossils

▶ Prehistoric Weevil DNA

In 1993, research in the field of fossil DNA took a tremendous leap forward when Dr. George Poinar, of the University of California at Berkeley, successfully extracted fragmented DNA from the tissue of a 125-million-year-old weevil encased in amber found in Lebanon. The weevil was so well preserved in the amber that even its muscle tissue was intact.

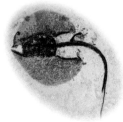

▶ Coelacanths: Living Fossils

Coelacanths are large, carnivorous, lobe-finned fish. Their fossil record dates back to over 350 million years

ago and, until recently, they were believed to have become extinct about 65 million years ago. In 1938, Marjorie Courtenay-Latimer, a museum curator in a small port village near Cape Town, South Africa, noticed an unusual blue-finned fish among the day's catch at the local docks—it was a coelacanth! A second coelacanth was recovered in 1952 by anglers, again off the African coast. It is believed that only a few hundred of the fish still survive and, in 1995, researchers declared the animal in danger of extinction.

- In 1998, Dr. Mark Erdmann confirmed at least two coelacanth specimens from North Sulawesi, Indonesia, 10,000 km from the African coast. The coelacanths were discovered living in volcanic caves below sea level. It is hoped that coelacanths live in many of the unexplored sea caves of the Indonesian archipelago.

IS THAT A FACT!

➥ The largest coprolite ever found is a 65-million-year-old mound of feces probably left by a *Tyrannosaurus rex.* It is 43 cm across and 15 cm high.

SECTION 5

Time Marches On

▶ Life in the Precambrian Era

The period of time spanning from the formation of Earth 4.6 billion years ago to 540 million years ago is called the Precambrian era. It encompasses more than 80 percent of the geologic time scale. Until the discovery of soft-bodied organisms in Australia in 1947, paleontologists believed that only single-celled microorganisms and blue-green algae lived during this period. Now scientists know that a wide variety of animals resembling jellyfish, annelids, and even echinoderms evolved in Precambrian seas between 590 and 700 million years ago. These are so far the oldest known multicellular organisms.

For background information about teaching strategies and issues, refer to the *Professional Reference for Teachers.*

The Rock and Fossil Record

The Rock and Fossil Record

 Pre-Reading Questions

Students may not know the answers to these questions before reading the chapter, so accept any reasonable response.

Suggested Answers

1. Students might mention both absolute and relative dating methods.

2. No; trace fossils are preserved evidence of animal activity and do not contain any animal parts.

3. Answers will vary. Students should note that scientists analyze the rock and fossil record and observe processes occurring today in order to form theories about the Earth's history.

Sections

 **Pre-Reading Questions**

1. How can you determine if some rocks and fossils are older than others?

2. Are fossils always made up of parts of plants or animals?

3. How do scientists study the Earth's history?

TIME STANDS STILL

Sealed in darkness for 49 million years, this beetle still shimmers with the same metallic hues that once helped it hide among ancient plants. This rare fossil was found in Messel, Germany. In the same rock formation, scientists have found fossilized crocodiles, bats, birds, and frogs. A living stag beetle *(below)* has a similar form and color. Do you think that these two beetles would live in similar environments? What do you think Messel, Germany, was like 49 million years ago? In this chapter, you will learn how scientists answer questions like these.

⚡ internet**connect**

 HRW On-line Resources

go.hrw.com
For worksheets and other teaching aids, visit the HRW Web site and type in the keyword: **HSTFOS**

 NSTA

www.scilinks.com
Use the *sci*LINKS numbers at the end of each chapter for additional resources on the **NSTA** Web site.

 Smithsonian Institution®

www.si.edu/hrw
Visit the Smithsonian Institution Web site for related on-line resources.

CNNfyi.com

www.cnnfyi.com
Visit the CNN Web site for current events coverage and classroom resources.

MAKING FOSSILS

How do scientists learn from fossils? In this activity, you will study "fossils" and identify the object that made each.

Procedure

1. You and three or four of your classmates will be given several pieces of **modeling clay** and a paper sack containing a few **small objects.**

2. Press each object firmly into a piece of clay. Try to leave a fossil imprint showing as much detail as possible.

3. After you have made an imprint of each object, exchange your model fossils with another group.

4. In your ScienceLog, describe the fossils you have received. List as many details as possible. What patterns and textures do you observe?

5. Work as a group to identify each fossil and check your results. Were you right?

Analysis

6. What kinds of details were important in identifying your fossils? What kinds of details were not preserved in the imprints? For example, can you tell the color of the objects?

7. Explain how Earth scientists follow similar methods when studying fossils.

START-UP
Activity

MAKING FOSSILS

MATERIALS

FOR EACH GROUP:
• several pieces of modeling clay
• a paper sack containing several small objects, such as coins, paper clips, buttons, army men, or any other objects with recognizable textures or shapes.

Answers to START-UP Activity

6. Sample answer: Textures and distinctive shapes were useful in identifying the model fossils. Small details, colors, and the internal structures of the objects were not preserved.

7. Sample answer: Earth scientists carefully observe fossil remains to determine what organism left them.

55

Focus

Earth's Story and Those Who First Listened

In this section, students explore the beginnings of modern geology by comparing and contrasting uniformitarianism and catastrophism—two early theories regarding geologic processes. Students learn that the forces that shaped the Earth around them are still at work today and that modern geology is a synthesis of both theories.

Bellringer

On the board write "The Present is the Key to the Past." Tell students that this phrase was the cornerstone of the uniformitarianist theory developed by geologist James Hutton in the late 1700s. Have students write a few sentences about how studying the present could reveal the story of Earth's history. Have students illustrate their comments with a few sketches of processes they can see today that also occurred millions of years ago.

1 Motivate

ACTIVITY

PORTFOLIO Have students design a poster announcing an upcoming debate between a catastrophist and a uniformitarian. Encourage students to use attention-catching phrases and illustrations that would attract supporters from both sides. Have them summarize the major points of both sides, and display the finished posters in the classroom.
Sheltered English

Terms to Learn

uniformitarianism
catastrophism

What You'll Do

◆ Identify the role of uniformitarianism in Earth science.
◆ Contrast uniformitarianism with catastrophism.
◆ Describe how the role of catastrophism in Earth science has changed.

Earth's Story and Those Who First Listened

Humans have wondered about Earth's history for thousands of years. But the branch of Earth science called *geology,* which involves the study of Earth's history, got a late start. The main concept of modern geology was not outlined until the late eighteenth century. Within a few decades, this concept replaced a more traditional concept of Earth's history. Today, both concepts are an essential part of Earth science.

The Principle of Uniformitarianism

In 1795, a philosopher and scientist named James Hutton published *Theory of the Earth,* in which he wrote that Earth's landforms are constantly changing. As shown in **Figure 1,** Hutton assumed that these changes result from geologic processes—such as the breakdown of rock and the transport of sediment—that remain uniform, or do not change, over time. This assumption is now called uniformitarianism. **Uniformitarianism** is a principle that states that the same geologic processes shaping the Earth today have been at work throughout Earth's history. "The present is the key to the past" is a phrase that best summarizes uniformitarianism.

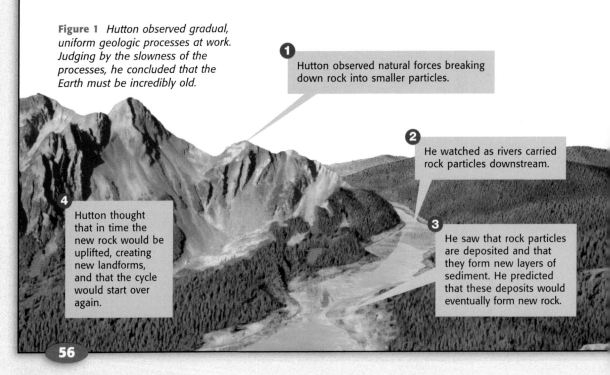

Figure 1 *Hutton observed gradual, uniform geologic processes at work. Judging by the slowness of the processes, he concluded that the Earth must be incredibly old.*

1 Hutton observed natural forces breaking down rock into smaller particles.

2 He watched as rivers carried rock particles downstream.

3 He saw that rock particles are deposited and that they form new layers of sediment. He predicted that these deposits would eventually form new rock.

4 Hutton thought that in time the new rock would be uplifted, creating new landforms, and that the cycle would start over again.

56

Multicultural CONNECTION

Many of the ideas that form the basis of modern geology came from Scottish scientists. Among the famous Scottish geologists are James Hutton, Charles Lyell, Sir James Hall, Roderick Murchison, and John Playfair. Have students research these or other Scottish geologists to discover the contributions they made to modern geology.

IS THAT A FACT!

James Hutton's colleague, Sir James Hall, dramatically demonstrated Hutton's theories by melting rock in a furnace and letting it cool, showing how it changed from one form to another. This demonstration struck a major blow against the catastrophists.

APPLY

Making Assumptions

Examine the photographs at right. List the letters of the photos in the order you think the photos were taken. Now think of all the assumptions that you made to infer that order. Write down as many of these assumptions as you can. Compare notes with your classmates. Did you get the same sequence? Were your assumptions similar?

In science, assumptions must also be made. For example, you assume that the sun will rise each day. Briefly explain the importance of being able to count on certain things always being the same. How does this apply to uniformitarianism?

Uniformitarianism Versus Catastrophism In Hutton's time most people thought that the Earth had existed for only thousands of years. This was not nearly enough time for the gradual geologic processes that Hutton described to have shaped our planet. But uniformitarianism was not immediately accepted. Instead, most scientists believed in catastrophism. **Catastrophism** is a principle that states that all geologic change occurs suddenly. Supporters of catastrophism claimed that the formation of all Earth's features, such as its mountains, canyons, and seas, could be explained by rare, sudden events called *catastrophes*. These unpredictable catastrophes caused rapid geologic changes over large areas—sometimes even globally.

Uniformitarianism Wins! Despite Hutton's observations, catastrophism remained geology's guiding principle for decades. It took the work of Charles Lyell, another scientist, for people to seriously consider uniformitarianism.

From 1830 to 1833, Lyell published three volumes collectively titled *Principles of Geology,* in which he reintroduced uniformitarianism. Armed with Hutton's notes and new evidence of his own, Lyell successfully challenged the principle of catastrophism. Lyell saw no reason to doubt that major geologic change happened the same way in the past as it does in the present—gradually.

Biology
CONNECTION

As a friend of Charles Lyell, Charles Darwin was greatly influenced by Lyell's unitarian ideas. Lyell's influence became clear when Darwin published *On the Origin of Species by Natural Selection* in 1859. Similar to uniformitarianism, Darwin's theory of evolution proposes that changes in species occur gradually over long periods of time.

Answers to APPLY

Answers will vary. Accept all reasonable responses.

REAL-WORLD CONNECTION

Use the following example to discuss uniformitarianism and catastrophism. Tell students to suppose they have a cousin. They see their cousin when she is born, again when she is 3 years old and again when she is 7 and 14. Students will notice a dramatic difference each time they see her. Ask students why they know those changes took place gradually instead of suddenly.
Sheltered English

DEBATE

Uniformitarianism Vs. Catastrophism Ask students to engage in a debate that might have taken place between James Hutton and the catastrophists. Emphasize to students representing the catastrophists that their argument had a strong theological base and was the accepted geologic theory of the time. Help students imagine the opposition James Hutton must have faced when he introduced his ideas. Students can advertise their debates with the posters they made in the Motivate activity.

internet**connect**

SCiLINKS
NSTA

TOPIC: Earth's Story
GO TO: www.scilinks.org
*sci***LINKS NUMBER:** HSTE130

SCIENCE
HUMOR

When Mr. Hutton studied Earth's tiers,
He proposed what was rejected for years:
That to form rocks of lime,
It takes EONS of time,
Not an evening, as proposed by his peers.

Directed Reading Worksheet Section 1

Teaching Transparency 118 "Hutton and the Principle of Uniformitarianism"

CROSS-DISCIPLINARY FOCUS

Language Arts Although Charles Darwin and Charles Lyell were avid correspondents and good friends, they did not agree on everything. Darwin was quick to accept the principle of uniformitarianism (he read Lyell's *Principles of Geology* before his famous 1831 HMS *Beagle* voyage), but Lyell did not readily embrace Darwin's theories of natural selection. It was not until much later in life that Charles Lyell became a vigorous supporter of Darwin's ideas. Invite students to write a script for a conversation that the two scientists might have had. Have them imagine that Darwin has just returned from his *Beagle* journey. What questions might Darwin and Lyell have exchanged? Students can present the conversations as short skits.

Quiz

1. What is catastrophism?
   (the idea that geologic change occurred suddenly as a result of infrequent disastrous events)

2. Describe uniformitarianism.
   (the view that the Earth is shaped by gradual changes that are still occurring today)

ALTERNATIVE ASSESSMENT

Writing Have students write a letter to Charles Lyell or James Hutton. The letter should explain why the student agrees or disagrees with the scientist's theories. Suggest that students end the letter with at least two questions that they would like to ask the scientist. Have students exchange letters and answer each other's questions.

BRAIN FOOD

Did you know that the first dinosaur bones were not identified until 1841? Hutton and Lyell developed their ideas without knowledge of these giants of prehistory.

Modern Geology—A Happy Medium

Today scientists realize that neither uniformitarianism nor catastrophism accounts for all of Earth's history. Although most geologic change is gradual and uniform, catastrophes do occur occasionally. For example, huge craters have been found where asteroids and comets are thought to have struck Earth in the past. Some of these strikes indeed may have been catastrophic. Some scientists think one such asteroid strike led to the extinction of the dinosaurs, as explained in **Figure 2**. The impact of an asteroid is thought to have spread debris into the atmosphere around the entire planet, blocking the sun's rays and causing major changes in the global climate.

Figure 2 *Today scientists think that sudden events are responsible for some changes in Earth's past. An asteroid hitting Earth, for example, may have led to the extinction of the dinosaurs 65 million years ago.*

internet connect

SCILINKS
NSTA

TOPIC: Earth's Story
GO TO: www.scilinks.org
*sci*LINKS **NUMBER:** HSTE130

SECTION REVIEW

1. Why do Earth scientists need the principle of uniformitarianism in order to make predictions?

2. What is the difference between uniformitarianism and catastrophism?

3. **Summarizing Data** How has the role of catastrophism in Earth science changed?

▼ *Answers to Section Review*

1. Scientists make predictions based on the past as well as the present. To make predictions, they must assume that geologic processes will be similar in the future.

2. Catastrophism states that the geologic history of the Earth was dominated by sudden, drastic changes that built features such as mountains, valleys, and oceans. Uniformi-tarianism argues that the Earth is shaped by slow, gradual processes that can still be observed today.

3. Geologists now agree that sudden catastrophic events such as asteroid impacts or volcanic eruptions can also cause geologic change.

Terms to Learn

relative dating
superposition
geologic column
unconformity

What You'll Do

- ◆ Explain how relative dating is used in geology.
- ◆ Explain the principle of superposition.
- ◆ Demonstrate an understanding of the geologic column.
- ◆ Identify two events and two features that disrupt rock sequences.
- ◆ Explain how physical features are used to determine relative ages.

Relative Dating: Which Came First?

Imagine that you are a detective investigating a crime scene. What is the first thing you would do? You might begin by dusting the scene for fingerprints or by searching for witnesses. As a detective, your goal is to figure out the sequence of events that took place before you arrived at the scene.

Geologists have a similar goal when investigating the Earth. They try to determine the order of events that led to how the Earth looks today. But instead of fingerprints and witnesses, geologists rely on rocks and fossils. Determining whether an object or event is older or younger than other objects or events is called **relative dating.**

The Principle of Superposition

Suppose you have an older brother who takes a lot of photographs of your family but never puts them into an album. He just piles them in a box. Over the years, he keeps adding new pictures to the top of the stack. Think about the family history recorded in those pictures. Where are the oldest pictures—the ones taken when you were a baby? Where are the most recent pictures—those taken last week?

Rock layers, such as the ones shown in **Figure 3,** are like stacked pictures. The oldest layers are at the bottom. As you move from bottom to top, the layers get more recent, or younger. Scientists call this superposition. **Superposition** is a principle that states that younger rocks lie above older rocks in undisturbed sequences. "Younger over older" is a phrase you can use to remember this principle.

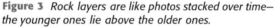

Figure 3 *Rock layers are like photos stacked over time—the younger ones lie above the older ones.*

59

Directed Reading Worksheet Section 2

Focus

Relative Dating: Which Came First?

In this section, students learn how the principle of superposition is used to interpret Earth's history. They will practice relative dating techniques and learn how the geologic column is used to understand the sequence of Earth's rock formations. The section concludes with a discussion of three types of unconformities that occur in rock layers.

🔔 Bellringer

Ask students to arrange the following sentences in a logical order to make a short story:

I stood in the checkout line.
I selected two apples.
I walked home from the store.
I gave the cashier money.
I went to the store.
The cashier gave me change.
I was hungry.
Sheltered English

1) Motivate

DEMONSTRATION

Stack several books on your desk. Tell students that the books represent layers of rock that were deposited at different times. Ask students: Which layer would be the oldest? (the one on the bottom)

Which rock layer is the youngest? (the one on top)

Ask students to discuss how they arrived at these answers, and tell them that they have just applied a basic geologic concept—the principle of superposition.

4. The book contains all of the chapters in the correct order. Similarly, the geologic column is a sequence of all the known rock layers and fossils. By using the geologic column, geologists can put rock layers in the correct order even if some layers are missing.

INDEPENDENT PRACTICE

The geologic column is an easy concept for students to understand if they get some hands-on practice. Before the lesson, you may wish to make photocopies of the exercise at the bottom of this page. Cut out the columns, and have students work independently to correctly align them.
Sheltered English

MISCONCEPTION //// ALERT \\\\

Emphasize to students that no single locality in the world has a continuous sequence of all the rocks formed throughout geologic history. The geologic column is an idealized sequence of rock layers that have accumulated around the world since the Earth formed. The geologic column was first pieced together in the mid-nineteenth century, and it is continually revised as geologists map more of the Earth.

Teaching Transparency 119
"Constructing the Geologic Column"

Activity

1. Write the titles of 10 chapters of this book on 10 note cards (one title on each note card).
2. Shuffle the cards and exchange them with a partner. Try to put your partner's titles in the correct order without using your book.
3. Compare your order with the order in the book.
4. Your work would have been easier if you had been allowed to use your book. How does this relate to geologists using the geologic column to put rock layers in order?

Disturbing Forces Some rock-layer sequences, however, are disturbed by forces from within the Earth. These forces can push other rocks into a sequence, tilt or fold rock layers, and break sequences into movable parts. Sometimes these forces even put older layers above younger layers, which goes against superposition. The disruptions of rock sequences caused by these forces pose a great challenge to geologists trying to determine the relative ages of rocks. Fortunately, geologists can get help from a very valuable tool—the geologic column.

The Geologic Column

To make their job easier, geologists combine data from all the known undisturbed rock sequences around the world. From this information, geologists create the *geologic column*. The **geologic column** is an ideal sequence of rock layers that contains all the known fossils and rock formations on Earth arranged from oldest to youngest.

Geologists rely on the geologic column to interpret rock sequences. For example, when geologists are not sure about the age of a rock sequence they are studying, they gather information about the sequence and compare it to the geologic column. Geologists also use the geologic column to identify the layers in puzzling rock sequences, such as sequences that have been folded over.

Constructing the Geologic Column

Here you can see three rock sequences (**a**, **b**, and **c**) from three different locations. Some rock layers appear in more than one sequence. Geologists construct the geologic column by piecing together different rock sequences from all over the world.

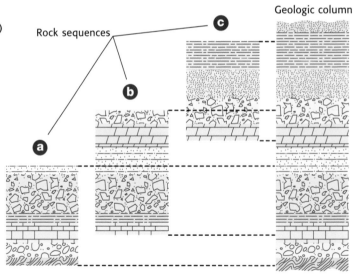

Rock sequences

Geologic column

60

internetconnect

SCiLINKS

NSTA

TOPIC: Relative Dating
GO TO: www.scilinks.org
*sci*LINKS NUMBER: HSTE135

Disturbed Rock Layers

Geologists often find features that cut through existing rock layers. Geologists use the relationships between rock layers and the features that cut across them to assign relative ages to the features and the layers. They know that those features are younger than the rock layers because the rock layers had to be present before the features could cut across them.

Faults and intrusions are examples of features that cut across rock layers. A *fault* is a break in the Earth's crust along which blocks of the crust slide relative to one another. Another cross-cutting feature is an intrusion. An *intrusion* is molten rock from the Earth's interior that squeezes into existing rock and cools. **Figure 4** illustrates both of these features.

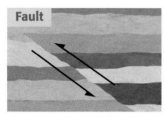
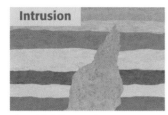

Figure 4 *A fault (left) and an intrusion (right) are always younger than the layers they cut across.*

Geologists assume that the way sediment is deposited to form rock layers—in horizontal layers—has not changed over time. According to this principle, if rock layers are not horizontal, something must have disturbed them after they formed. This principle allows geologists to determine the relative ages of rock layers and the events that disturbed them.

Folding and tilting are two additional types of events that disturb rock layers. *Folding* occurs when rock layers bend and buckle from Earth's internal forces. *Tilting* occurs when internal forces in the Earth slant rock layers without folding them. **Figure 5** illustrates the results of folding and tilting.

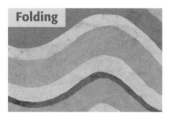

Figure 5 *Folding (left) and tilting (right) are events that are always younger than the rock layers they affect.*

61

GROUP ACTIVITY

Try to arrange a field trip to a local area with exposed rock strata. If possible, contact a geologist from a local university or a museum to accompany the group. In small groups of three or four, have students try to find at least two unconformities and explain their origins. Encourage students to make drawings of the rock formations that they observe, labeling the features that are described in this chapter.

REAL-WORLD CONNECTION

Road cuts are excellent places to study the geology of your area. Tell students that the next time they are in a car and pass a road cut, they should try to spot unconformities. One unconformity is at the point where soil meets the bedrock. If students want to explore a road cut by foot, remind them to exercise caution around unstable rocks and passing cars.

GOING FURTHER

Have students study **Figure 6** and then work independently to create a comic strip that continues the sequence of images in the figure. Students can illustrate events such as intrusions, tilting, folding, faulting, or volcanic deposition as well as unconformities. Have students share their illustrations with the class and explain the geologic history of their comic strip.

Teaching Transparency 120 "Formation of Unconformities"

BRAIN FOOD

Many high-rise apartment and office buildings exhibit something similar to an unconformity—they do not have a 13th floor. Instead, the floors skip from 12 to 14.

Gaps in the Record—Unconformities

Faults, intrusions, and the effects of folding and tilting can make dating rock layers a challenge. But sometimes layers of rock are missing altogether, creating a gap in the geologic record. To think of this another way, let's say that you stack your newspapers every day after reading them. Now let's suppose you want to look at a paper you read 10 days ago. You know that the paper you want should be 10 papers deep in the stack. But when you look, the paper is not there. What happened? Perhaps you forgot to put the paper in the stack. Now instead of a missing newspaper, imagine a missing rock layer.

Missing Evidence Missing rock layers create gaps in rock-layer sequences called unconformities. An **unconformity** is a surface that represents a missing part of the geologic column. Unconformities also represent missing time—time that was not recorded in layers of rock. When geologists find unconformities, they must question whether the "missing layers" were actually present or whether they were somehow removed. **Figure 6** shows how *nondeposition* and *erosion* create unconformities.

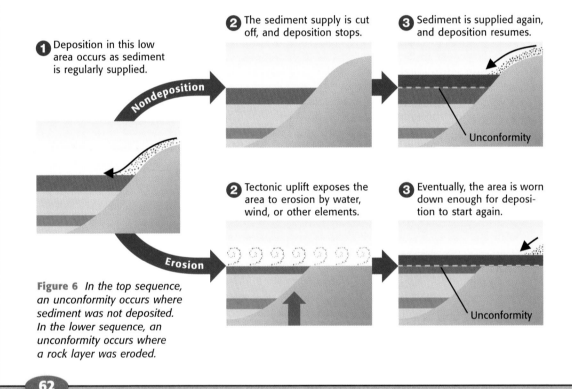

① Deposition in this low area occurs as sediment is regularly supplied.

Nondeposition

② The sediment supply is cut off, and deposition stops.

③ Sediment is supplied again, and deposition resumes.

Unconformity

Erosion

② Tectonic uplift exposes the area to erosion by water, wind, or other elements.

③ Eventually, the area is worn down enough for deposition to start again.

Unconformity

Figure 6 *In the top sequence, an unconformity occurs where sediment was not deposited. In the lower sequence, an unconformity occurs where a rock layer was eroded.*

62

Homework

Making Models Have students draw and label disconformities, nonconformities, and angular unconformities in their ScienceLog. Ask them to identify the youngest and the oldest rocks and include examples of intrusions, folds, and faults.

IS THAT A FACT!

Unconformities can represent a short gap in the geologic record or a very long one. The time gap can be as little as a few hundred years or as much as several billion years. Geologists must analyze many different variables to determine how much time an unconformity represents.

Types of Unconformities

Most unconformities form by both erosion and nondeposition. But other factors can complicate matters. To simplify the study of unconformities, geologists put them in three major categories—disconformities, nonconformities, and angular unconformities. The three diagrams at right illustrate these three categories.

Rock-Layer Puzzles

Geologists often find rock-layer sequences that have been affected by more than one of the events and features mentioned in this section. For example, an intrusion may squeeze into rock layers that contain an unconformity and that have been cut across by a fault. Determining the order of events that led to such a sequence is like piecing together a jigsaw puzzle.

SECTION REVIEW

1. In a rock-layer sequence that hasn't been disturbed, are older layers found on top of younger layers? What rule do you use to answer this question?

2. List five events or features that can disturb rock-layer sequences.

3. Consider a fault that cuts through all the layers of a rock-layer sequence. Is the fault older or younger than the layers? Explain.

4. **Analyzing Methods** Unlike other types of unconformities, disconformities are hard to recognize because all the layers are horizontal. How does a geologist know when he or she is looking at a disconformity?

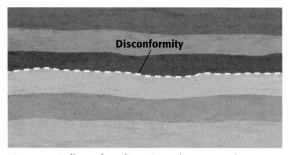

Figure 7 *A disconformity exists where part of a sequence of parallel rock layers is missing. While often hard to see, a disconformity is the most common type of unconformity.*

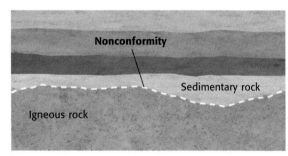

Figure 8 *A nonconformity exists where sedimentary rock layers lie on top of an eroded surface of non-layered igneous or metamorphic rock.*

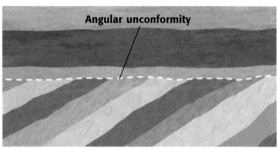

Figure 9 *An angular unconformity exists between horizontal rock layers and rock layers that are tilted or folded. The tilted or folded layers were eroded before horizontal layers formed above them.*

63

▼ **Answers to Section Review**

1. No; the younger layers are found on top. the principle of superposition

2. Answers will vary but should include a fault, an intrusion, a disconformity, a nonconformity, and an angular unconformity.

3. The fault is younger than the layers. The layers had to be present for the fault to cut across them.

4. Disconformities represent a gap in the geologic column. If part of the column is missing from the layers, then the geologist has observed a disconformity.

Absolute Dating: A Measure of Time

This section explains how absolute dating can determine the actual age of a fossil or a rock. Students will be able to explain the nature of radioactive decay and describe how radiometric dating measures the radioactive decay of different isotopes to calculate the age of the parent material.

🔔 Bellringer

Have students assess whether these statements describe relative or absolute age:

"She is my younger sister." (relative age)

"He is 12 years old." (absolute age)

Ask students to write a short paragraph explaining why geologists use both absolute and relative dating to interpret the past.

1 Motivate

ACTIVITY

Ask two students to be the geologists in this activity. The rest of the class will be radioactive isotopes in a newly formed rock sample. Tell the isotopes to stand up and that they have a half-life of 1 minute. Have the geologists go outside the classroom and wait. After 1 minute has elapsed, tell half of the isotopes to sit down. After another minute, ask half of the students left standing to sit down. Continue this pattern until one student remains standing. Ask the geologists to determine the age of the sample based on the number of original isotopes and the length of a half-life.

Terms to Learn

absolute dating
isotopes
radioactive decay
radiometric dating
half-life

What You'll Do

- ◆ Explain how radioactive decay occurs.
- ◆ Explain how radioactive decay relates to radiometric dating.
- ◆ List three types of radiometric dating.
- ◆ Determine the best type of radiometric dating to use to date an object.

Absolute Dating: A Measure of Time

By using relative dating, scientists can determine the relative ages of rock layers. To determine the actual age of a layer of rock or a fossil, however, scientists must rely on absolute dating. **Absolute dating** is a process of establishing the age of an object, such as a fossil or rock layer, by determining the number of years it has existed. In this section, we will concentrate on radiometric dating, which is the most common method of absolute dating.

Radioactive Decay

To determine the absolute ages of fossils and rocks, scientists most often analyze radioactive isotopes. **Isotopes** are atoms of the same element that have the same number of protons but have different numbers of neutrons. Most isotopes are stable, meaning that they stay in their original form. But some isotopes are unstable. Scientists call unstable isotopes *radioactive*. Radioactive isotopes tend to break down into stable isotopes of other elements in a process called **radioactive decay**. **Figure 10** shows how one type of radioactive decay occurs. Because radioactive decay occurs at a steady pace, scientists can use the relative amounts of stable and unstable isotopes present in an object to determine the object's age.

Unstable isotope
6 protons, 8 neutrons

Figure 10 *During radioactive decay, an unstable parent isotope breaks down into a stable daughter isotope.*

Radioactive decay
When the unstable isotope decays, a neutron is converted into a proton. In the process, an electron is released.

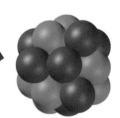

Stable isotope
7 protons, 7 neutrons

64

MISCONCEPTION ///ALERT\\\

Students may associate atomic decay with other types of organic decay they know about. Explain that some elements have forms called isotopes. Some isotopes have unstable atomic nuclei that tend to change, or decay. The chance that an atom will decay at any given moment is very small, but that chance is constant. Unstable atoms do not "wear out" or "grow old." From the moment they form to the moment they decay, they always have the same probability of decaying. For example, every potassium-40 atom in a sample has a 50:50 chance of decaying during the course of 1.3 billion years. After 1.3 billion years, half the P-40 atoms will have decayed. Every unstable isotope has a characteristic half-life. Some half-lives last only a ten-thousandth of a second!

Dating Rocks—How Does It Work? Consider a stream of molten lava flowing out of a volcano. As long as the lava is in liquid form, the daughter material that is already present and the parent material are free to mix and move around. But eventually the lava cools and becomes solid igneous rock. When this happens, the parent and daughter materials often end up in different minerals. Scientists know that any daughter material found in the same mineral as the parent material most likely formed after the lava became solid rock. Scientists compare the amount of new daughter material with the amount of parent material that remains. The more new daughter material there is, the older the rock is.

Radiometric Dating

If you know the rate of decay for an element in a rock, you can figure out the age of the rock. Determining the absolute age of a sample based on the ratio of parent material to daughter material is called **radiometric dating.** For example, let's say that it takes 10,000 years for half the parent material in a rock sample to decay into daughter material. You analyze the sample and find equal amounts of parent material and daughter material. This means that half the original radioactive isotope has decayed and that the sample must be about 10,000 years old.

What if one-fourth of your sample is parent material and three-fourths is daughter material? You would know that it took 10,000 years for half the original sample to decay and another 10,000 years for half of what remained to decay. The age of your sample would be 2 × 10,000, or 20,000, years. **Figure 11** shows how this steady decay works. The time it takes for one-half of a radioactive sample to decay is called a **half-life.**

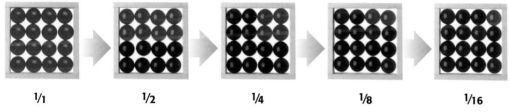

Figure 11 *After every half-life, the amount of parent material decreases by one-half.*

¹⁄₁   ¹⁄₂   ¹⁄₄   ¹⁄₈   ¹⁄₁₆

MATHBREAK

Get a Half-Life!

After observing the process illustrated in Figure 11, complete the chart below in your ScienceLog.

Parent left	Half-life in years	Age in years
¹⁄₈	?	30,000
?	1.3 billion	3.9 billion
¹⁄₄	10,000	?

65

Teaching Transparency 263
"Radioactive Decay and Half-life" LINK TO PHYSICAL SCIENCE

Directed Reading Worksheet Section 3

READING 📖 STRATEGY

Activity After students read the passage about radiometric dating, have them work together to define the terms *isotope, parent material, daughter material,* and *half-life.* Ask students to reproduce **Figure 11** in their ScienceLog and have them calculate the percentage of isotope remaining in each box. (100 percent, 50 percent, 25 percent, 12.5 percent, and 6.25 percent)

MATH and MORE

To help students understand the concept of a half-life, have them calculate how old an object is when $\frac{1}{4}$, $\frac{1}{8}$, $\frac{1}{32}$, and $\frac{1}{64}$ of its carbon-14 remains. The half-life for carbon-14 is 5,730 years. (11,460; 17,190; 28,650; 34,380)

Answers to MATHBREAK

(10,000; $\frac{1}{8}$, 20,000)

CONNECT TO PHYSICAL SCIENCE

The unstable isotope shown in **Figure 10** is carbon-14, which decays to a stable nitrogen-14. Have students use two different colors of modeling clay to construct the nuclei of other unstable isotopes. Ask students to identify the protons and neutrons in each model. Discuss the difference between atomic mass and atomic number. Ask students to identify isotopes of the same element, and help them explain radioactive decay by using their model. Use Teaching Transparency 263 to lead into a discussion of half-lives and radioactive decay.

CROSS-DISCIPLINARY FOCUS

History Have students work together in small groups to research Effigy Mounds National Monument. Each group of students could create a display with photographs, articles, and interesting information about the artifacts found there. Encourage students to find out more about how absolute dating is used at other archaeological sites.

The carbon-14 dating method reports the age of a substance as the number of years before present (abbreviated B.P.). The term *before present* uses the year 1950 as a reference point. Ask students why scientists chose one year as a reference. (If scientists used the current year as a reference, the age of a specimen would change every year.)

---

internetconnect

*sci*LINKS.
NSTA

TOPIC: Absolute Dating
GO TO: www.scilinks.org
*sci*LINKS **NUMBER:** HSTE140

Did you know that scientists have radiometrically dated moon rocks? The ages they have determined suggest that the moon formed when the Earth was still molten.

Types of Radiometric Dating

Imagine traveling back through the centuries to a time long before Columbus arrived in America. You are standing along the bluffs of what will one day be called the Mississippi River. You see dozens of people building large mounds. Who are these people, and what are they building?

The people you saw in your time travel were American Indians, and the structures they were building were burial mounds. The area you imagined is now an archaeological site called Effigy Mounds National Monument. **Figure 12** shows one of these mounds.

According to archaeologists, people lived at Effigy Mounds from 2,500 years ago to 600 years ago. How do archaeologists know these dates? They have dated bones and other objects in the mounds using radiometric dating. Scientists use different radiometric dating techniques based on the estimated age of an object. As you read on, think about how the half-life of an isotope relates to the age of the object being dated. Which technique would you use to date the burial mounds?

Figure 12 *This burial mound at Effigy Mounds resembles a snake.*

Uranium-Lead Method Uranium-238 is a radioactive isotope that eventually decays to lead-206. The half-life of uranium-238 is 4.5 billion years. The older the rock is, the more daughter material (lead-206) there will be in the rock. Uranium-lead dating can be used for rocks more than 10 million years old. Younger rocks do not contain enough daughter material to be accurately measured by this method.

66

IS THAT A FACT!

The oldest rock sample on record is a metamorphic gneiss from northern Canada, dated at 3.9 billion years old. Zircon crystals from Australia were found to be 4.2 billion years old, but they are part of much younger rock.

SCIENCE HUMOR

Q: What is the first thing you have to do before you date a dinosaur?

A: Ask it out.

Potassium-Argon Method   Another isotope used for radiometric dating is potassium-40. Potassium-40 has a half-life of 1.3 billion years, and it eventually decays to argon and calcium. Geologists measure argon as the daughter material for radiometric dating. This method is mainly used to date rocks older than 100,000 years.

Carbon-14 Method   The carbon-14 method works differently from the two methods already mentioned. The element carbon is normally found in three forms, the stable isotopes carbon-12 and carbon-13 and the radioactive isotope carbon-14. These carbon isotopes combine with oxygen to form the gas carbon dioxide, which is taken in by plants during photosynthesis. As long as a plant is alive, new carbon dioxide with a constant carbon-14 to carbon-12 ratio is continually taken in. Animals that eat plants contain the same ratio of carbon isotopes.

Once a plant or animal dies, however, no new carbon is taken in. The amount of carbon-14 begins to decrease as the plant or animal decays, and the ratio of carbon-14 to carbon-12 decreases. This decrease can be measured in a laboratory, such as the one shown in **Figure 13**. Because the half-life of carbon-14 is only 5,730 years, this dating method is mainly used for dating things that lived within the last 50,000 years.

Figure 13 *Some samples containing carbon must be cleaned and burned before their age can be determined.*

SECTION REVIEW

1. Explain how radioactive decay occurs.

2. How does radioactive decay relate to radiometric dating?

3. List three types of radiometric dating.

4. **Applying Concepts**   Which radiometric-dating method would be most appropriate for dating artifacts found at Effigy Mounds? Explain.

internet connect

SCI LINKS
NSTA

TOPIC: Absolute Dating
GO TO: www.scilinks.org
*sci*LINKS NUMBER: HSTE140

67

▼ *Answers to Section Review*

1. Radioactive decay occurs as a radioactive isotope breaks down into a stable isotope. This happens as the isotope loses an electron and a neutron becomes a proton.

2. Radioactive decay occurs at a constant rate. By determining the ratio between the parent material and the daughter material in an object, scientists can determine how old the object is.

3. uranium-lead, carbon-14, and potassium-argon

4. Carbon-14 would be the best method to date artifacts from Effigy Mounds. This is because carbon-14 has a relatively short half-life of 5,730 years.

Quiz

1. When using the carbon-14 dating method, which sample would be older, a sample with a ratio of carbon-14 to carbon-12 of 2 to 1 or a sample with a ratio of 3 to 1? (the sample with a 2 to 1 ratio)

2. What is a half-life? (the time it takes for one-half of a radioactive isotope to decay)

ALTERNATIVE ASSESSMENT

Display three different "fossils" for students. Tell students that the first sample is about 30,000 years old, the second is about 1 million years old, and the last came from the Paleozoic era, around 400 million years ago. Ask students to state which dating method they would use to determine the absolute age of each fossil.

CONNECT TO
LIFE SCIENCE

Carbon-14 is constantly created in the atmosphere by cosmic radiation. There is one atom of radioactive carbon-14 for every trillion atoms of carbon-12 in the atmosphere. Plants absorb carbon-14 directly through their leaves as carbon dioxide. Animals take in carbon-14 indirectly when they eat plants. Although carbon-14 disintegrates at a constant rate, it is continuously renewed as long as an organism remains alive. When an organism dies, it stops absorbing new carbon-14 and its radiocarbon "clock" is set.

Looking at Fossils

This section describes different types of fossils and how they are formed. Students learn how fossils provide information about the organisms that left them behind as well as the environment they inhabited. Students will also discover how index fossils are used to determine the relative age of rock layers.

🔔 Bellringer

Tell students that a fossil is any naturally preserved evidence of life. Ask them to write a few sentences to describe the fossil record of their own lives that might be found 65 million years from now. Stress to students that fossils must be naturally preserved. Have students share their ideas with the class.

Sheltered English

1 Motivate

GROUP ACTIVITY

Carbon impressions of plants can form when leaves are buried in sediment. As the plant decays, a thin film of carbon is left behind. Have students work in groups to make carbon "fossil" imprints. To each group, distribute a leaf, two sheets of white paper, and a piece of carbon paper. Instruct the groups to place their leaf on a sheet of white paper and cover it with the carbon paper, carbon side up. Next, cover the carbon paper with another sheet of white paper. Now have groups rub over the leaf using the side of a ruler. Ask them to describe which features were preserved and which were lost.

Terms to Learn

fossil	coprolite
permineralization	mold
petrification	cast
trace fossil	index fossil

What You'll Do

- Describe how different types of fossils are formed.
- List the types of fossils that are not part of organisms.
- Demonstrate how fossils can be used to determine changes in environments and in the organisms the fossils came from.
- Describe index fossils, and explain how they are used.

Looking at Fossils

Imagine you and your classmates are on a cross-country science field trip to Coralville, a town in east-central Iowa. Your teacher takes your class to a nearby stone quarry and points to a large rock wall that looks just like a coral reef. "This is how Coralville got its name," your teacher explains. "There used to be a living coral reef right here. What you see today is a fossilized coral reef." But you know that coral reefs are found in warm tropical oceans and that Iowa is more than 1,000 km away from any ocean! How did this huge coral reef end up in the middle of Iowa? To answer this question, you need to learn about fossils.

Fossilized Organisms

A **fossil** is any naturally preserved evidence of life. Fossils exist in many forms. The most easily recognizable fossils are preserved organisms, such as the stingray shown at right, or parts of organisms. Usually these fossils occur in rock. But as you will see, other materials can also preserve evidence of life.

Fossils in Rocks   When organisms die, the soft, fleshy parts of their bodies decompose, leaving only the hard parts. Occasionally, these hard parts get buried quickly in sediment and are preserved while the sediment turns to rock.

It takes more time for hard body parts such as bones, shells, and wood to decompose. For this reason, organisms with hard body parts are more likely to become fossils than those with only soft parts.

Mineral Replacement   Organisms can also be preserved by **permineralization,** a process in which minerals fill in pore spaces of an organism's tissues. Minerals can also replace the original tissues of organisms. **Petrification** of an organism, shown in **Figure 14,** occurs when the organism's tissues are completely replaced by minerals.

Figure 14 *These pieces of petrified wood are made of stone.*

SCIENTISTS AT ODDS

The discovery of dinosaur fossils in the American northwest during the later half of the nineteenth century led to a frenzy of amateur paleontology known as the Bone Rush. Paleontologists trying to make a name for themselves would stop at nothing to discover a new species of dinosaur. In the 1870s, two American paleontologists, Edward Drinker Cope and Othniel Charles Marsh, were bitter rivals. In 1878, Marsh and Cope were both excavating fossils near Como Bluff, Wyoming. They had separate excavations and did not want to share findings. Both groups found more fossils than they could carry. To prevent the other group from taking their finds, they smashed all the fossils they couldn't carry!

Fossils in Amber Imagine a fly or a mosquito landing in a drop of tree sap and getting stuck. Suppose that the insect gets covered by more sap. When the sap hardens, the insect will be preserved inside. Hardened tree sap is called *amber*. Some of our best insect fossils are found in amber, as shown in **Figure 15**.

Mummification When organisms die in dry places, such as deserts, they can sometimes dry out so fast that there isn't enough time for even their soft parts to decay. This process is called *mummification*. Mummified organisms don't decay because the bacteria that feed on dead organisms can't live without water. Some food, like dried fruit and beef jerky, is preserved in a similar way.

Figure 15 *This insect is perfectly preserved in amber.*

Frozen Fossils Imagine a huge animal that looks like an elephant with long hair walking along a glacier 12,000 years ago. It's a woolly mammoth. Suddenly, the beast slips and falls between two huge pieces of ice into a deep crack. With no way out, the animal freezes and is preserved until the glacier thaws thousands of years later. Scientists find fossils of woolly mammoths and many other organisms when glaciers thaw. These frozen specimens are some of the best fossils.

Fossils in Tar There are places where tar occurs naturally in thick, sticky pools. One such place is the La Brea tar pits, in Los Angeles County, California. These pits of thick oil and tar were present when saber-toothed cats roamed the Earth 40,000 years ago, as shown in **Figure 16.**

Much of what we know about these extinct cats comes from fossils found in the La Brea tar pits. But saber-toothed cats are not the only organisms found in the pits. Scientists have found fossils of many other mammals as well as plants, snails, birds, salamanders, and insects.

Figure 16 *Many animals, including saber-toothed cats, became fossils after sinking in tar pits.*

2 Teach

READING STRATEGY

Writing **Activity** Ask students to write short paragraphs exploring possible scenarios for each type of fossilization described in this section. Encourage students to illustrate each scenario and to include details of the paleo-environment at the time of fossilization.
Sheltered English

ACTIVITY

Making Fossils Distribute the following materials to groups of students:

> several leaves or small shells, a small amount of petroleum jelly, plaster of Paris, water, waxed paper, a square of heavy cardboard, and a milk carton

Have each group fill the container halfway with plaster. Add some water, and combine the mixture to form a smooth, thick paste. Pour the plaster mixture onto the cardboard square covered by waxed paper. The plaster should be 5 mm thick. Coat the leaves or the shells with petroleum jelly, and place them jelly side down into the plaster. Allow the plaster to dry for 24 hours before removing the leaves or the shells. Groups may wish to create a fossil record of a mystery environment and exchange it for another group to interpret.

MISCONCEPTION ALERT

Many people assume that when they see dinosaur bones in a museum, they are looking at the actual bones that made up the dinosaur. It is important to point out that paleontologists rarely display the actual fossilized dinosaur bones, instead they make casts of the bones. Using the casts, they make fiberglass reproductions of the bones. The fiberglass bones are much lighter than the originals and can stand on their own.

DEBATE

Have students debate the pros and cons of amateur fossil collecting. They should understand that amateur fossil collectors have made some amazing discoveries and have advanced paleontology. On the other hand, amateur fossil collectors have lost important information by improperly removing fossils or not recording data about locations or associated fossils. Have them conclude the debate by writing a handbook for amateur fossil collectors.

Answer to Self-Check

Coprolites and tracks are trace fossils because they are evidence of animal activity rather than fossilized organisms.

BRAIN FOOD

In 1997, the most complete skeleton of a *Tyrannosaurus rex* ever found was auctioned. The dinosaur, named Sue, was purchased for $8.36 million by the Field Museum of Natural History in Chicago. Scientists were relieved because they feared that a private collector would buy the fossil skeleton and that scientists and the public would not be able to view it. Have students find out more about the bitter custody battle involving Sue, the U.S. government, the Cheyenne Indians, a private rancher, and a commercial paleontology company. Ask students how they feel about people owning and controlling fossils. At what point is it okay to own a fossil, and at what point should scientists be in control of a fossil?

Other Types of Fossils

What happens when scientists cannot find any remains of plants or animals? Is there anything else that might indicate an organism's former presence?

Trace Fossils Any naturally preserved evidence of an animal's activity is called a **trace fossil.** An easily recognizable type of trace fossil is a *track.* Just like animals today, the animals in the past left tracks. These ancient tracks became fossils when they filled with sediment that eventually turned to rock.

Imagine that the tracks shown here were made by a ferocious *Tyrannosaurus rex.* While the animal that made them is long gone, the fossil tracks remain as evidence that it once prowled the Earth.

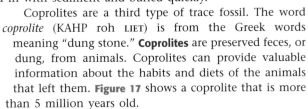

Burrows are another type of trace fossil. Burrows are shelters made by animals that dig into the ground. Like tracks, burrows are preserved when they are filled in with sediment and buried quickly.

Coprolites are a third type of trace fossil. The word *coprolite* (KAHP roh LIET) is from the Greek words meaning "dung stone." **Coprolites** are preserved feces, or dung, from animals. Coprolites can provide valuable information about the habits and diets of the animals that left them. **Figure 17** shows a coprolite that is more than 5 million years old.

Figure 17 *This coprolite came from a prehistoric mammal.*

✓ Self-Check

Why are tracks and coprolites considered trace fossils? *(See page 216 to check your answer.)*

Molds and Casts A **mold** is a cavity in the ground or rock where a plant or animal was buried. Often the cavity has been filled in, leaving a cast of the original organism. A **cast** is an object created when sediment fills a mold and becomes rock. A cast shows what the outside of the organism looked like. **Figure 18** shows a mold and cast from the same organism.

Figure 18 *The ammonite cast on the left formed when sediment filled the ammonite mold on the right and became rock.*

Science Bloopers

How *Brontosaurus* lost its name is a story full of science bloopers. In 1877, Othniel Marsh hastily described a new species of dinosaur based on a few vertebrae and part of a pelvis. He named this dinosaur *Apatosaurus.* In 1879, Marsh went on to announce the discovery of another new dinosaur, the *Brontosaurus,* which was also based on incomplete remains. Not until 1903 was it discovered that the new dinosaurs were actually members of the same species! It was decided that the dinosaur should be called *Apatosaurus* instead of *Brontosaurus.* Controversy continued when, in the 1970s, scientists found that Marsh had put the wrong skull on *Apatosaurus.*

Using Fossils to Interpret the Past

By examining fossils, scientists can find out what was happening in the environment when the sediments surrounding the fossils were deposited. Scientists can also interpret how plants and animals have changed over time by studying fossils from different parts of the geologic column.

Changes in Environments

Fossils can reveal changes that have occurred in parts of the Earth. By studying the coral-reef fossils and applying the principle of uniformitarianism, for example, scientists have determined that Iowa was once covered by a shallow sea. This is hard to believe when you look at Iowa's landscape today!

Iowa is just one example of where inconsistent fossils have been found. Who would have expected fossils of coral to be found in the landlocked state of Iowa? Likewise, who would have expected fossils of marine organisms on the top of a mountain? But that is exactly what scientists found on mountaintops in Canada, as shown in **Figure 19.** The presence of these fossils means that these rocks were once below the surface of an ocean.

Figure 19 *Scientists often find rocks that contain marine fossils on mountaintops. These rocks were pushed up from below sea level millions of years ago.*

Changes in Life   Older rock layers contain organisms different from those found in younger rock layers. The record stored in the rocks shows a change in life-forms over the years. For example, rock layers that contain fish fossils are found beneath the oldest rock layers that contain fossils of amphibians. Amphibians, such as frogs and salamanders, are animals with characteristics that allow them to live both on land and in water. On top of these rock layers are the oldest layers that contain fossils of reptiles, most of which lived only on land. Using the principle of superposition, we know that fish existed before amphibians because fish were found in a lower layer of rock. In the same way, we know that amphibians existed before reptiles.

GOING FURTHER

Have students research the methods used by paleontologists to excavate fossils. Show students a collection of tools that might be used by paleontologists and ask them to think about the purpose of each item. Tools include picks and brushes, trowels, stakes and string, a tape measure, a compass, plaster, and sifting screens. Organize a dig, or have students demonstrate some paleontological techniques in class.

COOPERATIVE LEARNING

Have small groups search in magazines for photographs representing five different biomes. Then have them order the five photographs in a sequence. Tell them to imagine that they are paleontologists and that this sequence represents roughly 300 million years in the geologic history of a single location. Have them study their photographs and brainstorm about what the fossil record for each biome might contain. How would the fossil record indicate the environmental changes that occurred between each photograph? Have the group members work together to write a press release announcing their great discovery—a complete, continuous record of 300 million years of environmental change! Students can describe how they made their discovery and the field techniques they used. They can show illustrations of the fossils they found and explain why these fossils suggest the environmental changes shown in the sequence of photographs.

71

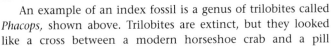

4) Close

Quiz

1. Would a shark tooth make a good index fossil? Why or why not? (A shark tooth would not make a good index fossil because sharks have existed for more than 200 million years; index fossils are useful because they existed for a short period of time.)

2. Why do the frigid temperatures of Siberia and the sticky tar of the La Brea Tar Pits preserve fossils so well? (Both environments retard the decay of an organism and help preserve it.)

ALTERNATIVE ASSESSMENT

Have students prepare a "how-to" guide for the fossilization processes described in this section. Students should imagine that they are instructing an untrained person in how to preserve an organism using sedimentation, amber, mummification, tar, ice, and permineralization. Emphasize that this assignment should read like a recipe; details are important.

Homework

Modern Index Fossils Which organisms would make good index fossils for marking the end of the twentieth century? Have students research species that have become extinct during the last 100 years and illustrate what their fossils might look like.

Critical Thinking Worksheet
"Adiós Alamosaurus!"

Using Fossils to Date Rocks

Geologists sometimes use *index fossils* to date rocks while in the field. **Index fossils** are fossils of organisms that lived during a relatively short, well-defined time span. Whenever geologists find an index fossil in a rock layer, they know where in the geologic column the rock layer fits. This enables them to give the layer a date without directly using radiometric dating. Good index fossils also have a wide distribution around the world.

An example of an index fossil is a genus of trilobites called *Phacops*, shown above. Trilobites are extinct, but they looked like a cross between a modern horseshoe crab and a pill bug. *Phacops* lived in shallow oceans about 400 million years ago. Where geologists find a fossil of this trilobite, they can assume that the surrounding rock is about 400 million years old.

Another good index fossil is a genus of ammonites called *Tropites*, shown in **Figure 20**. Ammonites were marine animals that looked a lot like modern squids, but they lived in coiled shells with complex inner walls. *Tropites* lived between 230 million and 208 million years ago. Where geologists find them in a rock layer, they know that the rock layer is between 208 million and 230 million years old.

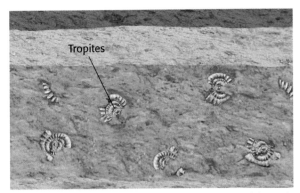

Figure 20 Tropites, *a genus of ammonites, existed for only about 20 million years, which makes it a good index fossil.*

internetconnect

SCiLINKS.
NSTA

TOPIC: Looking at Fossils
GO TO: www.scilinks.org
*sci*LINKS **NUMBER:** HSTE145

SECTION REVIEW

1. Describe two ways that fossils can form.

2. List two types of fossils that are not part of an organism.

3. What are index fossils? How do scientists use them to date rocks?

4. **Making Inferences** If you find rock layers containing fish fossils in a desert, what can you infer about that area of the desert?

▼ **Answers to Section Review**

1. Answers will vary. Fossils can form as organisms are deposited in layers of sediment. If the sediment becomes rock, the organism may be preserved as a fossil. Permineralization is another way fossils can form. In this process, minerals form in the pore spaces between an organism's tissues. Petrification occurs if the tissues are completely replaced by minerals.

2. Answers will vary. Students may mention animal burrows, coprolites, or animal tracks.

3. Index fossils are fossils of organisms that lived during a relatively short, defined period of time. Index fossils help scientists date a rock layer without directly using radiometric dating.

4. Answers will vary. The desert was once an ocean, stream, or lake.

Terms to Learn

geologic time scale
eon
era
period
epoch

What You'll Do

◆ Demonstrate an understanding of the geologic time scale.
◆ Identify important dates on the geologic time scale.
◆ Identify the eon we know the most about, and explain why we know more about it than about other eons.

Time Marches On

Remember the stack of family pictures mentioned in Section 2? The oldest pictures were on the bottom, and the newest ones were on the top. By looking through the pictures in order, you could see the sequence of events and changes that occurred in your family's history. In studying the history of the Earth, scientists follow a similar process. But instead of looking at pictures, they analyze rock layers and the fossils they contain.

Rock Layers and Geologic Time

One of the best places in North America to see the Earth's history recorded in rock layers is in Grand Canyon National Park, shown in **Figure 21.** The Colorado River has cut the canyon nearly 2 km deep in some places. During this process, countless layers of rock have been eroded by the river. These layers represent nearly 2 billion years of geologic time!

Figure 21 *The rock layers in the Grand Canyon correspond to a very large section of the geologic column.*

Biology
CONNECTION

The Grand Canyon is so wide and deep that organisms on either side of the canyon took different evolutionary paths. As the Colorado River formed the canyon, groups of individuals from the same species became separated and could no longer interact. Over millions of years, these groups developed differently and became different species.

73

Marineris were on Earth, it would stretch across the United States from New York to Los Angeles. Ask students to hypothesize how such a vast system of canyons formed on Mars. (The canyons may have formed from tectonic activity. The flow of water on the surface of Mars may have eroded the canyon further.)

The Grand Canyon may be big, but Valles Marineris, on Mars, is much bigger. The Valles Marineris is a system of canyons 4,000 km long. The canyons have a maximum depth of 7–10 km. If Valles

Focus

Time Marches On

In this section, students are introduced to the geologic time scale. The section discusses the important biological and geological events of each eon and era. The section concludes with a QuickLab in which students construct their own geologic time scale to help them understand the length of each eon.

Bellringer

Post the following question for students:

> If the history of Earth was the length of one calendar year, what do you think is the date of the arrival of modern humans? (7:40 P.M., December 31)

1 Motivate

DISCUSSION

After students study the photograph of the Grand Canyon in **Figure 21,** ask them how they can identify different rock layers. (Each layer has a different thickness and color.)

Where are the oldest layers? (near the base of the canyon)

Why is the Grand Canyon such an important place to study the geologic history of western North America? (The Colorado River has cut through nearly 2 billion years of geologic history.)

If the Earth is 4.6 billion years old, how much of Earth's history do the layers of the Grand Canyon represent? (less than half)

Directed Reading Worksheet Section 5

READING 📖 STRATEGY

Mnemonics Help students devise mnemonic sentences to learn and remember the eons of geologic history. For example. "**H**appy **A**ardvarks **Pr**ance for **Ph**otographers" could be used to recall the **H**adean, **A**rchean, **Pr**oterozoic, and **Ph**anerozoic eons. Other mnemonic sentences will help students learn the eras, periods, and epochs.

Sheltered English

CONNECT TO
LIFE SCIENCE

The study of Earth's history has given rise to highly specific subdivisions of Earth science. Paleobotany, for example, studies the history of the plant kingdom. Have interested students find out how plant and pollen fossils can provide clues about past environments and how they have changed over time.

MEETING INDIVIDUAL NEEDS

Learners Having Difficulty As you begin to discuss the geologic time scale, write the names of the four eons on the board. Ask students to use the text to help you list the characteristics of each eon. Have students find the dates of each eon, the biological events that define it, and other facts. Have students copy the information in their ScienceLog for future study and review.

Sheltered English

Teaching Transparency 121
"The Geologic Time Scale"

The Geologic Time Scale

While the rock layers in the Grand Canyon represent the time that passed as they formed, the geologic column represents the billions of years that have passed since the first rocks formed on Earth. Geologists must grapple with the time represented by the geologic column as well as the time between Earth's formation and the formation of Earth's oldest known rocks. Altogether, geologists study 4.6 billion years of Earth's history! To make their job easier, geologists have created the geologic time scale. The **geologic time scale,** which is shown in **Figure 22,** is a scale that divides Earth's 4.6-billion-year history into distinct intervals of time.

Figure 22 *The geologic time scale accounts for Earth's entire history. It is divided into four major parts called* eons.

Phanerozoic eon

(540 million years ago–present)
The rock and fossil record mainly represents the Phanerozoic eon, which is the eon in which we live.

Proterozoic eon

(2.5 billion years ago–540 million years ago)
The first organisms with well-developed cells appeared during this eon.

Archean eon

(3.8 billion years ago–2.5 billion years ago)
The earliest known rocks on Earth formed during this eon.

Hadean eon

(4.6 billion years ago–3.8 billion years ago)
The only rocks that scientists have found from this eon are meteorites and rocks from the moon.

Geologic Time Scale				
	Era	Period	Epoch	Millions of years ago
PHANEROZOIC EON	Cenozoic	Quaternary	Holocene	0.01
			Pleistocene	1.8
		Tertiary	Pliocene	5.3
			Miocene	23.8
			Oligocene	33.7
			Eocene	54.8
			Paleocene	65
	Mesozoic	Cretaceous		144
		Jurassic		206
		Triassic		248
	Paleozoic	Permian		290
		Pennsylvanian		323
		Mississippian		354
		Devonian		417
		Silurian		443
		Ordovician		490
		Cambrian		540
PROTEROZOIC EON				2,500
ARCHEAN EON				3,800
HADEAN EON				4,600

74

Homework

Research Before the theory of plate tectonics and the invention of radiometric dating, scientists developed many elaborate experiments to determine the age of the Earth. In the mid-1700s, a French scientist estimated the age of Earth to be 75,000 years old. He based his estimate on the cooling rate of iron cannonballs.

By the 1930s, the estimated age of Earth reached 1 billion years, but it was not until the middle of this century that we determined the current estimate at 4.6 billion. Have interested students research the different methods that were used in the past to estimate the age of Earth.

Divisions of Time Geologists have divided Earth's history into sections of time, as shown on the geologic time scale in Figure 22. The largest divisions of geologic time are **eons.** The four eons in turn are divided into **eras,** which are the second-largest divisions of geologic time. Eras are divided into **periods,** which are the third-largest divisions of geologic time. Some periods are divided into **epochs** (EP uhks), which are the fourth-largest division of geologic time. Look again at Figure 22. Can you figure out what epoch we live in?

The boundaries between geologic time intervals represent major changes on Earth. These changes include the appearance or disappearance of life-forms, changes in the global climate, and changes in rock types. For example, each of the three eras of the Phanerozoic eon are characterized by unique life-forms.

The Paleozoic Era *Paleozoic* means "old life." The Paleozoic era lasted from about 540 to 248 million years ago. It is the first era that is well represented by fossils.

At the beginning of the Paleozoic era, there were no land organisms. Imagine how empty the landscape must have looked! By the middle of the era, plants started appearing on land. By the end of the era, amphibians were living partially on the land, and insects were abundant. **Figure 23** shows what the land might have looked like late in the Paleozoic era. The Paleozoic era came to an end with a mass extinction—nearly 90 percent of all species perished.

Living in the Past
How do scientists know what life was like in prehistoric times? Turn to page 85 to learn how one paleontologist finds out.

Figure 23 *Jungles were present during the Paleozoic era, but there were no birds singing in the trees and no monkeys swinging from the branches. Birds and mammals didn't evolve until much later.*

75

BRAIN FOOD
Ask students to think about the following quote: "The Earth does not belong to us; we belong to the Earth." Ask students to write a poem about how our place in the geologic time scale supports that statement.

internet connect
SC/LINKS **TOPIC:** Geologic Time
NSTA **GO TO:** www.scilinks.org
sciLINKS NUMBER: HSTE150

DEBATE

The Ancestry of Dinosaurs
Have students research and debate the ancestry of dinosaurs. Are they related more closely to reptiles or to birds? One side can gather evidence to support the theory that dinosaurs were cold-blooded and were more closely related to today's reptiles. The other side can use evidence to show that dinosaurs were more likely warmblooded and related to present-day birds.

MISCONCEPTION ///ALERT\\\

Illustrations of dinosaurs and ancient environments are based on artists' conceptions. For example, scientists are sure about the skeletal structure of most dinosaurs, but skin type and skin color are open to interpretation. *Tyrannosaurus rex* might not have had lips, and *Triceratops* might not have had cheeks. Artists have drawn these types of features on dinosaurs because these make the dinosaurs look familiar. The actual fossils do not suggest these types of features at all. In addition, most if not all movies about prehistoric life are abundant with paleontological inaccuracies. A classic example is the depiction of prehistoric humans and dinosaurs coexisting at the same time period. Show parts of these films to see how many inaccuracies students can point out.

The Mesozoic Era *Mesozoic* means "middle life." The Mesozoic era lasted from about 248 million years ago until about 65 million years ago. This era is also known as the Age of Reptiles. Dinosaurs, such as the ones shown in **Figure 24**, inhabited the land and the water.

Although reptiles dominated the Mesozoic era, birds and small mammals began to evolve late in the era. Most scientists think that birds evolved directly from a type of dinosaur. By the end of the Mesozoic era, about 50 percent of all species on Earth, including the dinosaurs, became extinct.

Figure 24 *Imagine walking in the desert and bumping into these fierce creatures! It's a good thing humans didn't evolve in the Mesozoic era, which was dominated by dinosaurs.*

The Cenozoic Era *Cenozoic* means "recent life." The Cenozoic era began about 65 million years ago and continues to the present. We live in the Cenozoic era.

Whereas the Mesozoic era is called the Age of Reptiles, the Cenozoic era is called the Age of Mammals. After the mass extinction at the end of the Mesozoic era, mammals became abundant on Earth, as shown in **Figure 25**. Many types of mammals that lived earlier in the Cenozoic era are now extinct, including woolly mammoths, saber-toothed cats, and giant sloths.

Figure 25 *Thousands of species of mammals evolved during the Cenozoic era. This scene shows species from the early Cenozoic era that are now extinct.*

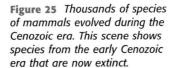

76

Homework

Prehistoric Animals Ask each student to choose a favorite prehistoric animal. Then have students find information about that animal and the time period it lived in. University Web sites are an excellent place to look for this information. Students can present their information as an oral presentation or as a poster.

IS THAT A FACT!

How long and heavy were the heaviest dinosaurs? Some dinosaurs were almost as large as blue whales, and the average elephant weighs less than the tongue of a blue whale.

Can You Imagine 4.6 Billion Years?

It's hard to picture 4.6 billion of anything, especially years. As humans, we do quite well to live to be 100 years old. Given this perspective, it is very difficult to think of Earth as being billions of years old. One way to do this is to organize the geologic time scale into the frame of 12 hours, with the first moment of Earth's history being noon and the present moment being midnight. This has been done on the Earth-history clock shown in **Figure 26**. On the Earth-history clock, the millions of years of evolution that you just read about occurred within the last hour. Human civilizations appeared within the last second! Perhaps you now have a better understanding of just how old the Earth is and just how brief humans' existence has been.

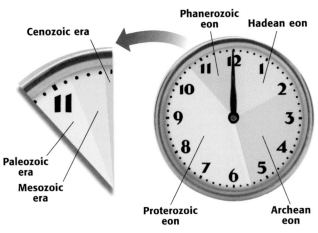

Figure 26 *On the Earth-history clock, which organizes Earth's history into the frame of 12 hours, 1 hour equals 383 million years, 1 minute equals 6.4 million years, and 1 second equals 106,000 years.*

SECTION REVIEW

1. How many eras are in the Phanerozoic eon? List them.

2. In this section, extinctions at the end of two geologic time intervals are mentioned. What are these two intervals, and when did each interval end?

3. Which eon do we know the most about? Why?

4. **Making Predictions** What future event might mark the end of the Cenozoic era?

internetconnect

SCiLINKS.
NSTA

TOPIC: Geologic Time
GO TO: www.scilinks.org
*sci*LINKS NUMBER: HSTE150

QuickLab

Make a Time Scale

1. Using a pair of **scissors,** cut a length of **adding-machine tape** 46 cm long.

2. Starting at one end of the tape, use a **ruler** and a **black marker** to draw a line across the width of the tape at the following measurements: 5.4 cm, 25 cm, and 38 cm.

3. Using **colored markers,** color the sections of tape as follows:
   0 cm–5.4 cm = green
   5.4 cm–25 cm = blue
   25 cm–38 cm = red
   38 cm–46 cm = yellow

4. Your tape represents the geologic time scale, and the present moment is at 46 cm. What is the name of each time interval on your scale?

4) Close

QuickLab

Answers to QuickLab

4. yellow = Phanerozoic;
   red = Proterozoic;
   blue = Archean;
   green = Hadean

Quiz

1. What are the largest divisions of time in the geologic time scale? (eons)

2. During which era did plants start to appear on land? (Paleozoic)

3. Which group of animals has been on Earth for a longer period of time, birds or humans? (birds)

ALTERNATIVE ASSESSMENT

PORTFOLIO

Making A Geologic History Book Have students work independently to make construction-paper cutouts of fossils that might be found in each era of Earth's history. Encourage students to create both plant and animal fossils. Students should then paste each era's fossils on construction paper "rock" layers. Students should create five layers for each era, and attach all the layers together so that they fold out accordion-style. Students can then annotate each layer, describing the time period the rocks and fossils were deposited, and paste in small illustrations of what the environment was like. Students can display their accordion books for the class to enjoy.

▼ Answers to Section Review

1. There are three eras: Cenozoic, Mesozoic, and Paleozoic.

2. The Paleozoic era ended about 248 million years ago, and the Mesozoic era ended about 65 million years ago.

3. We know the most about the Phanerozoic eon because the rock and fossil record from that eon is the most detailed and complete.

4. **Making Predictions** Answers will vary. Sample answers:
   the extinction of humans
   the extinction of most wild animal species
   the evolution of a new, widespread group of organisms
   a major change in the Earth's climate

How DO You Stack Up?
Teacher's Notes

Time Required

Two 45-minute class periods

Lab Ratings

EASY ——————→ HARD

TEACHER PREP
STUDENT SET-UP
CONCEPT LEVEL
CLEAN UP

MATERIALS

The materials listed on the student page are enough for each group. The activity works best if the class is divided into five groups.

Safety Caution

Remind students to review all safety cautions and icons before beginning this lab activity.

Preparation Notes

You may need to review correlation and the principle of superposition before performing this activity. Also be certain that your students understand what an index fossil is.

Thicknesses of layers given in the lab are the thicknesses on the stratigraphic sections only. The rock layers represented by the sections would probably be much thicker. However, the relative thicknesses of the layers are represented in the measurements given (i.e., a layer that is 4 cm thick is twice as thick as a layer that is 2 cm thick).

Discovery Lab

How DO You Stack Up?

According to the *principle of superposition,* in undisturbed sequences of sedimentary rock, the oldest layers are on the bottom. Geologists use this principle to determine the relative age of the rocks in a small area. In this activity, you will model what geologists do by drawing sections of different rock outcrops. Then you will create a part of the geologic column, showing the geologic history of the area that contains all of the outcrops.

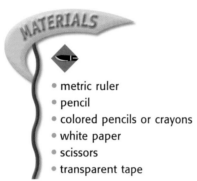

MATERIALS

- metric ruler
- pencil
- colored pencils or crayons
- white paper
- scissors
- transparent tape

Procedure

1. Use a metric ruler and a pencil to draw four boxes on a blank sheet of paper. Each box should be 3 cm wide and at least 6 cm tall. (You can trace the boxes shown on the next page.)

2. With colored pencils, copy the illustrations of the four outcrops on the next page. Use colors and patterns similar to those shown.

3. Pay close attention to the contact between layers—straight or wavy. Straight lines represent bedding planes, where deposition was continuous. Wavy lines represent unconformities, where rock layers may be missing. The top of each outcrop is incomplete, so it should be a jagged line. (Assume that the bottom of the lowest layer is a bedding plane.)

4. Use a black crayon or pencil to add the symbols representing fossils to the layers in your drawings. Pay attention to the variety of fossil shapes and the layers that they are in.

5. Write the outcrop number on the back of each section.

6. Carefully cut the outcrops out of the paper, and lay the individual outcrops next to each other on your desk or table.

7. Find layers that have the same rocks and contain the same fossils. Move each outcrop up or down to align similar layers next to each other.

78

Dwight Patton
Carroll T. Welch Middle School
Horizon City, Texas

8 If unconformities appear in any of the outcrops, rock layers may be missing. You may need to examine other sections to find out what fits between the layers above and below the unconformities. Leave room for these layers by cutting the outcrops along the unconformities (wavy lines).

9 Eventually, you should be able to make a geologic column that represents all four of the outcrops. It will show rock types and fossils for all the known layers in the area.

10 Tape the pieces of paper together in a pattern that represents the complete geologic column.

Analysis

11 How many layers are in this part of the geologic column you modeled?

12 Which is the oldest layer in your column? Which rock layer is the youngest? Describe these layers in terms of rock type and the fossils they contain.

13 Which, if any, fossils can be used as index fossils for a single layer? Why are these fossils considered index fossils?

14 List the fossils in your column from oldest to youngest. Label the oldest and youngest fossils.

15 Look at the unconformity in Outcrop 2. Which rock layers are partially or completely missing? Explain how you know this.

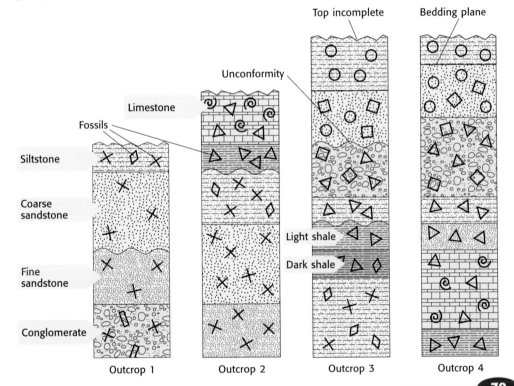

 Datasheets for LabBook

Lab Notes

Explain that the geologic column for the entire Earth is constructed from smaller columns similar to the hypothetical column in this lab. Stratigraphic sections are pieced together to form short columns, and short columns are pieced together to form longer columns. All columns put together make up the geologic column for the entire Earth.

Answers

11. There are 12 layers in this part of the geologic column.

12. The conglomerate containing rectangle and X fossils is the oldest. The siltstone containing circle fossils is the youngest.

13. Index fossils: the circles or the X's and diamonds in the siltstone; the squares and circles or the X's in the coarse sandstone; the squares and triangles or the X's and rectangles in the conglomerate; the triangles or X's in the fine sandstone. These fossils are considered index fossils because they existed for a short range of geologic time. To determine the absolute age of the fossils, radiometric dating would be necessary.

14. The relative age of the fossils from oldest to youngest is rectangles, X's, diamonds, triangles, spirals, squares, and circles.

15. In Outcrop 2, part of the siltstone and all of the shale are missing. This can be determined by comparing the outcrop with the geologic column.

Chapter Highlights

SECTION 1

uniformitarianism a principle that states that the same geologic processes shaping the Earth today have been at work throughout Earth's history

catastrophism a principle that states that all geologic change occurs suddenly

SECTION 2

relative dating determining whether an object or event is older or younger than other objects or events

superposition a principle that states that younger rocks lie above older rocks in undisturbed sequences

geologic column an ideal sequence of rock layers that contains all the known fossils and rock formations on Earth arranged from oldest to youngest

unconformity a surface that represents a missing part of the geologic column

SECTION 3

absolute dating the process of establishing the age of an object, such as a fossil or rock layer, by determining the number of years it has existed

isotopes atoms of the same element that have the same number of protons but have different numbers of neutrons

radioactive decay a process in which radioactive isotopes tend to break down into stable isotopes of other elements

radiometric dating determining the absolute age of a sample based on the ratio of parent material to daughter material

half-life for a particular radioactive sample, the time it takes for one-half of the sample to decay

Chapter Highlights

SECTION 1

Vocabulary

uniformitarianism (p. 56)

catastrophism (p. 57)

Section Notes

- Scientists use the principle of uniformitarianism to interpret the past and make predictions.

- According to uniformitarianism, geologic change is gradual. According to catastrophism, geologic change is sudden.

- Before Hutton and Lyell, most scientists believed all geologic change was catastrophic. After Hutton and Lyell, most scientists rejected catastrophism. Today most scientists favor uniformitarianism, but they recognize some geologic change as catastrophic.

SECTION 2

Vocabulary

relative dating (p. 59)

superposition (p. 59)

geologic column (p. 60)

unconformity (p. 62)

Section Notes

- Geologists use relative dating to determine the relative age of objects.

- Geologists assume that younger layers lie above older layers in undisturbed rock-layer sequences. This is called superposition.

- The entire rock and fossil record is represented by the geologic column.

- Geologists examine the relationships between rock layers and the structures that cut across them in order to determine relative ages.

- Geologists also determine relative ages by assuming that all rock layers were originally horizontal.

- Unconformities form where rock layers are missing, and they represent time that is not recorded in the rock record.

☑ Skills Check

Math Concepts

HALF-LIVES Remember from Figure 11 on page 65 that the ratio of parent material to daughter material decreases by one-half with each half-life. An easy way to think of this is to multiply the ratio by $1/2$ for each half-life. This is shown below.

$$\frac{1}{1} \times \frac{1}{2} = \frac{1}{2}; \quad \frac{1}{2} \times \frac{1}{2} = \frac{1}{4};$$
$$\frac{1}{4} \times \frac{1}{2} = \frac{1}{8}; \text{ and } \frac{1}{8} \times \frac{1}{2} = \frac{1}{16}$$

Visual Understanding

FAULTS AND UNCONFORMITIES It is important to realize that faults and unconformities are not bodies of rock. They are types of surfaces where bodies of rock contact each other.

80

Lab and Activity Highlights

How DO You Stack Up? `PG 78`

Datasheets for LabBooks
(blackline masters for these labs)

SECTION 4

fossil any naturally preserved evidence of life

permineralization a process in which minerals fill in pore spaces of an organism's tissues

petrification a process in which an organism's tissues are completely replaced by minerals

trace fossil any naturally preserved evidence of an animal's activity

coprolites preserved feces, or dung, from animals

mold a cavity in the ground or rock where a plant or animal was buried

cast an object created when sediment fills a mold and becomes rock

index fossil a fossil of an organism that lived during a relatively short, well-defined time span; a fossil that is used to date the rock layers in which it is found

SECTION 5

geologic time scale a scale that divides Earth's 4.6-billion-year history into distinct intervals of time

eon the largest division of geologic time

era the second-largest division of geologic time

period the third-largest division of geologic time

epoch the fourth-largest division of geologic time

SECTION 3

Vocabulary

absolute dating *(p. 64)*

isotopes *(p. 64)*

radioactive decay *(p. 64)*

radiometric dating *(p. 65)*

half-life *(p. 65)*

Section Notes

- During radioactive decay, an unstable parent isotope of one element decays at a constant rate into a stable daughter isotope of a different element.

- The absolute age of samples of some rocks and fossils can be determined by the ratio of unstable isotopes to stable isotopes in the samples. This is called radiometric dating.

- The radiometric-dating method scientists use depends on the estimated age of the object they are dating.

SECTION 4

Vocabulary

fossil *(p. 68)*

permineralization *(p. 68)*

petrification *(p. 68)*

trace fossil *(p. 70)*

coprolite *(p. 70)*

mold *(p. 70)*

cast *(p. 70)*

index fossil *(p. 72)*

Section Notes

- Any naturally preserved evidence of life is considered a fossil.

- There are many ways fossils can form, such as mineral replacement, mummification, and freezing.

- Fossils can be used to show how environments and organisms have changed over time.

- Fossils, especially index fossils, can be used to date rocks.

SECTION 5

Vocabulary

geologic time scale *(p. 74)*

eon *(p. 75)*

era *(p. 75)*

period *(p. 75)*

epoch *(p. 75)*

Section Notes

- The history of the Earth is recorded in rock layers.

- The 4.6 billion years of Earth's history is represented on the geologic time scale, including the intervals not represented in the rock and fossil record.

- There are several different time intervals on the geologic time scale.

- Scientists know very little about the Earth's early history. This is because the rock and fossil record primarily represents the last eon of Earth's history.

---

  internetconnect

GO TO: go.hrw.com

Visit the **HRW** Web site for a variety of learning tools related to this chapter. Just type in the keyword:

KEYWORD: HSTFOS

 SCI LINKS
N S T A

GO TO: www.scilinks.org

Visit the **National Science Teachers Association** on-line Web site for Internet resources related to this chapter. Just type in the *sci*LINKS number for more information about the topic:

TOPIC: Earth's Story	*sci*LINKS NUMBER: HSTE130
TOPIC: Relative Dating	*sci*LINKS NUMBER: HSTE135
TOPIC: Absolute Dating	*sci*LINKS NUMBER: HSTE140
TOPIC: Looking at Fossils	*sci*LINKS NUMBER: HSTE145
TOPIC: Geologic Time	*sci*LINKS NUMBER: HSTE150

81

Lab and Activity Highlights

LabBank

 Inquiry Labs,
A Penny for Your Thoughts

EcoLabs & Field Activities,
Rock of Ages

Labs You Can Eat,
Geopancakes

 Long-Term Projects & Research Ideas,
The Hard Rock Chronicles

 Vocabulary Review Worksheet

 Blackline masters of these Chapter Highlights can be found in the **Study Guide.**

Chapter Review
Answers

USING VOCABULARY

1. Uniformitarianism is the theory that gradual geologic processes that we observe in the present were also active in the past. This theory argues that slow gradual change shapes the Earth. Catastrophism is the theory that past episodes of sudden and drastic change are responsible for the major geologic features of the Earth.

2. Relative dating is a method of comparing the age of a rock or fossil with the age of other objects or events. For example, a fault is always younger than the layers it disturbs. Absolute dating is a method of determining the age of something in years.

3. A mold is the cavity created in ground or rock where an organism was buried. A cast forms when material fills the mold and becomes rock.

4. An eon is the largest division of geologic time. The Phanerozoic eon is divided into three eras.

5. The geologic time scale is the history of the Earth divided into eons, eras, periods, and epochs. The geologic column is an idealized sequence of rock layers that contains all known fossils and rock formations arranged from oldest to youngest.

UNDERSTANDING CONCEPTS

Multiple Choice

6. c
7. b
8. b
9. d
10. a
11. d
12. d
13. c

Chapter Review

For each pair of terms, explain the difference in their meaning.

1. uniformitarianism/catastrophism

2. relative dating/absolute dating

3. mold/cast

4. eon/era

5. geologic time scale/geologic column

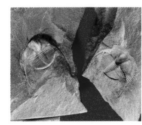

UNDERSTANDING CONCEPTS

Multiple Choice

6. Which of the following words does not describe catastrophic geologic change?
   a. sudden
   b. widespread
   c. gradual
   d. rare

7. Scientists assign relative ages by using
   a. potassium-argon dating.
   b. the principle of superposition.
   c. radioactive half-lives.
   d. the ratios of isotopes.

8. Rock layers cut by a fault formed
   a. after the fault.
   b. before the fault.
   c. at the same time as the fault.
   d. Cannot be determined

9. If the half-life of an unstable element is 5,000 years, what percentage of the parent material will be left after 10,000 years?
   a. 100   c. 50
   b. 75   d. 25

10. Of the following unstable isotopes, which has the longest half-life?
    a. uranium-238
    b. potassium-40
    c. carbon-14

11. Fossils can be
    a. petrified.
    b. dried out.
    c. frozen.
    d. All of the above

12. Of the following geologic time intervals, which is the shortest?
    a. an eon
    b. a period
    c. an era
    d. an epoch

13. If Earth's history is put on a scale of 12 hours, human civilizations would have been around for
    a. hours.
    b. minutes.
    c. less than 1 second.

Short Answer

14. What is the principle of superposition? How is it used by geologists?

15. Describe how plant and animal remains become petrified.

16. Explain how a fossil cast forms.

Short Answer

14. The principle of superposition states that, in undisturbed rock sequences, younger rock layers lie above older rock layers. Geologists use this principle to assign relative ages to rock layers.

15. Petrification occurs as the tissues of organisms are completely replaced by minerals.

16. A fossil cast forms when sediment fills in a fossil mold and becomes rock.

Concept Mapping

17. Use the following terms to create a concept map: age, absolute dating, half-life, radioactive decay, radiometric dating, relative dating, superposition, geologic column, isotopes.

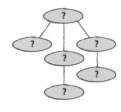

CRITICAL THINKING AND PROBLEM SOLVING

Write one or two sentences to answer the following questions:

18. You may have heard the term *petrified wood*. Why doesn't a "petrified" tree contain any wood?

19. How do tracks and burrows end up in the rock and fossil record?

20. How do you know that an intrusion is younger than its surrounding rock layers?

MATH IN SCIENCE

21. Copy the graph below onto a separate sheet of paper. Place a dot on the *y*-axis at 100 percent. Then place a dot on the graph at each half-life to show how much of the parent material is left. Connect the points with a curved line. Will the percentage of parent material ever reach zero? Explain.

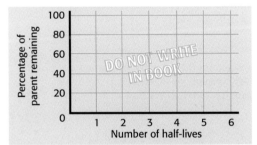

INTERPRETING GRAPHICS

Examine the drawing below, and answer the following questions.

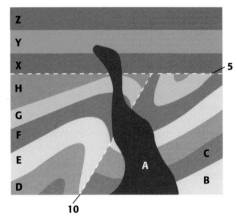

22. Is intrusion A younger or older than layer X?

23. What kind of unconformity is marked by 5?

24. Is intrusion A younger or older than fault 10? Why?

25. Other than the intrusion and faulting, what event occurred in layers **B, C, D, E, F, G,** and **H**? Number this event, the intrusion, and the faulting in the order they occurred.

Reading Check-up Take a minute to review your answers to the Pre-Reading Questions found at the bottom of page 54. Have your answers changed? If necessary, revise your answers based on what you have learned since you began this chapter.

Concept Mapping

17. 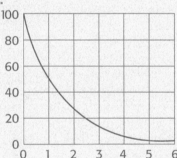 An answer to this exercise can be found in the front of this book.

CRITICAL THINKING AND PROBLEM SOLVING

18. The petrified tree does not contain any wood because the wood tissue in the tree was completely replaced by minerals.

19. Animals leave tracks and create burrows in soil. Sediment fills in these features and buries them quickly. Over time, the sediment becomes rock and preserves these trace fossils.

20. The intrusion is always younger because the rock layers had to be present before the intrusion could disturb them.

MATH IN SCIENCE

21.

Mathematically, the percentage of parent material will never reach zero. In a real sample, however, all of the parent material will eventually decay.

INTERPRETING GRAPHICS

22. younger

23. an angular unconformity

24. Intrusion A is younger than fault 10 because the intrusion is not disturbed by the fault.

25. Erosion; the fault occurred first, then layers eroded, and finally the intrusion occurred.

Concept Mapping Transparency 6

Blackline masters of this Chapter Review can be found in the **Study Guide**.

Science, Technology, and Society

CAT Scanning Fossils

Teaching Strategy

You may want to devote class time to illustrate how a three-dimensional CAT scan is derived from hundreds of two-dimensional X rays. If students have trouble visualizing this, you can use a three-dimensional model.

Obtain a sliced loaf of bread. After numbering each slice in order with either a marker or with flagged toothpicks, randomly distribute a slice to each student, and have students trace the slice onto a piece of paper, adding details to the interior of the tracing as desired. This tracing corresponds to two-dimensional X rays. Call out the slice numbers sequentially, and have students bring the slices to the front of the classroom in order. As each slice is received, place the slice in a stack so students can see the three-dimensional shape emerge. The three-dimensional shape corresponds to the three-dimensional image of a fossil after all of the X rays have been "stacked" by a computer.

Imagine that you've just found the fossilized skull of a small prehistoric mammal. You examine it very carefully, taking note of its size, shape, and external features. But you also want to look at features inside the skull, like the tiny bones of the middle ear. Can you do it without damaging the fossil? In the past it would have been impossible. Today, though, scientists are using medical technology to do this kind of detailed examination.

Breaking Bones

Paleontologists want to learn all they can about the fossils they study. They want to know about internal structures as well as external ones. Paleontologists usually grind a fossil away layer by layer, recording their observations as they go. Unfortunately, by the time they finish analyzing all the internal structures, the fossil is destroyed! This is a real problem if you want to show someone else your discovery.

Scientists with X-ray Vision

Now paleontologists have another choice. *Computerized axial tomography* (CAT scanning) is quickly replacing the more destructive method of studying internal structures. Originally designed as medical technology to examine the inside of the human skull, CAT scans provide interior views of a fossil without even touching its surface.

To understand how a CAT scan works, imagine a dolphin jumping through a hoop. As the dolphin passes through the hoop a CAT scan machine takes an X-ray picture of it from *every point around the hoop*. In effect, the machine takes a series of cross-section X-ray pictures of the dolphin. A computer then assembles these "slices" to create a three-dimensional picture of the dolphin. Every part of the dolphin's insides can then be studied without dissecting the dolphin.

When a paleontologist needs to reconstruct an entire skull, a series of two-dimensional "slice" shots is taken and the "slices" are combined through computer imaging to produce a three-dimensional image of the skull—inside and out!

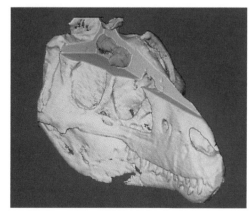

▲ *This CAT scan shows the size and location of the dinosaur* Nanotyrannosaurus rex's *brain.*

What's Hidden Inside?

Using CAT scans, scientists have learned much more about the internal structures of fossils. They have used CAT scans to look at the skeletons of embryos inside fossilized eggs and to study fragile bones still embedded in rock.

On Your Own

▶ What are the advantages of using CAT scans over conventional X rays? Find out by doing some research on your own.

84

Sample Answer to On Your Own

A conventional X ray gives an image of all layers of the skull at one time, superimposed on each other, making it difficult to see details behind opaque layers of rock or fossilized bone. CAT scans can produce virtual "sections" through an object, making it possible to see all of the internal features clearly.

CAREERS

PALEONTOLOGIST

Jack Horner found his first fossil bones at age 7 or 8 while collecting rocks at his father's quarry. From then on, he was hooked on dinosaurs. "I became a paleontologist because I like to dig in the dirt, discover things, and piece together puzzles," Horner says. As one of the world's leading experts on dinosaurs, Horner is curator of paleontology at the Museum of the Rockies, in Bozeman, Montana.

A mother nuzzles her babies in a nest. Nearby, another mother lets out a worried yelp; one of her babies has crawled out of its nest and is scampering away. The mother quickly captures her baby and returns it to safety. Puppies? Birds? No—dinosaurs! Or so Jack Horner believes.

Horner has come to this conclusion by comparing dinosaur fossils with modern alligators and birds. "I am studying how dinosaur bones developed, and I'm comparing them with the development of bones of alligators and birds so that we can learn more about dinosaur growth and nesting behaviors," Horner says. "I think that birds probably evolved from dinosaurs. If I find fossils of several nests close to each other, that tells me that the dinosaurs that built those nests may have lived together in a group."

Meeting the Challenge

As a child, Horner had difficulties in school because he had a learning disability called dyslexia. But no learning disability could dampen Horner's enthusiasm for science, especially the study of dinosaurs. "I like dinosaurs and figuring out what the world looked like at different times in the past. I've always liked the detective work that's involved in paleontology. You can't study a living dinosaur, so you have to figure out everything using clues from the past."

Boning Up on the Latest . . .

One of Horner's current projects is analyzing whether *Tyrannosaurus rex* was a vicious predator, as is often pictured, or a scavenger, eating other animals' kills. The more he studies fossil clues, the more Horner leans toward accepting the scavenger hypothesis. "Predatory animals require certain characteristics in order to be efficient killers. They need to be able to run fast, and they need to be able to maneuver and leap," Horner explains. "*T. rex* couldn't run fast, wasn't agile, and couldn't jump around or even fall down without doing serious damage to itself or even dying."

Decide for Yourself

▶ Observe the behavior of birds in your area. Focus on one or two species. Note their eating habits, the sounds they make, and their interactions with other birds. Do you think birds might have evolved from dinosaurs? Use your observations to support your theory.

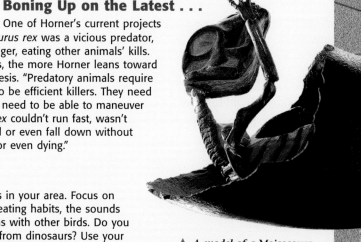

▲ *A model of a* Maisasaura *hatching.*

85

Background

As Jack Horner compared the behavior of modern birds with the fossil evidence of dinosaurs, he began to think that dinosaurs behaved more like birds than lizards. Further evidence led him to hypothesize that birds evolved from dinosaurs. For example, evidence suggests that some dinosaurs guarded their eggs and took care of their young, much like birds do.

Other scientists disagree with the "birds from dinosaurs" theory, and the relationship between dinosaurs and modern birds remains a hotly debated topic among scientists.

Answer to Decide for Yourself
Answers will vary.

Chapter Organizer

CHAPTER ORGANIZATION	TIME MINUTES	OBJECTIVES	LABS, INVESTIGATIONS, AND DEMONSTRATIONS
Chapter Opener pp. 86–87	45	National Standards: SAI 1, SPSP 5, ES 1b, 2a	**Start-Up Activity,** Continental Collisions, p. 87
Section 1 Inside the Earth	90	▶ Identify and describe the layers of the Earth by what they are made of. ▶ Identify and describe the layers of the Earth by their physical properties. ▶ Define *tectonic plate.* ▶ Explain how scientists know about the structure of Earth's interior. UCP 2, SAI 1, SPSP 5, ES 1a	**QuickLab,** Floating Mountains, p. 93 **Labs You Can Eat,** Rescue Near the Center of the Earth **Whiz-Bang Demonstrations,** Thar She Blows!
Section 2 Restless Continents	90	▶ Describe Wegener's theory of continental drift, and explain why it was not accepted at first. ▶ Explain how sea-floor spreading provides a way for continents to move. ▶ Describe how new oceanic crust forms at mid-ocean ridges. ▶ Explain how magnetic reversals provide evidence for sea-floor spreading. UCP 2, HNS 1, ES 2a	**Labs You Can Eat,** Cracks in the Hard-Boiled Earth
Section 3 The Theory of Plate Tectonics	90	▶ Describe the three forces thought to move tectonic plates. ▶ Describe the three types of tectonic plate boundaries. ▶ Explain how scientists measure the rate at which tectonic plates move. UCP 2, SPSP 4, 5, HNS 1, 3, ES 1b; Labs SAI 1, ST 1	**Making Models,** Convection Connection, p. 000 **Datasheets for LabBook,** Convection Connection, Datasheet 13 **Labs You Can Eat,** Dough Fault of Your Own
Section 4 Deforming the Earth's Crust	90	▶ Describe major types of folds. ▶ Explain how the three major types of faults differ. ▶ Name and describe the most common types of mountains. ▶ Explain how various types of mountains form. SAI 1, ES 1b, 1c, 2a; Labs UCP 2, SAI 1	**Demonstration,** p. 103 in ATE **Making Models,** Oh, the Pressure! p. 110 **Datasheets for LabBook,** Oh, the Pressure! **Long-Term Projects & Research Ideas,** Legend Has It

See page **T23** *for a complete correlation of this book with the*

NATIONAL SCIENCE EDUCATION STANDARDS.

TECHNOLOGY RESOURCES

 Guided Reading Audio CD English or Spanish, Chapter 4

 One-Stop Planner CD-ROM with Test Generator

 CNN Scientists in Action, Studying Sea Floor Tectonics, Segment 10

 Earth Science Videodisc The Dynamic Earth: 10427–32232 Plate Tectonics: 10608–21420 Deformation of the Crust: 21421–24901

Chapter 4 • Plate Tectonics

CLASSROOM WORKSHEETS, TRANSPARENCIES, AND RESOURCES	SCIENCE INTEGRATION AND CONNECTIONS	REVIEW AND ASSESSMENT
Directed Reading Worksheet **Science Puzzlers, Twisters & Teasers**		
Directed Reading Worksheet, Section 1 **Transparency 122,** The Composition of the Earth **Transparency 123,** The Earth's Crust, Lithosphere, and Asthenosphere **Transparency 124,** The Earth's Mesosphere, Outer Core, and Inner Core **Transparency 125,** The Tectonic Plates **Reinforcement Worksheet,** The Layered Earth **Critical Thinking Worksheet,** Planet of Waves	**Math and More,** p. 89 in ATE **Connect to Physical Science,** p. 89 in ATE **MathBreak,** Using Models, p. 90 **Connect to Physical Science,** p. 90 in ATE **Biology Connection,** p. 91 **Cross-Disciplinary Focus,** p. 92 in ATE **Multicultural Connection,** p. 93 in ATE	**Section Review,** p. 94 **Quiz,** p. 94 in ATE **Alternative Assessment,** p. 94 in ATE
Directed Reading Worksheet, Section 2 **Transparency 28,** Evolution of the Galápagos Finches **Transparency 126,** The Breakup of Pangaea	**Connect to Life Science,** p. 96 in ATE **Connect to Physical Science,** p. 97 in ATE **Physics Connection,** p. 98	**Section Review,** p. 98 **Quiz,** p. 98 in ATE **Alternative Assessment,** p. 98 in ATE
Directed Reading Worksheet, Section 3 **Teaching Transparencies 127–129** **Math Skills for Science Worksheet,** A Shortcut for Multiplying Large Numbers **Reinforcement Worksheet,** A Moving Jigsaw Puzzle	**Cross-Disciplinary Focus,** p. 100 in ATE **Math and More,** p. 101 in ATE **Science, Technology, and Society:** Living on the Mid-Atlantic Ridge, p. 116 **Scientific Debate:** Continental Drift, p. 117	**Homework,** p. 101 in ATE **Section Review,** p. 102 **Quiz,** p. 102 in ATE **Alternative Assessment,** p. 102 in ATE
Directed Reading Worksheet, Section 4	**Cross-Disciplinary Focus,** p. 104 in ATE **Connect to Life Science,** p. 105 in ATE **Apply,** p. 106 **Multicultural Connection,** pp. 107, 109 in ATE **Connect to Astronomy,** p. 107 in ATE	**Homework,** p. 104 in ATE **Self-Check,** p. 105 **Section Review,** p. 109 **Quiz,** p. 109 in ATE **Alternative Assessment,** p. 109 in ATE

 internet**connect**

 Holt, Rinehart and Winston On-line Resources
go.hrw.com

For worksheets and other teaching aids related to this chapter, visit the HRW Web site and type in the keyword: **HSTTEC**

 National Science Teachers Association
www.scilinks.org

Encourage students to use the *sci*LINKS numbers listed in the internet connect boxes to access information and resources on the **NSTA** Web site.

END-OF-CHAPTER REVIEW AND ASSESSMENT

Chapter Review in Study Guide
Vocabulary and Notes in Study Guide
Chapter Tests with Performance-Based Assessment, Chapter 4 Test, Performance-Based Assessment 4
Concept Mapping Transparency 7

Chapter Resources & Worksheets

Visual Resources

TEACHING TRANSPARENCIES

#122 — Holt Science and Technology — Teaching Transparency **122** — The Composition of the Earth

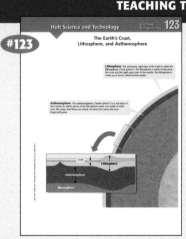

#123 — Holt Science and Technology — Teaching Transparency **123** — The Earth's Crust, Lithosphere, and Asthenosphere

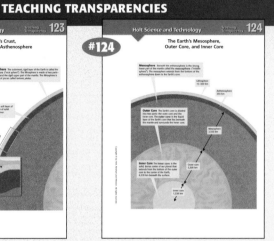

#124 — Holt Science and Technology — Teaching Transparency **124** — The Earth's Mesosphere, Outer Core, and Inner Core

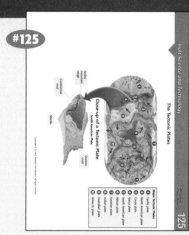

#125 — Holt Science and Technology — The Tectonic Plates

TEACHING TRANSPARENCIES

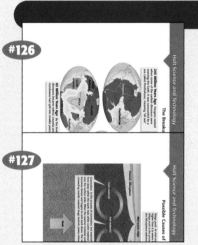

#126 — Holt Science and Technology — The Breaku...

#127 — Holt Science and Technology — Possible Causes of

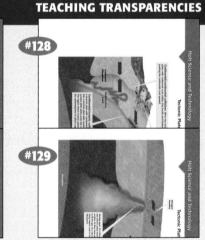

#128 — Holt Science and Technology — Tectonic Plate

#129 — Holt Science and Technology — Tectonic Plat

#28 — Holt Science and Technology — Evolution of the Galápagos Finches

LINK TO LIFE SCIENCE

CONCEPT MAPPING TRANSPARENCY

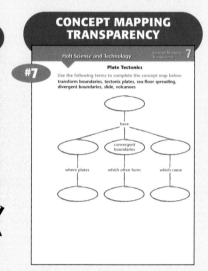

#7 — Holt Science and Technology — Concept Mapping Transparency **7**

Plate Tectonics

Use the following terms to complete the concept map below: transform boundaries, tectonic plates, sea-floor spreading, divergent boundaries, slide, volcanoes

Meeting Individual Needs

DIRECTED READING

#4 — DIRECTED READING WORKSHEET

Plate Tectonics

Chapter Introduction
As you begin this chapter, answer the following.
1. Read the title of the chapter. List three things that you already know about this subject.

2. Write two questions about this subject that you would like answered by the time you finish this chapter.

Start-Up Activity (p. 000)
3. What will you do in this activity?

Section 1: Inside the Earth (p. 00)
4. Earth's layers of rock are classified by their _____ and their _____.

REINFORCEMENT & VOCABULARY REVIEW

#4 — REINFORCEMENT WORKSHEET

The Layered Earth

Complete this worksheet after you finish reading Chapter 6, Section 1.
Use the following terms to label the diagram. Then fill in the blanks in the sentences that follow. Each word should be used only once.

crust   outer core   mantle
lithosphere   inner core   mesosphere
asthenosphere   tectonic plate

Who Am I?
I am part of the lithosphere but I move around on top of the asthenosphere. I am a _____.

Where Are We?
We have journeyed to the center of the Earth and when we got there we discovered that the core has two parts! One part is liquid and this is called the _____. The other part is dense and solid and this is called the _____.

Complete this worksheet after you finish reading Chapter 6, Section 3. The theory of plate tectonics explains that the Earth's lithosphere is divided into tectonic plates. These tectonic plates move in relation to one another. An area where two plates meet is called a boundary. There are three types of boundaries and each defines the type of motion that takes place when two plates meet. Using the hints below, label the diagram.

Types of Boundaries
convergent: This word is the adjective of the word *converge* and so they share the same basic meaning. Pretend you and a friend are on opposite sides of a room and walk towards a chair that is at the center of the room. When you meet each other at the chair you have converged on the chair. In other words you have come together so that you meet at the same place.
divergent: This word comes from the word *diverge*. This word means the exact opposite of the word converge. In this case you and a friend stand back to back at the center of the room and walk away from each other.
transform: This word means to change the form or appearance of something. It does not specify in what way, just that a change is taking place.

#4 — VOCABULARY REVIEW WORKSHEET

An Earthly Anagram

After finishing Chapter 6, give this puzzle a try!
Use the clues to help you unscramble the words given. Write your answer in the spaces provided.

1. The layer of Earth on which we live: RCSUT
   _____

2. The layer of Earth that has the most mass: METNAL
   _____

3. This layer of Earth is made mostly of iron: RCEO
   _____

4. The physical layer of the Earth made up of #1 and #2: LHETPHESROI
   _____

5. Pieces of the lithosphere: ENCCITTO TPSAEL
   _____

6. The physical layer of the Earth on which #5 float: SEEOHNTAPSRHE
   _____

7. The strong physical layer of the Earth that is part of #2: OEISEMPSHR
   _____

8. The liquid, physical layer of the Earth beneath #2: ROUTE ECRO
   _____

9. The solid, dense center of our planet: NNERI CREO
   _____

10. The theory that continents move apart from one another: TCOITAENLNN FDTRI
    _____

11. The tectonic process that takes place along mid-ocean ridges: AES RFOOL REGIDANSP
    _____

SCIENCE PUZZLERS, TWISTERS & TEASERS

#4 — SCIENCE PUZZLERS, TWISTERS & TEASERS

Plate Tectonics

Tectonic Rhyme Time
1. Professor Bankston, an inventor/architect, has made some creations. Some sound more creative than others. Each of the clues below indicates a two-word rhyming answer that describes one of professor Bankston's creations. Write the words in the blank.

   a. the amount of force put on a given material, and a machine for applying that force
      _____

   b. the outermost layer of earth, and oxidation particles that cover the iron portion of it
      _____

   c. the surface along which rocks break and slide past each other, and an impenetrable room in which to store it
      _____

   d. extends from the bottom of the mantle to the center of the earth, and the place where you can buy parts of it
      _____

The Blame Game—Whose Fault Is It?
2. Amanda blames others for everything. Below are some questions her teacher has asked her about faults, and the jumbled responses she gave in return. Write the correct responses below.

   Teacher: Amanda, why did the hanging wall move up relative to the footwall?
   Amanda: It was Reese V.'s fault!
   a. _____

   Teacher: O.K. Amanda, let's try again. Why did the hanging wall move down relative to the footwall?
   Amanda: It was Ron Lam's fault!
   b. _____

Review & Assessment

STUDY GUIDE

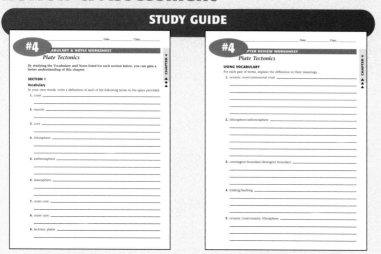

CHAPTER TESTS WITH PERFORMANCE-BASED ASSESSMENT

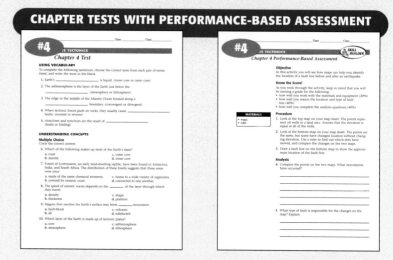

Lab Worksheets

LABS YOU CAN EAT

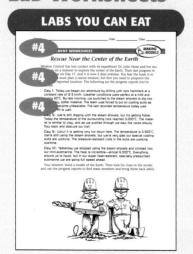

WHIZ-BANG DEMONSTRATIONS

LONG-TERM PROJECTS & RESEARCH IDEAS

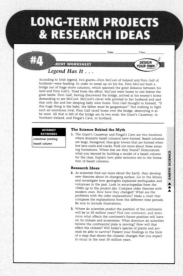

DATASHEETS FOR LABBOOK

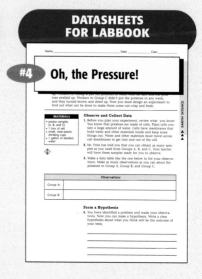

Applications & Extensions

CRITICAL THINKING & PROBLEM SOLVING

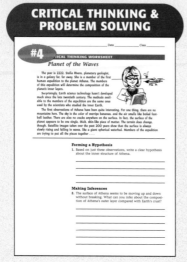

SCIENTISTS IN ACTION

SECTION 1

SECTION 1

Inside the Earth

▶ Continents and the Earth's Crust

Continents are large, continuous landmasses composed of crust that is generally much older than the surrounding oceanic crust. The core of a continent, called a craton, is generally composed of ancient, crystalline igneous and metamorphic rock. Cratons are relatively thick and make up the most stable part of continents. They range from 200 million to 3.9 billion years of age.

▶ Heat Within the Earth

The Earth's internal heat contributes to the process of differentiation—the division of the Earth into layers with distinct characteristics. This heat has three main sources:

- the decay of radioactive elements

- the collapse of iron into Earth's core during its formation

- leftover energy from the accretion and compression of particles that coalesced to form Earth

▶ Earth's Inner Core

Research conducted in 1996 suggests that the solid inner core of the Earth spins faster than the rest of the planet. This 2,456 km wide ball of hot iron moves at a speed that would allow it to lap Earth's surface once every 400 years. This information may give scientists clues about how the Earth formed.

- The Earth's outer core is a hot, electrically conducting liquid thought to be continuously moved by convection. This layer's conductivity combines with the differential spin of the Earth's inner core to create powerful electric currents that, in turn, generate the Earth's magnetic field.

IS THAT A FACT!

- ➤ Earth's magnetic poles have reversed more than 177 times in the last 85 million years. The most recent switch occurred within the last 2 million

years. With complex computer models, scientists are beginning to understand how this process happens, but they are still unable to predict the next time the poles will reverse or how life on Earth will be affected by this change.

SECTION 2

Restless Continents

▶ Continental Drift: An Old Idea

The idea that the continents were once joined together was not a new idea in Alfred Wegener's time. In 1620, Francis Bacon noted that the continents seemed to fit together like a jigsaw puzzle, but no one could understand how they moved. In 1858, a French scientist named Antonio Snider-Pellegrini cited fossil evidence that suggested the continents had been joined. Wegener's studies in 1915 were the first exhaustive research on the topic, combining evidence from many disciplines. In 1958, an American geologist named Frank Taylor pointed out geologic similarities between South America and Africa. But neither scientist could explain how the continents had separated, and their observations were dismissed. It was not until the discovery of sea-floor spreading that the continental drift hypothesis was accepted.

▶ Testing the Continental Drift Hypothesis

After sea-floor spreading was discovered in the 1960s, research groups tested Wegener's hypothesis using as many methods as possible:

- The edges of continental slopes were mapped with sonar and shown to fit together even better than the coastlines did.

- New radiometric dating methods showed that rocks in corresponding parts of Africa and South America formed at the same time.

- The dating of igneous rocks around mid-ocean ridges showed a symmetrical pattern, with older rocks located farther away from the rifts. Few rocks older than 180 million years were discovered on the ocean floor. This indicates that the oceanic lithosphere is continuously recycled.

- Scientists found that zones of magnetic reversals also followed a symmetrical pattern on either side of mid-ocean ridges, matching the pattern revealed by the ages of those rocks.

- The horizontal magnetic reversals recorded in the ocean floor matched those recorded in vertical sequences of lava flows on continents.

▶ Harry Hammond Hess (1906–1969)

Henry Hess was an American geologist who proposed the idea of sea-floor spreading in 1960, thus playing a key role in developing the theory of plate tectonics. Hess suggested that convection within the Earth was continuously creating new ocean floor at the mid-ocean ridges. He also theorized that rocks would be older at increasing distances from these ridges, an expectation confirmed by research beginning in 1963. Hess also correctly explained the subduction of oceanic crust beneath less dense continental crust.

SECTION 3

The Theory of Plate Tectonics

▶ Trenches

Where an oceanic plate subducts under another tectonic plate, a long, steep-sided trench forms on the sea floor. On average, subduction trenches are 2,000–4,000 m lower than the rest of the ocean floor. Nevertheless, some animals, including species of sea cucumbers, sea anemones, and marine worms, are capable of living in the cold, pressurized depths of ocean trenches.

IS THAT A FACT!

- ➤ The Mariana Trench, which is 2,500 km long and 11,033 m below sea level at its deepest, is the deepest known point on Earth. This trench is located where the Pacific plate is subducted beneath the Philippine plate.

SECTION 4

Deforming the Earth's Crust

▶ Fault Versus Fold

Tectonic activity exerts a tremendous amount of pressure on crustal rocks; whether they bend or break depends on several factors:

- type of stress—If stress is applied gradually, rocks often fold; if stress is applied suddenly, rocks tend to fault.

- composition of rock—Brittle rocks, such as sandstone, tend to break; ductile (easily bent) rocks, such as shale, tend to fold.

- temperature—As the temperature at the point of stress increases, rocks are more likely to fold rather than fault.

For background information about teaching strategies and issues, refer to the *Professional Reference for Teachers.*

Plate Tectonics

CHAPTER 4

Pre-Reading Questions

Students may not know the answers to these questions before reading the chapter, so accept any reasonable response.

Suggested Answers

1. Mountain ranges move because they are part of tectonic plates, which move around on top of the asthenosphere.

2. Mountains can form in three main ways: when rock layers are folded as tectonic plates collide; when the crust is stretched due to tension, forming a large number of normal faults; and when volcanoes are formed as molten rock erupts onto the Earth's surface.

CHAPTER 4

Plate Tectonics

Sections

Pre-Reading Questions

1. Why do entire mountain ranges move?
2. How do mountains form?

WHEN CONTINENTS COLLIDE

The Himalayas are the highest mountains on Earth. They are located between India and Asia in a region where two continents are slowly crashing into each other. This photo shows the highest mountain of all—Mount Everest. At an elevation of 8,848 m, the air at the top of Mount Everest is so thin that climbers must bring their own oxygen! In this chapter you will learn about how and where different types of mountains form. You will also learn about how scientists came up with *plate tectonics*, the theory that revolutionized geology.

Mountain climbers must brave extreme conditions when climbing mountains such as Mount Everest.

86

internet connect

HRW On-line Resources

go.hrw.com

For worksheets and other teaching aids, visit the HRW Web site and type in the keyword: **HSTTEC**

SCiLINKS
NSTA

www.scilinks.com

Use the *sci*LINKS numbers at the end of each chapter for additional resources on the **NSTA** Web site.

Smithsonian Institution

www.si.edu/hrw

Visit the Smithsonian Institution Web site for related on-line resources.

CNNfyi.com

www.cnnfyi.com

Visit the CNN Web site for current events coverage and classroom resources.

START-UP Activity

CONTINENTAL COLLISIONS

As you can see, continents not only move, but they can also crash into each other. In this activity, you will model the collision of two continents.

Procedure

1. Obtain **two stacks of paper,** each about 1 cm thick.

2. Place the two stacks of paper on a **flat surface,** such as a desk.

3. Very slowly, push the stacks of paper together so that they collide. Continue to push the stacks until the paper in one of the stacks folds over.

4. Repeat step 3, but this time push the two stacks together at a different angle. For example, if you pushed the flat edges together in step 3, try pushing the corners of the paper together this time.

Analysis

5. What happens to the stacks of paper when they collide with each other?

6. Do all of the pieces of paper get pushed upward? If not, what happens to those pieces that do not get pushed upward?

7. What type of landform does this model predict as the result of a continental collision?

87

START-UP Activity

CONTINENTAL COLLISIONS

MATERIALS
FOR EACH STUDENT:
• two stacks of paper
• flat surface

Answers to START-UP Activity

5. The stacks of paper buckle and fold over. One stack of paper slid under the other.

6. No, some pieces of paper slid under the opposite stack, while others slid into the other stack.

7. Continental collisions form large mountain ranges like the Himalayas.

Focus

Inside the Earth

This section describes the classification of the Earth according to composition (crust, mantle, and core) and according to physical structure (lithosphere, asthenosphere, mesosphere, outer core, and inner core). Students then learn about *tectonic plates*. The section concludes with a discussion of how scientists study seismic waves to map the Earth's interior.

 Bellringer

On the board or an overhead projector, pose the following question to your students at the beginning of class:

If you journeyed to the center of the Earth, what do you think you would see along the way?

Have students draw an illustration of their journey in their ScienceLog. Sheltered English

1) Motivate

COOPERATIVE LEARNING

Pose the following situation to small groups of students for discussion: Measurements show that the land west of the San Andreas Fault, in California, is moving toward the northwest at a rate of 5 cm per year relative to the land east of the fault. What forces do you think cause this movement? Where do these forces come from? When groups agree on a hypothesis, have them create illustrations or a model they can use to explain their theory to the class.

Terms to Learn

crust	mesosphere
mantle	outer core
core	inner core
lithosphere	tectonic plate
asthenosphere	

What You'll Do

- ◆ Identify and describe the layers of the Earth by what they are made of.
- ◆ Identify and describe the layers of the Earth by their physical properties.
- ◆ Define *tectonic plate.*
- ◆ Explain how scientists know about the structure of Earth's interior.

Inside the Earth

The Earth is not just a ball of solid rock. It is made of several layers with different physical properties and compositions. As you will discover, scientists think about the Earth's layers in two ways—by their *composition* and by their *physical properties*.

Earth's layers are made of different mixtures of elements. This is what is meant by differences in composition. Many of the Earth's layers also have different physical properties. Physical properties include temperature, density, and ability to flow. Let's first take a look at the composition of the Earth.

The Composition of the Earth

The Earth is divided into three layers—the *crust, mantle,* and *core*—based on what each one is made of. The lightest materials make up the outermost layer, and the densest materials make up the inner layers. This is because lighter materials tend to float up, while heavier materials sink.

The Crust The **crust** is the outermost layer of the Earth. Ranging from 5 to 100 km thick, it is also the thinnest layer of the Earth. And because it is the layer we live on, we know more about this layer than we know about the other two.

There are two types of crust—continental and oceanic. *Continental crust* has a composition similar to granite. It has an average thickness of 30 km. *Oceanic crust* has a composition similar to basalt. It is generally between 5 and 8 km thick. Because basalt is denser than granite, oceanic crust is denser than continental crust.

Figure 1 *Oceanic crust is thinner but denser than continental crust.*

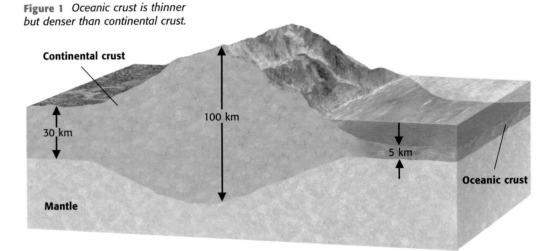

Continental crust

30 km

100 km

5 km

Oceanic crust

Mantle

Directed Reading Worksheet Section 1

IS THAT A FACT!

Two lines of evidence indicate that Earth's core is a mixture of iron and nickel. The core's density, which is similar to a mixture of iron and nickel, was determined by studying the way seismic waves travel through it. The Earth's magnetic field also suggests this composition.

The Mantle The **mantle** is the layer of the Earth between the crust and the core. Compared with the crust, the mantle is extremely thick and contains most of the Earth's mass.

No one has ever seen what the mantle really looks like. It is just too far down to drill for a sample. Scientists must infer what the composition and other characteristics of the mantle are from observations they make on the Earth's surface. In some places mantle rock has been pushed up to the surface by tectonic forces, allowing scientists to observe the rock directly.

As you can see in **Figure 2,** another place scientists look is on the ocean floor, where molten rock from the mantle flows out of active volcanoes. These underwater volcanoes are like windows through the crust into the mantle. The "windows" have given us strong clues about the composition of the mantle. Scientists have learned that the mantle's composition is similar to that of the mineral olivine, which has large amounts of iron and magnesium compared with other common minerals.

Figure 2 *Volcanic vents on the ocean floor, such as this one off the coast of Hawaii, allow magma to escape from the mantle beneath oceanic crust.*

The Core By studying the different layers that make up the Earth, geologists can get an idea of which elements each is made of. They think that the Earth's *core* is made mostly of iron, with smaller amounts of nickel and possibly some sulfur and oxygen. The **core** extends from the bottom of the mantle to the center of the Earth. As you can see in **Figure 3,** the diameter of the planet Mars is slightly smaller than that of the Earth's core.

Figure 3 *The Earth is made up of three layers, as shown here.*

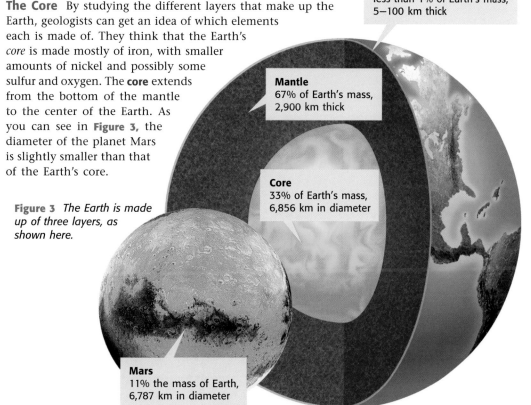

Crust
less than 1% of Earth's mass,
5–100 km thick

Mantle
67% of Earth's mass,
2,900 km thick

Core
33% of Earth's mass,
6,856 km in diameter

Mars
11% the mass of Earth,
6,787 km in diameter

89

MISCONCEPTION ALERT

Explain the differences between radius, diameter, and thickness. In **Figure 3,** the crust and mantle are shells measured by their thickness. The core is a sphere, so it is measured by its diameter or radius.

READING STRATEGY

Prediction Guide Before students read this page, ask them the following question: If you could burrow to the center of the Earth, what would you expect to happen to the pressure, the temperature, and the solidity of matter? Each successive layer will:

a. become hotter, have higher pressure, and become more liquid

b. become cooler, have higher pressure, and become harder

c. become hotter, have lower pressure, and become more liquid

d. become hotter and have higher pressure; the solidity of layers will depend on temperature and pressure

(answer: d)

CONNECT TO PHYSICAL SCIENCE

The composition of the core is probably similar throughout. Why, then, is part of the core liquid and the rest solid? You would think that if the outer core were hot enough to be in a liquid state, the inner core would be at least as hot, if not hotter. The difference in physical states is due not to differences in temperature but to differences in pressure. Even though the inner core is extremely hot, the high pressure keeps the material in a solid state. The outer core, on the other hand, has less pressure. The pressure in the outer core is just low enough that the hot iron can stay in a liquid state.

÷ 5 ÷ Ω ≤ ∞ +Ω √ 9 ∞ ≤ Σ 2

MATH BREAK

Using Models
Imagine that you are building a model of the Earth that is going to have a radius of 1 m. You find out that the average radius of the Earth is 6,378 km and that the thickness of the lithosphere is about 150 km. What percentage of the Earth's radius is the lithosphere? How thick (in centimeters) would you make the lithosphere in your model?

The Structure of the Earth

So far we have talked about the composition of the Earth. Another way to look at how the Earth is made is to examine the physical properties of its layers. The Earth is divided into five main physical layers—the *lithosphere, asthenosphere, mesosphere, outer core,* and *inner core.* As shown below, each layer has its own set of physical properties.

Lithosphere The outermost, rigid layer of the Earth is called the **lithosphere** ("rock sphere"). The lithosphere is made of two parts—the crust and the rigid upper part of the mantle. The lithosphere is divided into pieces called *tectonic plates.*

Asthenosphere The **asthenosphere** ("weak sphere") is a soft layer of the mantle on which pieces of the lithosphere move. It is made of solid rock that, like putty, flows very slowly—at about the same rate your fingernails grow.

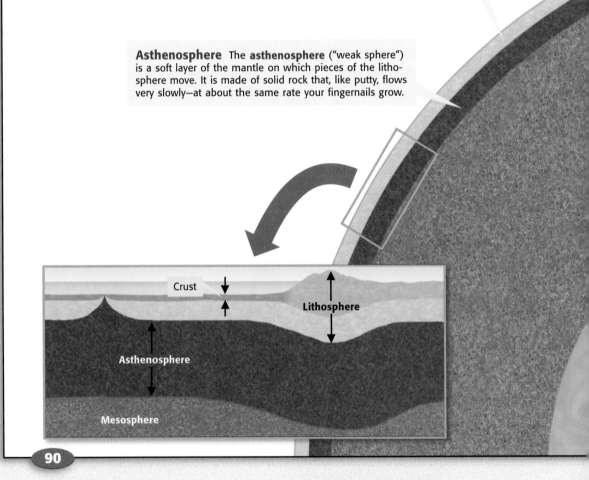

Teaching Transparency 123
"The Earth's Crust, Lithosphere, and Asthenosphere"

MISCONCEPTION ALERT

Be sure students understand that the two systems of naming Earth's layers describe different properties. *Crust, mantle,* and *core* describe differences in chemical makeup; *lithosphere, asthenosphere,* and *mesosphere* describe differences in the response of the material to stress caused by differences in temperature and pressure.

Mesosphere Beneath the asthenosphere is the strong, lower part of the mantle called the **mesosphere** ("middle sphere"). The mesosphere extends from the bottom of the asthenosphere down to the Earth's core.

Biology CONNECTION

Scientists call the part of the Earth where life is possible the *biosphere*. The biosphere is the layer of the Earth above the crust and below the uppermost part of the atmosphere. It includes the oceans, the land surface, and the lower part of the atmosphere.

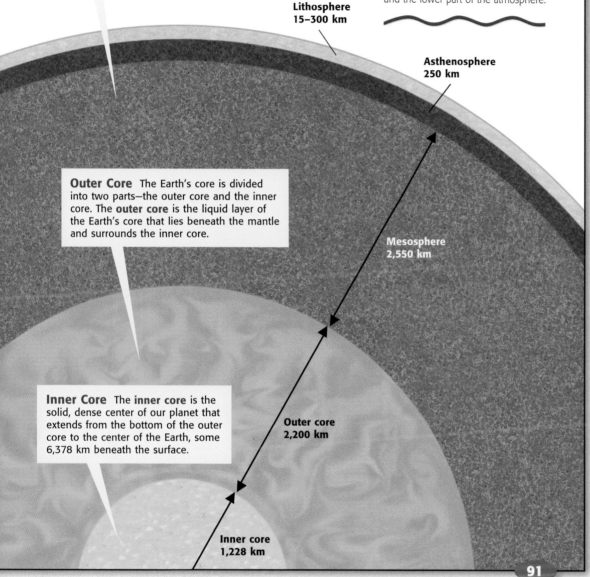

Lithosphere
15–300 km

Asthenosphere
250 km

Mesosphere
2,550 km

Outer core
2,200 km

Inner core
1,228 km

Outer Core The Earth's core is divided into two parts—the outer core and the inner core. The **outer core** is the liquid layer of the Earth's core that lies beneath the mantle and surrounds the inner core.

Inner Core The **inner core** is the solid, dense center of our planet that extends from the bottom of the outer core to the center of the Earth, some 6,378 km beneath the surface.

91

IS THAT A FACT!

The center of the Earth's core is hotter than the surface of the sun! The temperature of Earth's inner core reaches 6,000°C. The photosphere of the sun, which we see as its surface, has a temperature of 5,500°C. The sun's core temperature, however, is 15,000,000°C.

internetconnect

SCiLINKS.
NSTA

TOPIC: Composition of the Earth
GO TO: www.scilinks.org
*sci*LINKS NUMBER: HSTE155

TOPIC: Structure of the Earth
GO TO: www.scilinks.org
*sci*LINKS NUMBER: HSTE160

Teaching Transparency 124
"The Earth's Mesosphere, Outer Core, and Inner Core"

Writing **Language Arts** *Tectonic* comes from the Greek word *tektonikos*, meaning "of a builder." Ask students to consider how this meaning is appropriate for tectonic plates. In what ways are tectonic plates responsible for building features on the Earth's surface? Have students write a poem that describes how the movement of tectonic plates slowly shapes the landscape around us.

BRAIN FOOD

The deepest hole ever drilled into the continental crust was in the Kola Peninsula, in Russia, in 1984. It was 12,226 m deep! It is very difficult to drill much deeper than that because the deeper you go, the hotter it gets. If you drill too deep, the hot rock flows around the drill bit, filling the hole faster than it can be drilled.

Have students calculate the depth, in kilometers, of the deepest human-made hole. Did it extend to the asthenosphere? (12.2 km; no)

Teaching Transparency 125
"The Tectonic Plates"
"Close-up of a Tectonic Plate"

Tectonic Plates

Tectonic plates are pieces of the lithosphere that move around on top of the asthenosphere. But what exactly does a tectonic plate look like? How big are tectonic plates? How and why do they move around? To answer these questions, start by thinking of the lithosphere as a giant jigsaw puzzle.

Figure 4 *Tectonic plates fit together like the pieces of a jigsaw puzzle. On this map, the relative motions of some of the major tectonic plates are shown with arrows.*

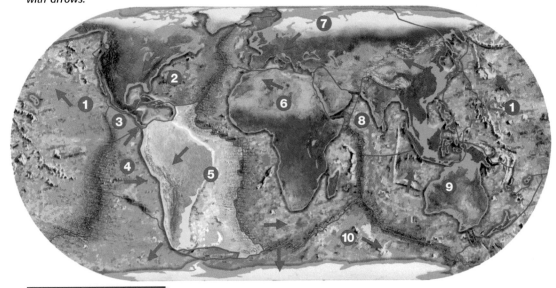

Major Tectonic Plates

1. Pacific plate
2. North American plate
3. Cocos plate
4. Nazca plate
5. South American plate
6. African plate
7. Eurasian plate
8. Indian plate
9. Australian plate
10. Antarctic plate

A Giant Jigsaw Puzzle Look at the world map above. All of the plates have names, some of which you may already be familiar with. Some of the major tectonic plates are listed in the key at left. Notice that each tectonic plate fits the other tectonic plates that surround it. The lithosphere is like a jigsaw puzzle, and the tectonic plates are like the pieces of a jigsaw puzzle.

You will also notice that not all tectonic plates are the same. Compare the size of the North American plate with that of the Cocos plate. But tectonic plates are different in other ways too. For example, the North American plate has an entire continent on it, while the Cocos plate only has oceanic crust. Like the North American plate, some tectonic plates include both continental *and* oceanic crust.

MISCONCEPTION ALERT

Be sure students realize that tectonic plates are not always neatly divided along continental lines. For example, the North American plate includes the North American continent, Greenland, half of Iceland, and part of Eurasia. All six of the Earth's large continental plates contain a continent and a large section of oceanic lithosphere. Some of the smaller tectonic plates contain only oceanic crust.

A Tectonic Plate Close-up What would a tectonic plate look like if you could lift it out of its place? **Figure 5** shows what the South American plate might look like if you could. Notice that this tectonic plate consists of both oceanic and continental crust, just like the North American plate.

The thickest part of this tectonic plate is on the South American continent, under the Andes mountain range. The thinnest part of the South American plate is at the Mid-Atlantic Ridge.

South American Plate

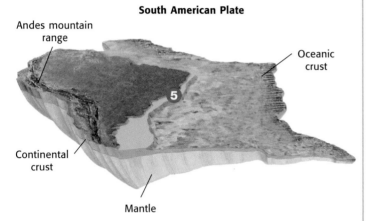

Figure 5 *The South American plate is one of the many pieces of the spherical "jigsaw puzzle" we call the lithosphere.*

Tip of the Iceberg If you could look at a tectonic plate from the side, you would see that mountain ranges are like the tips of icebergs—there is much more material below the surface than above. Mountain ranges that occur in continental crust have very deep roots relative to their height. For example, the Rocky Mountains rise less than 5 km above sea level, but their roots go down to about 60 km *below* sea level.

But if continental crust is so much thicker than oceanic crust, why doesn't it sink down below the oceanic crust? Think back to the difference between continental and oceanic crust. Continental crust stands much higher than oceanic crust because it is both thicker and less dense. Both kinds of crust are less dense than the mantle and "float" on top of the asthenosphere, similar to the way ice floats on top of water.

 **QuickLab**

Floating Mountains

1. Take a large **block** of wood and place it in a clear plastic **container.** The block of wood represents the mantle part of the lithosphere.

2. Fill the container with **water** at least 10 cm deep. The water represents the asthenosphere. Use a ruler to measure how far the top of the wood block sits above the surface of the water.

3. Now try loading the block of wood with several different **wooden objects,** each with a different weight. These objects represent different amounts of crustal material loaded onto the lithosphere during mountain building. Measure how far the block sinks under each different weight.

4. What can you conclude about how the tectonic plate reacts to increasing weight of crustal material?

5. What happens to a tectonic plate when the crustal material is removed?

TRY at HOME

 Multicultural CONNECTION

The contact between the crust and the mantle is called the Mohorovičić discontinuity, or the Moho. The discontinuity is caused by a density difference between the crust and the mantle. It was discovered by a Croatian geologist named Andrija Mohorovičić. While investigating a 1909 earthquake in Croatia, he noticed there had been two sets of seismic waves. He theorized that the existence of these two sets was caused by a density difference between the crust and the mantle. Further studies indicated that the discontinuity is found worldwide. Have interested students find out more about the Moho and Gutenberg discontinuities.

3 Extend

QuickLab

MATERIALS
• block of wood • plastic container • water • wooden objects

Teacher Notes: In step 3, the wooden objects should each weigh less than the original wooden block. Explain to students that removing the wooden objects is analogous to large-scale erosion of crustal materials.

Answers to QuickLab

4. As a tectonic plate is weighed down with crustal material, it sinks lower into the asthenosphere.

5. When the weight is removed, the tectonic plate rises back up to its former level.

GROUP ACTIVITY

Pair students and have them plan and build a three-dimensional model of a tectonic plate on the asthenosphere. Students might use materials such as cardboard, wood, and clay. Remind students to label the continental crust, oceanic crust, and lithosphere, as well as any surface topographical features, such as mountain ranges. When models are complete, have students display them and give a brief presentation to the class. Students can use their models later in this chapter to simulate convergent, divergent, and transform motion.
Sheltered English

Reinforcement Worksheet
"The Layered Earth"

USING THE FIGURE

The key for **Figure 6** shows the speeds of only one type of seismic wave—the compression, or P wave. P waves can travel through both liquids and solids and thus can travel through the liquid outer core, unlike other seismic waves. Have students describe what happens when the speed of seismic waves changes. (They also change direction.)

Quiz

1. The crust is the Earth's only solid layer. (false)

2. The inner core of the Earth is solid and made primarily of iron. (true)

3. Temperature and pressure increase toward the center of the Earth. (true)

4. The asthenosphere is the thinnest layer. (false)

ALTERNATIVE ASSESSMENT

 Have students write a story describing their own "journey to the center of the Earth," or they may choose to write a travel guide that describes the experience of traveling through Earth's different layers. Have students draw and color-code a model of Earth to include with their project. Emphasize that this model must show layers defined by chemical composition (crust, mantle, and core) and by physical traits (lithosphere, asthenosphere, mesosphere, outer core, and inner core.)

 Critical Thinking Worksheet "Planet of Waves"

Mapping the Earth's Interior

How do we know all these things about the deepest parts of the Earth, where no one has ever been? Scientists have never even drilled through the crust, which is only a thin skin on the surface of the Earth. So how do we know so much about the mantle and the core?

Would you be surprised to know that the answers come from earthquakes? When an earthquake occurs, vibrations called seismic waves are produced. *Seismic waves are vibrations that travel through the Earth.* Depending on the density and strength of material they pass through, seismic waves travel at different speeds. For example, a seismic wave traveling through solid rock will go faster than a seismic wave traveling through a liquid.

When an earthquake occurs, *seismographs* measure the difference in the arrival times of seismic waves and record them. Seismologists can then use these measurements to calculate the density and thickness of each physical layer of the Earth. **Figure 6** shows how one kind of seismic wave travels through the Earth.

Earthquake

Path of seismic wave

Lithosphere 7–8 km/second

Asthenosphere 7–11 km/second

Mesosphere 11–13 km/second

Outer core 7–10 km/second

Inner core 11–12 km/second

Figure 6 *The speed of seismic waves depends on the density of the material they travel through. The denser the material, the faster seismic waves move.*

internet connect

*SCi*LINKS
NSTA

TOPIC: Composition of the Earth, Structure of the Earth
GO TO: www.scilinks.org
*sci*LINKS **NUMBER:** HSTE155, HSTE160

SECTION REVIEW

1. What is the difference between continental and oceanic crust?

2. How is the lithosphere different from the asthenosphere?

3. How do scientists know about the structure of the Earth's interior? Explain.

4. **Analyzing Relationships** Explain the difference between the crust and the lithosphere.

▼ *Answers to Section Review*

1. Oceanic crust is thin and dense compared with continental crust. Continental crust and granite have a similar composition, and oceanic crust and basalt have a similar composition.

2. The lithosphere is rigid and is divided into tectonic plates. The asthenosphere is a layer of soft mantle material that flows very slowly.

3. Scientists measure the different speeds at which seismic waves travel through different parts of the Earth. This indicates the density and thickness of each layer the waves pass through.

4. The crust and the lithosphere are the outermost layers of the Earth, but the lithosphere includes the crust and the rigid, uppermost part of the mantle.

Terms to Learn

continental drift
sea-floor spreading

What You'll Do

◆ Describe Wegener's theory of continental drift, and explain why it was not accepted at first.

◆ Explain how sea-floor spreading provides a way for continents to move.

◆ Describe how new oceanic crust forms at mid-ocean ridges.

◆ Explain how magnetic reversals provide evidence for sea-floor spreading.

Restless Continents

Take a look at **Figure 7.** It shows how continents would fit together if you removed the Atlantic Ocean and moved the land together. Is it just coincidence that the coastlines fit together so well? Is it possible that the continents were actually together sometime in the past?

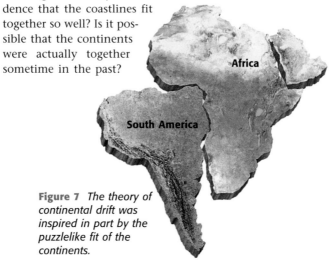

Figure 7 *The theory of continental drift was inspired in part by the puzzlelike fit of the continents.*

Wegener's Theory of Continental Drift

One scientist who looked at the pieces of this puzzle was Alfred Wegener (VEG e nuhr). In the early 1900s he wrote about his theory of *continental drift*. **Continental drift** is the theory that continents can drift apart from one another and have done so in the past. This theory seemed to explain a lot of puzzling observations, including the very good fit of some of the continents.

Continental drift also explained why fossils of the same plant and animal species are found on both sides of the Atlantic Ocean. Many of these ancient species could not have made it across the Atlantic Ocean. As you can see in **Figure 8,** without continental drift, this pattern of fossil findings would be hard to explain. In addition to fossils, similar types of rock and evidence of the same ancient climatic conditions were found on several continents.

Mesosaurus

Glossopteris

Figure 8 *Fossils of* Mesosaurus, *a small, aquatic reptile, and* Glossopteris, *an ancient plant species, have been found on several continents.*

95

IS THAT A FACT!

By the time Alfred Wegener was 32, he had set a world record for balloon flight, earned a doctorate in astronomy, made two meteorological expeditions to Greenland, and written the paper that was the main catalyst for the greatest geologic insight of the twentieth century.

WEIRD SCIENCE

In **Figure 7,** the southern tips of South America and Africa do not touch, while **Figure 8** indicates that they did touch in the past. According to one interpretation, the southern tip of South America was wrapped around the southern tip of Africa when the two continents were together.

Focus

Restless Continents

This section explains how, over millions of years, continents have moved to their present locations. Students learn about continental drift—the theory that the Earth's continents were originally united as the giant landmass called Pangaea and have since drifted apart. The section explains that support for this theory came when mid-ocean ridges were discovered. In turn, the phenomenon of sea-floor spreading was evidenced by the record of reversals of the Earth's magnetic field present in oceanic crust.

Bellringer

Ask students to explain why the following statement is true or false:

The United States is moving westward.

1 Motivate

DISCUSSION

Show students a map of the world, and demonstrate how the continents seem to fit together, as shown in **Figure 7.** Ask them to help you write a list of other evidence that supports Wegener's theories. (Students might suggest similar fossils on continents that were once joined, similar rock strata and crust thickness, or the continuity of ancient geologic features, such as mountain chains or faults.)

 Directed Reading Worksheet Section 2

GUIDED PRACTICE

Have students work in small groups to create a model of Pangaea. Provide each group with two world maps. With pencils, students can mark hypothetical glacial grooves extending from the poles of both maps. Have them cut the continents out of one map and treat them as puzzle pieces, seeing how they best fit together. Refer to both the complete and the altered maps, and help students explain and demonstrate how each continent moved from its original position. Sheltered English

CONNECT TO
LIFE SCIENCE

Before Pangaea broke up, dinosaurs roamed the entire continent. The populations were very widespread. As Pangaea began to break up, the populations of dinosaurs were fragmented and isolated on the new continents. The fossil record indicates that dinosaurs began to evolve divergently as a result. By the time dinosaurs became extinct, about 65 million years ago, there was great diversity among the different dinosaurs. Use the Teaching Transparencies listed below to discuss natural selection and the breakup of Pangaea. Have groups of students research different dinosaurs that lived after the breakup of Pangaea and speculate why these dinosaurs evolved the way they did.

Teaching Transparency 28
"Evolution of the Galápagos Finches" LINK TO LIFE SCIENCE

Teaching Transparency 126
"The Breakup of Pangaea"

Continental drift also explained puzzling evidence left by ancient glaciers. Glaciers cut grooves in the ground that indicate the direction they traveled. When you look at the placement of today's continents, these glacial activities do not seem to be related. But when you bring all of these continental pieces back to their original arrangement, the glacial grooves match! Along with fossil evidence, glacial grooves supported Wegener's idea of continental drift.

The Breakup of Pangaea

Wegener studied many observations before establishing his theory of continental drift. He thought that all the separate continents of today were once joined in a single landmass that he called *Pangaea,* which is Greek for "all earth." As shown in **Figure 9,** almost all of Earth's landmasses were joined together in one huge continent 245 million years ago.

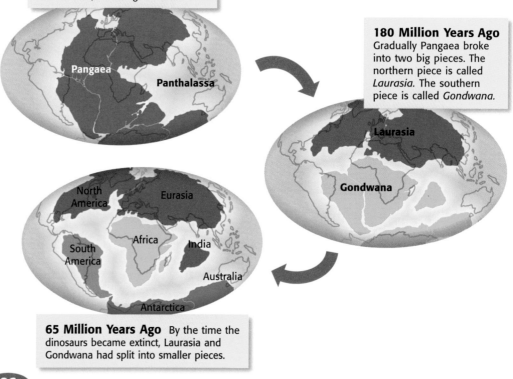

245 Million Years Ago Pangaea existed when some of the earliest dinosaurs were roaming the Earth. It was surrounded by a sea called *Panthalassa,* meaning "all sea."

Figure 9 Over time, Earth's continents have changed shape and traveled great distances.

180 Million Years Ago Gradually Pangaea broke into two big pieces. The northern piece is called *Laurasia.* The southern piece is called *Gondwana.*

65 Million Years Ago By the time the dinosaurs became extinct, Laurasia and Gondwana had split into smaller pieces.

96

MISCONCEPTION ///ALERT\\\

Pangaea was not the only supercontinent that existed. Some 500 million years before Pangaea began to form, another supercontinent dominated the globe—Rodinia. Some scientists speculate that the formation of supercontinents occurs as a cycle of accretion and breakup. If this is true, there may have been as many as 10 different supercontinents in the last 3 billion years and there may be more in the future!

Sea-Floor Spreading

When Wegener put forth his theory of continental drift, many scientists would not accept his theory. What force of nature, they wondered, could move entire continents? In Wegener's day, no one could answer that question. It wasn't until many years later that new evidence provided some clues.

In **Figure 10** you will notice that there is a chain of submerged mountains running through the center of the Atlantic Ocean. The chain is called the Mid-Atlantic Ridge, part of a worldwide system of ocean ridges. Mid-ocean ridges are underwater mountain chains that run through Earth's ocean basins.

Mid-ocean ridges are places where sea-floor spreading takes place. **Sea-floor spreading** is the process by which new oceanic lithosphere is created as older materials are pulled away. As tectonic plates move away from each other, the sea floor spreads apart and magma rises to fill in the gap. Notice in **Figure 11** that the crust increases in age the farther it is from the mid-ocean ridge. This is because new crust continually forms from molten material at the ridge. The oldest crust in the Atlantic Ocean is found along the edges of the continents. It dates back to the time of the dinosaurs. The newest crust is in the center of the ocean. This crust has just formed!

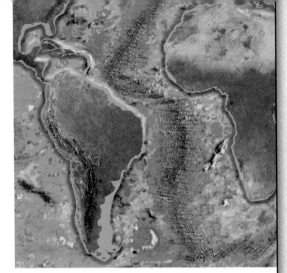

Figure 10 *The Mid-Atlantic Ridge is part of the longest mountain chain in the world.*

Figure 11 *Sea-floor spreading creates new oceanic lithosphere at mid-ocean ridges.*

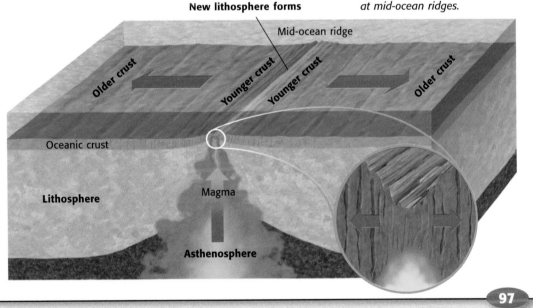

New lithosphere forms

Mid-ocean ridge

Older crust

Younger crust

Younger crust

Older crust

Oceanic crust

Lithosphere

Magma

Asthenosphere

97

Scientists at Odds

Many geologists ridiculed Wegener's theories because they had been taught that continents and ocean basins were fixed in their positions. These scientists knew of no force that could move an entire continent, and they discounted the overwhelming evidence that continental drift had occurred.

---

3) Extend

USING THE FIGURE

Have students use **Figure 11** to explain the forces that pull rocks outward from mid-ocean ridges. Guide their explanations by asking the following questions:

- Why does molten rock from the mantle come to the surface at the ridges?
- Why does the ocean floor spread apart at the ridges?
- Why is rock formed at the ridges called *new* rock?

Stress that mid-ocean ridges are not always in the middle of an ocean. Have students compare the locations of mid-ocean ridges in **Figure 4.**

CONNECT TO PHYSICAL SCIENCE

Explain that researchers used sonar to discover that the ocean floor is not flat. In the 1950s, scientists broadcast sound waves toward the sea floor and measured how long it took the waves to return. The echoes revealed the existence of oceanic valleys and mountains. In short, the ocean floors turned out to be as varied as the continents! Scientists were most amazed to find a chain of undersea mountains snaking thousands of kilometers around the globe—the mid-ocean ridges.

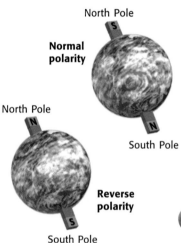

BRAIN FOOD

Why is the south pole of the bar magnet in **Figure 12** located at the Earth's north pole during "normal polarity"? Explain to students that magnetic attraction occurs between the opposite poles of magnets. The north-seeking pole of a compass needle actually points to the south pole of Earth's magnetic field. Thus, during periods of "normal polarity" what we call the Earth's magnetic north pole is actually the south pole of Earth's magnetic field. This concept can be easily demonstrated by placing the south pole of a bar magnet next to a compass. The compass needle will point toward the south pole of the bar magnet in the same way it tends to point toward the south pole of Earth's magnetic field, what we call magnetic north.

Quiz

1. If the Earth's crust is growing at mid-ocean ridges, why doesn't the Earth itself grow larger? (because the Earth's crust is part of the rock cycle)

2. What was Pangaea? (the large landmass that later broke up to form two supercontinents and then fragmented further to form the six continents of today)

ALTERNATIVE ASSESSMENT

Writing Have students write a paragraph explaining how sea-floor spreading causes continents to move apart. Students should also include a diagram of this process.

Physics CONNECTION

All matter has the property of magnetism, though in most cases it is very weak compared with that of magnets. This explains why researchers have been able to levitate a frog—by creating a very strong magnetic field beneath it!

Magnetic Reversals

Some of the most important evidence of sea-floor spreading comes from magnetic reversals recorded in the ocean floor. Throughout Earth's history, the north and south magnetic poles have changed places many times. When Earth's magnetic poles change place, this is called a *magnetic reversal*.

The molten rock at the mid-ocean ridges contains tiny grains of magnetic minerals. These mineral grains act like compasses. They align with the magnetic field of the Earth. Once the molten rock cools, the record of these tiny compasses is literally set in stone. This record is then carried slowly away from the spreading center as sea-floor spreading occurs. As you can see in **Figure 12,** when the Earth's magnetic field reverses, a new band is started, and this time the magnetic mineral grains point in the opposite direction. The new rock records the direction of the Earth's magnetic field. This record of magnetic reversals was the final proof that sea-floor spreading does occur.

Figure 12 *Magnetic reversals in oceanic crust are shown here as bands of light and dark blue oceanic crust.*

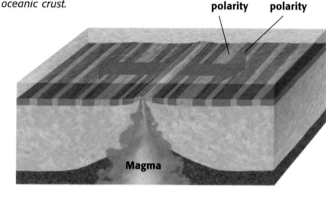

SECTION REVIEW

1. List three puzzling occurrences that the theory of continental drift helped to explain, and describe how it explained them.

2. Explain why Wegener's theory of continental drift was not accepted at first.

3. Identifying Relationships Explain how the processes of sea-floor spreading and magnetic reversal produce bands of oceanic crust that have different magnetic polarities.

▼ *Answers to Section Review*

1. Occurrences include the puzzlelike fit of the continents, the match of glacial grooves, the occurrence of fossils of the same species on different continents, and the distribution of rock types and ancient climatic zones. Continental drift explained that these coincidences exist because at one time, all the continents were joined together in one large landmass.

2. Wegener's theory of continental drift described the movement of continents but did not explain the force that moved them.

3. During sea-floor spreading, new oceanic crust forms on either side of the mid-ocean ridge. The changing polarity of the Earth's magnetic poles causes the new oceanic crust to have alternating bands of normal and reverse polarity.

The Theory of Plate Tectonics

The proof of sea-floor spreading supported Wegener's original idea that the continents move. But because both oceanic and continental crust appear to move, a new theory was devised to explain both continental drift and sea-floor spreading—the theory of *plate tectonics*. **Plate tectonics** is the theory that the Earth's lithosphere is divided into tectonic plates that move around on top of the asthenosphere.

Possible Causes of Tectonic Plate Motion

An incredible amount of energy is needed to move something as massive as a tectonic plate! We still don't know exactly why tectonic plates move as they do, but recently scientists have come up with some possible answers, as shown in **Figure 13**. Notice how all three are affected by heat and gravity.

Figure 13 Three Possible Driving Forces of Plate Tectonics

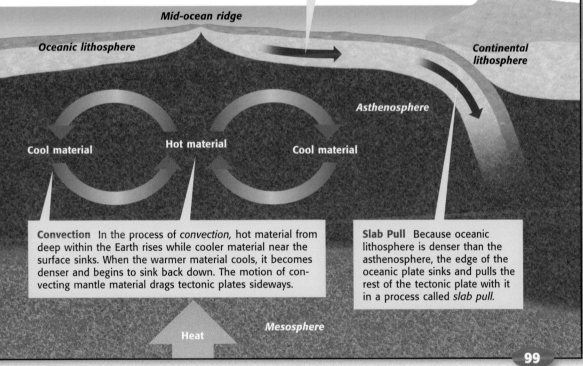

Ridge Push At mid-ocean ridges, the oceanic lithosphere is higher than it is where it sinks beneath continental lithosphere. *Ridge push* is the process by which an oceanic plate slides down the lithosphere-asthenosphere boundary.

Mid-ocean ridge

Oceanic lithosphere

Continental lithosphere

Asthenosphere

Cool material   Hot material   Cool material

Convection In the process of *convection,* hot material from deep within the Earth rises while cooler material near the surface sinks. When the warmer material cools, it becomes denser and begins to sink back down. The motion of convecting mantle material drags tectonic plates sideways.

Slab Pull Because oceanic lithosphere is denser than the asthenosphere, the edge of the oceanic plate sinks and pulls the rest of the tectonic plate with it in a process called *slab pull.*

Heat   Mesosphere

99

IS THAT A FACT!

Convection currents circulate material deep inside the Earth in a long, slow movement. The material cools near the surface and then sinks again into the depths. A single particle can take hundreds of millions of years to make a complete circle.

 Teaching Transparency 127 "Possible Causes of Tectonic Plate Motion"

 Directed Reading Worksheet Section 3

2) Teach

MEETING INDIVIDUAL NEEDS

Advanced Learners Challenge students to explain why continental/oceanic and oceanic/oceanic convergent boundaries result in subduction, whereas continental/continental convergent boundaries do not. Then have them:

• create an illustrated chart showing the five types of boundary movements

• write captions explaining both how the boundaries move and the forces responsible for their movement

DISCUSSION

Ask students to imagine trying to push a heavy crate along a concrete sidewalk. When you start to push, the box doesn't move. But as you push harder, the box finally slips a little and then stops again. Tectonic plates tend to move in similar jerks and jolts. When they move with a sudden jerk, an earthquake occurs. Sheltered English

INDEPENDENT PRACTICE

Have students refer back to **Figure 4** to locate examples of different types of tectonic plate boundaries given in **Figure 14.** (Teaching Transparencies 128 and 129 reproduce **Figure 14** for classroom use.) Test students' understanding of tectonic plate boundaries by asking them to identify which kind of boundary each red line in **Figure 4** represents.

Tectonic Plate Boundaries

All tectonic plates have boundaries with other tectonic plates. These boundaries are divided into three main types depending on how the tectonic plates move relative to one another. Tectonic plates can collide, separate, or slide past each other. **Figure 14** shows some examples of tectonic plate boundaries.

Convergent Boundaries When two tectonic plates push into one another, the boundary where they meet is called a **convergent boundary.** What happens at a convergent boundary depends on what kind of crust—continental or oceanic—the leading edge of each tectonic plate has. As you can see below, there are three types of convergent boundaries—continental/continental, continental/oceanic, and oceanic/oceanic.

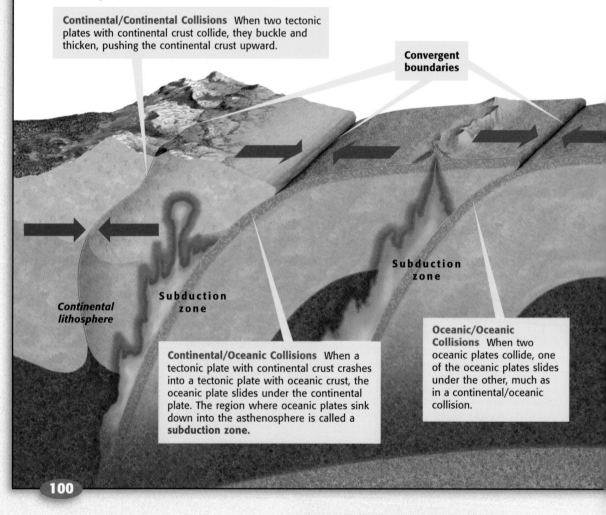

Figure 14 *This diagram shows five tectonic plate boundaries. Notice that there are three types of convergent boundaries.*

Continental/Continental Collisions When two tectonic plates with continental crust collide, they buckle and thicken, pushing the continental crust upward.

Convergent boundaries

Continental lithosphere

Subduction zone

Continental/Oceanic Collisions When a tectonic plate with continental crust crashes into a tectonic plate with oceanic crust, the oceanic plate slides under the continental plate. The region where oceanic plates sink down into the asthenosphere is called a **subduction zone.**

Subduction zone

Oceanic/Oceanic Collisions When two oceanic plates collide, one of the oceanic plates slides under the other, much as in a continental/oceanic collision.

100

Teaching Transparency 128 "Tectonic Plate Boundaries: A"

Teaching Transparency 129 "Tectonic Plate Boundaries: B"

CROSS-DISCIPLINARY FOCUS

Writing **Language Arts** Have students write a short story about a rock, from its formation from magma at an oceanic ridge to its subduction at a tectonic plate boundary.

Divergent Boundaries When two tectonic plates move away from one another, the boundary between them is called a **divergent boundary.** Remember sea-floor spreading? Divergent boundaries are where new oceanic lithosphere forms. The mid-ocean ridges that mark the spreading centers are the most common type of divergent boundary. However, divergent boundaries can also be found on continents.

Transform Boundaries When two tectonic plates slide past each other horizontally, the boundary between them is called a **transform boundary.** The San Andreas Fault, in southern California, is a good example of a transform boundary. This fault marks the place where the Pacific plate and the North American plate slide past each other.

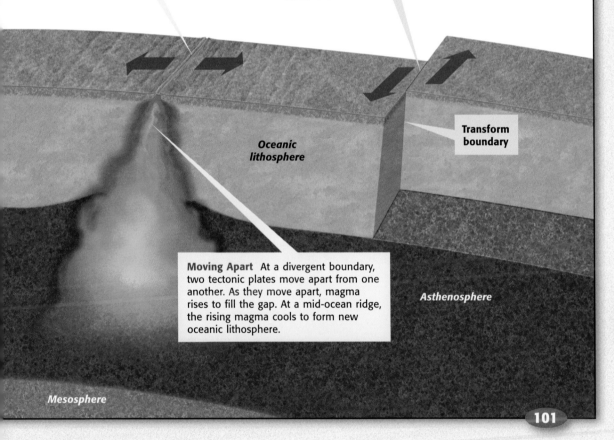

Divergent boundary

Sliding Past At a transform boundary, two tectonic plates slide past one another. Because tectonic plates are not smooth, they grind and jerk as they slide, producing earthquakes!

Oceanic lithosphere

Transform boundary

Moving Apart At a divergent boundary, two tectonic plates move apart from one another. As they move apart, magma rises to fill the gap. At a mid-ocean ridge, the rising magma cools to form new oceanic lithosphere.

Asthenosphere

Mesosphere

101

Homework

PORTFOLIO

Writing Assignment Alfred Wegener wrote, "If it turns out that sense and meaning are now becoming evident in the whole history of the Earth's development, why should we hesitate to toss the old views overboard?"

Ask students to think about why the acceptance of new ideas in science is a slow process. Ask students to explain why continental drift and another controversial theory took a long time to be accepted.

Quiz

1. Why are there several categories of convergent plate boundaries? (Plates that are pushed together behave differently, depending on their composition and density.)

2. Tell where you would expect to see the following features:

   a. tall, wrinkled mountains in the middle of a continent (convergent continental/continental boundary)

   b. a long parallel ridge on the ocean floor surrounded by parallel zones of magnetic reversal (divergent boundary)

3. Explain the process of subduction. (A denser oceanic plate is forced beneath a less-dense oceanic or continental plate at a convergent boundary. Gravity pulls the oceanic plate into the asthenosphere, where it begins to melt.)

ALTERNATIVE ASSESSMENT

Have students work in groups or with a partner to make models of different kinds of tectonic plate boundaries using modeling clay. Have students label their models, add appropriate surface features, and explain the processes responsible for the features.

Sheltered English

Reinforcement Worksheet
"A Moving Jigsaw Puzzle"

internet**connect**

SCi**LINKS**
NSTA
TOPIC: Tectonic Plates
GO TO: www.scilinks.org
*sci*LINKS NUMBER: HSTE165

Tracking Tectonic Plate Motion

Just how fast do tectonic plates move? The answer to this question depends on many factors, such as the type of tectonic plate, the shape of the tectonic plate, and the way it interacts with the tectonic plates that surround it. Tectonic movements are generally so slow and gradual that you can't see or feel them—they are measured in centimeters per year.

One exception to this rule is the San Andreas Fault, in California. The Pacific plate and the North American plate do not slide past each other smoothly nor continuously. Instead, this movement happens in jerks and jolts. Sections of the fault remain stationary for years and then suddenly shift several meters, causing an earthquake. Large shifts that occur at the San Andreas fault can be measured right on the surface. Unfortunately for scientists, however, most movements of tectonic plates are very difficult to measure. So how do they do it?

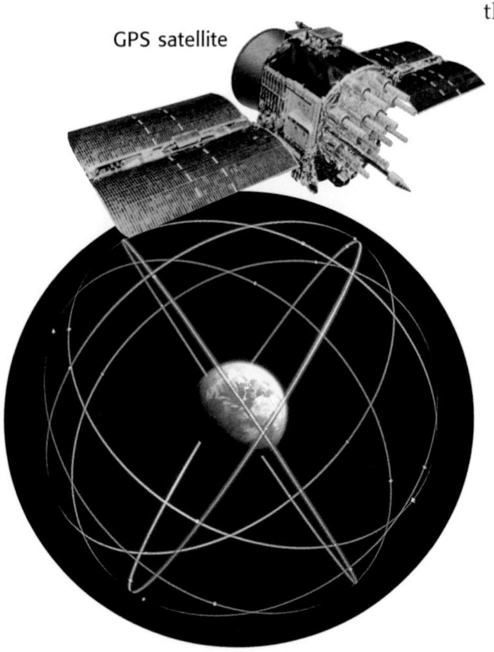

The Global Positioning System Scientists use a network of satellites called the *Global Positioning System* (GPS), shown in **Figure 15,** to measure the rate of tectonic plate movement. Radio signals are continuously beamed from satellites to GPS ground stations, which record the exact distance between the satellites and the ground station. Over time, these distances change slightly. By recording the time it takes for the GPS ground stations to move a given distance, scientists can measure the rate of motion of each tectonic plate.

GPS satellite

Figure 15 *The image above shows the orbits of the GPS satellites.*

internet**connect**

SCi**LINKS**
NSTA
TOPIC: Tectonic Plates
GO TO: www.scilinks.org
*sci*LINKS NUMBER: HSTE165

SECTION REVIEW

1. List and describe three possible driving forces of tectonic plate motion.

2. How do the three types of convergent boundaries differ from one another?

3. Explain how scientists measure the rate at which tectonic plates move.

4. **Identifying Relationships** When convection takes place in the mantle, why does cooler material sink, while warmer material rises?

▼ *Answers to Section Review*

1. Ridge push occurs when an oceanic plate slides down the tilted slope of the lithosphere/asthenosphere boundary. Slab pull occurs when the sinking edge of an oceanic plate pulls the rest of the plate down with it into the subduction zone. Convection occurs when hot mantle material in the asthenosphere convects, dragging the tectonic plate sideways.

2. Convergent boundaries can occur between two oceanic plates, two continental plates, or between an oceanic and a continental plate.

3. They measure tectonic plate movement by using a network of satellites to track the movement of GPS ground stations over long periods of time.

4. Cooler material sinks because it is denser than warmer material.

Deforming the Earth's Crust

Terms to Learn

stress   fault
compression   normal fault
tension   reverse fault
folding   strike-slip fault

What You'll Do

◆ Describe major types of folds.
◆ Explain how the three major types of faults differ.
◆ Name and describe the most common types of mountains.
◆ Explain how various types of mountains form.

Have you ever tried to bend something, only to have it break? Try this: take a long, uncooked piece of spaghetti, and bend it very slowly, and only a little. Now bend it again, but this time much farther and faster. What happened to it the second time? How can the same material bend at one time and break at another? The answer is that the *stress* you put on it was different. **Stress** is the amount of force per unit area that is put on a given material. The same principle works on the rocks in the Earth's crust. The conditions under which a rock is stressed determine its behavior.

Rocks Get Stressed

When rock changes its shape due to stress, this reaction is called *deformation*. In the example above, you saw the spaghetti deform in two different ways—by bending and by breaking. **Figure 16** illustrates this concept. The same thing happens in rock layers. Rock layers can bend when stress is placed on them. But when more stress is placed on them, they can break. Rocks can deform due to the forces of plate tectonics.

The type of stress that occurs when an object is squeezed, as when two tectonic plates collide, is called **compression.** Compression can have some spectacular results. The Rocky Mountains and the Cascade Range are two examples of compression at a convergent plate boundary.

Another form of stress is *tension.* **Tension** is stress that occurs when forces act to stretch an object. As you might guess, tension occurs at divergent plate boundaries, when two tectonic plates pull away from each other. In the following pages you will learn how these two tectonic forces—compression and tension—bend and break rock to form some of the common landforms you already know.

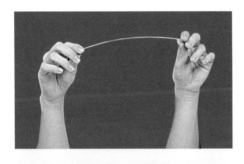

Figure 16 *With a small amount of stress, uncooked spaghetti bends. Additional stress causes it to break.*

103

Science Bloopers

In the 1800s, some scientists believed mountains formed as the result of Earth's shrinking. The theory proposed that Earth had once been a ball of semimolten rock; as it cooled, it shrank and wrinkles formed on the surface, much as an apple skin wrinkles as the fruit dries. This popular theory was not discarded until the structure and age of the Earth were better understood in the twentieth century.

Focus

Deforming the Earth's Crust

This section explores effects of tectonic forces on the Earth's crust. Students learn how stress on rock causes it to fold or fault in various ways. The section then discusses how different types of mountains form from the action of tectonic forces and volcanic activity.

Bellringer

Display photographs of several types of mountains. Have students write a description of each example and suggest how it might have formed.

1 Motivate

DEMONSTRATION

Display two thin strips of modeling clay, one frozen and one at room temperature. Have a volunteer demonstrate what happens when the warm clay is bent. (It folds.)

Ask students to predict what will happen to the frozen clay when a force is applied to it. Provide protective gloves, and have a second volunteer attempt to bend the frozen clay. (It should break.)

Discuss factors that affect the way a rock reacts to stress. (temperature, composition, and the characteristics of the force applied)

 Directed Reading Worksheet Section 4

READING 📖 STRATEGY

Activity As students read this section, have them sketch the following examples in their ScienceLog:

- folds that illustrate anticlines and synclines
- a fold that illustrates a monocline
- a normal fault
- a reverse fault
- a strike-slip fault

Have students label each sketch clearly, provide a caption, and draw arrows showing the direction of the forces causing the deformation. Sheltered English

CROSS-DISCIPLINARY FOCUS

Geography Plate tectonics play an important role in the formation of most mountain ranges. Mountain ranges in turn influence the weather around them. Because mountains are high, they influence the flow of air in a region, causing a rain shadow effect. Have interested students select a mountain range and learn more about how it affects the weather in its area. Tell students they should find out what rain shadows are and give a few geographic examples of them. Students should also explore how a certain mountain range supports a variety of ecosystems.

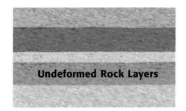

Undeformed Rock Layers

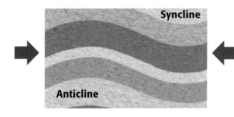

Syncline

Anticline

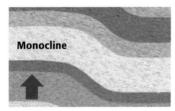

Monocline

Figure 17 *When tectonic forces put stress on rock layers, they can cause the layers to bend and fold.* Anticlines *and* synclines *form when horizontal stress acts on rock.* Monoclines *form when vertical stress acts on rock.*

Figure 18 *The larger photo at right shows mountain-sized folds in the Rocky Mountains. The smaller photo shows a rock with much smaller folds.*

Folding

Folding occurs when rock layers bend due to stress in the Earth's crust. We assume that all sedimentary rock layers started out as horizontal layers. So when you see a fold, you know that deformation has taken place. Depending on how the rock layers deform, different types of folds are made. **Figure 17** shows the two most common types—*anticlines* and *synclines*.

Another type of fold is a *monocline*. In a monocline, rock layers are folded so that both ends of the fold are still horizontal. Imagine taking a stack of paper and laying it on a table top. Think of all the sheets of paper as different rock layers. Now put a book under one end of the stack. You can see that both ends of the sheets are still horizontal, but all the sheets are bent in the middle.

Folds can be large or small. Take a look at **Figure 18.** The largest folds are measured in kilometers. They can make up the entire side of a mountain. Other folds are still obvious but much smaller. Note the size of the pocket knife in the smaller photo. Now look at the smallest folds. You would measure these folds in centimeters.

104

Homework

Making Models Have students select a topographic feature in your state that resulted from the deformation of the Earth's crust and find out about how it formed. Tell them to choose appropriate materials and create a model of the formation. Point out that they may need to create a cutaway view to show layers within the formation. Finally, ask students to write labels explaining the formation's features and the tectonic forces that caused them.

Faulting

While some rock layers bend and fold when stress is applied, other rock layers break. The surface along which rocks break and slide past each other is called a **fault.** The blocks of crust on each side of the fault are called *fault blocks.*

If a fault is not vertical, it is useful to distinguish between its two sides—the *hanging wall* and the *footwall.* **Figure 19** shows the difference between a hanging wall and a footwall. Depending on how the hanging wall and foot-wall move relative to each other, one of two main types of faults can form.

Normal Faults A *normal fault* is shown in **Figure 20.** The movement of a **normal fault** causes the hanging wall to move down relative to the footwall. Normal faults usually occur when tectonic forces cause tension that pulls rocks apart.

Reverse Faults A *reverse fault* is shown in **Figure 21.** The movement of a **reverse fault** causes the hanging wall to move up relative to the footwall—the "reverse" of a normal fault. Reverse faults usually happen when tectonic forces cause compression that pushes rocks together.

Self-Check

How is folding different from faulting? *(See page 216 to check your answer.)*

Fault

Footwall   Hanging wall

Figure 19 *The position of a fault block determines whether it is a hanging wall or a footwall.*

Normal Fault

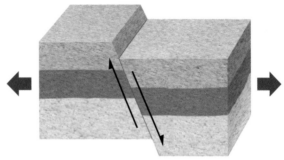

Figure 20 *When rocks are pulled apart due to tension, normal faults often result.*

Reverse Fault

Figure 21 *When rocks are pushed together by compression, reverse faults often result.*

105

Answers to Self-Check

When folding occurs, sedimentary rock strata bend but do not break. When faulting occurs, sedimentary rock strata break along a fault and the fault blocks on either side move relative to each other.

ACTIVITY

Making Models Have students use two blocks of wood to model the three types of fault movements. Tell students to sand one side of each block until it is smooth and to score another side until it is rough.

Inform students that the San Andreas Fault is a strike-slip fault. As they demonstrate the strike-slip movement, have them:

- slide smooth wood surfaces together
- slide rough wood surfaces together
- compare the amounts of resistance
- explain why movement at a strike-slip fault causes earthquakes

MISCONCEPTION ///ALERT\\\

It is important that students understand the relationship between strike-slip faults and the transform boundaries where tectonic plates meet. Some transform boundaries are actually systems of hundreds or thousands of strike-slip faults. The San Andreas Fault is an example of a particularly large strike-slip fault located between the Pacific and North American plates. In addition to the San Andreas Fault, a number of other strike-slip faults make up this transform boundary. Such large-scale strike-slip faults are often called transform faults. Strike-slip faults are not always associated with tectonic plate boundaries, however.

Figure 22 *The photo at left is a normal fault. The photo at right is a reverse fault.*

Telling the Difference It's easy to tell the difference between a normal fault and a reverse fault in diagrams with arrows. But what about the faults in **Figure 22?** You can certainly see the faults, but which one is a normal fault, and which one is a reverse fault? In the top left photo, one side has obviously moved relative to the other. You can tell this is a normal fault by looking at the sequence of sedimentary rock layers. You can see by the relative positions of the two dark layers that the hanging wall has moved down relative to the footwall.

Strike-slip Faults A third major type of fault is called a *strike-slip fault*. **Strike-slip faults** occur when opposing forces cause rock to break and move horizontally. If you were standing on one side of a strike-slip fault looking across the fault when it moved, the ground on the other side would appear to move to your left or right.

Tectonics and Natural Gas

Natural gas is used in many homes and factories as a source of energy. Some companies explore for sources of natural gas just as other companies explore for oil and coal. Like oil, natural gas travels upward through rock layers until it hits a layer through which it cannot travel and becomes trapped. Imagine that you are searching for pockets of trapped natural gas. Would you expect to find these pockets associated with anticlines, synclines, or faults? Explain your answer in your ScienceLog. Include drawings to help in your explanation.

106

Answers to APPLY

Pockets of natural gas would tend to get trapped in anticlines and faults because impermeable layers in these structures can seal off upward movement of the gas. In a syncline, the natural gas will still travel upward along the bottom of an impermeable layer.

Plate Tectonics and Mountain Building

You have just learned about several ways the Earth's crust changes due to the forces of plate tectonics. When tectonic plates collide, land features that start out as small folds and faults can eventually become great mountain ranges. The reason mountains exist is that tectonic plates are continually moving around and bumping into one another. As you can see in **Figure 23**, most major mountain ranges form at the edges of tectonic plates.

When tectonic plates undergo compression or tension, they can form mountains in several different ways. Let's take a look at three of the most common types of mountains—*folded mountains, fault-block mountains,* and *volcanic mountains.*

Folded Mountains *Folded mountains* form when rock layers are squeezed together and pushed upward. If you take a pile of paper on a table top and push on opposite edges of the pile, you will see how a folded mountain forms. You saw how these layers crunched together in Figure 17. **Figure 24** shows an example of a folded mountain range that formed at a convergent boundary.

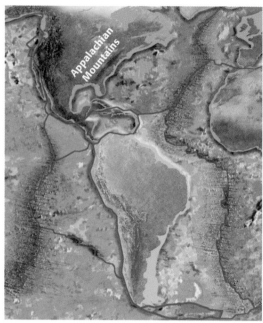

Figure 23 *Most of the world's major mountain ranges form at tectonic plate boundaries. Notice that the Appalachian Mountains, however, are located in the middle of the North American plate.*

Figure 24 *Once as mighty as the Himalayas, the Appalachians have been worn down by hundreds of millions of years of weathering and erosion.*

3 Extend

RETEACHING

After students have read this section, invite volunteers to sketch examples of each type of mountain on the board. Ask other students to explain how each mountain type forms. Have them refer to the diagram and add labels and arrows to show the direction of forces at work.

Sheltered English

ACTIVITY

Tell students to locate photographs of mountains in magazines, books, or on the Internet. Have them cut out, copy, or print these images and mount them on paper. Then have them write the type of mountain and a description of how it formed on a card and tape the card to the back of the photo.

Number and post the photos around the room so that students can view the "gallery" and write their own guesses about each mountain. Have students check their guesses against the cards.

internet**connect**

TOPIC: Faults
GO TO: www.scilinks.org
*sci*LINKS NUMBER: HSTE170

TOPIC: Mountain Building
GO TO: www.scilinks.org
*sci*LINKS NUMBER: HSTE175

Look back at Figure 23. The Appalachians are in the middle of the North American plate. How can this be? Shouldn't they be at the edge of a tectonic plate? Follow along in this diagram to find the answer.

1 About 500 million years ago, the landmasses that would become North America and Africa were on a collision course.

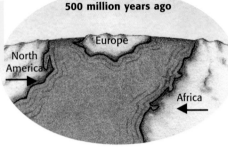
500 million years ago

2 About 390 million years ago, these tectonic plates collided, and the crust between them buckled and folded, forming the Appalachian Mountains.

390 million years ago
Appalachian Mountains

3 About 208 million years ago, North America and Africa began to break apart, and a mid-ocean ridge formed between them. By 65 million years ago, a huge amount of new oceanic lithosphere had formed between the two tectonic plates. Because of this, the Appalachian Mountains were no longer at a tectonic plate boundary at all.

65 million years ago

Fault-block Mountains Where tectonic forces put enough tension on the Earth's crust, a large number of normal faults can result. *Fault-block mountains* form when this faulting causes large blocks of the Earth's crust to drop down relative to other blocks. **Figure 25** shows one way this can happen.

Figure 25 *When the crust is subjected to tension, the rock can break along a series of normal faults, resulting in fault-block mountains.*

108

IS THAT A FACT!

When the Appalachian Mountains formed, they were probably very similar to the Himalayas. The Appalachians were of a comparable height and must have been characterized by frequent seismic activity.

The Appalachians are about 350 million years older than the Himalayas, however, and have been worn down steadily by weathering and erosion over hundreds of millions of years.

Figure 26 *The Tetons formed as a result of tectonic forces that stretched the Earth's crust, causing it to break in a series of normal faults. Compare this photo with the illustration in Figure 25.*

When sedimentary rock layers are tilted up by faulting, they can produce mountains with sharp, jagged peaks. As you can see in **Figure 26,** the Tetons, in western Wyoming, are a spectacular example of this type of mountain.

Volcanic Mountains   Most of the world's major volcanic mountains are located at convergent boundaries. *Volcanic mountains* form when molten rock erupts onto the Earth's surface. Unlike folded and fault-block mountains, volcanic mountains form from new material being added to the Earth's surface. Most volcanic mountains tend to form over the type of convergent boundaries that include subduction zones. There are so many volcanic mountains around the rim of the Pacific Ocean that early explorers named it the *Ring of Fire.*

SECTION REVIEW

1. What is the difference between an anticline and a syncline?

2. What is the difference between a normal fault and a reverse fault?

3. Name and describe the type of tectonic stress that forms folded mountains.

4. Name and describe the type of tectonic stress that forms fault-block mountains.

5. **Making Predictions** If a fault occurs in an area where rock layers have been folded, which type of fault is it likely to be? Why?

```
internetconnect
SCiLINKS
NSTA
TOPIC: Faults, Mountain Building
GO TO: www.scilinks.org
sciLINKS NUMBER: HSTE170, HSTE175
```

▼ *Answers to Section Review*

1. An anticline is shaped like an upside-down bowl, while a syncline resembles a bowl that is right side up.

2. In a normal fault, the hanging wall moves down relative to the footwall. In a reverse fault, the hanging wall moves up relative to the footwall.

3. Folded mountains form when compression acts on rock strata (such as when two continental plates collide) so that the layers of rock are pushed up into huge folds.

4. Fault-block mountains form when tension pulls rock apart, causing a large number of normal faults to form. When some of these fault blocks drop down relative to others, fault-block mountains form.

5. A reverse fault is likely to form because both reverse faults and folding occur in areas where compression takes place.

Quiz

1. What three features form when rock layers bend? (anticlines, synclines, and monoclines)

2. Why are the Appalachian Mountains now located in the middle of the North American plate? (The Appalachians formed when North America and Africa collided. In time, the plates separated and so much new crust was created that the mountains were no longer at the plate boundary.)

ALTERNATIVE ASSESSMENT

PORTFOLIO   Have students choose a mountain range to research. Then ask students to identify in writing the relationship between the mountain range and the forces that created it. Students can summarize their findings in a letter informing scientists living in the 1700s how mountains form and what causes earthquakes.

🌐 Multicultural CONNECTION

Although cultures living in mountainous regions are some of the world's most impoverished populations, they inhabit remarkably diverse ecosystems and have developed innovative technologies to live at high altitudes, where resources may be scarce. Encourage students to learn about a culture living in the Andes, the Himalayas, the Alps, or the Appalachians. Students should give a presentation about the culture they studied and conclude with a round-table discussion of the problems and opportunities mountain cultures face.

Oh, the Pressure!
Teacher's Notes

Time Required

One 45-minute class period

Lab Ratings

EASY ———————→ HARD

TEACHER PREP 🧪🧪🧪
STUDENT SET-UP 🧪🧪
CONCEPT LEVEL 🧪🧪🧪
CLEAN UP 🧪🧪🧪

MATERIALS

The materials listed on the student page are enough for a group of 3–4 students.

Safety Caution

Remind students to review all safety cautions and icons before beginning this lab activity.

Lab Notes

Homemade modeling dough may be substituted for modeling clay in this activity. In step 3, students may find it easier to trim each layer of clay with the plastic knife before stacking the layers together.

Students should realize that stress is equivalent to pressure or force. Explain to them that rocks can undergo stress without deforming. When the stress becomes too much, the rocks become folded or faulted. This deformation is also called *strain*. Stress and the result of stress (strain) are two different things.

Making Models Lab

USING SCIENTIFIC **METHODS**

Oh, the Pressure!

When scientists want to understand natural processes, such as mountain formation, they often make models to help them. Models are useful in studying how rocks react to the forces of plate tectonics. In a short amount of time, a model can demonstrate geological processes that take millions of years. Do the following activity to find out how folding and faulting happen in the Earth's crust.

MATERIALS

- modeling clay in 4 different colors
- 5 cm × 15 cm strip of poster board
- soup can or rolling pin
- newspaper
- colored pencils
- plastic knife
- 5 cm × 5 cm squares of poster board (2)

Ask a Question

① What types of forces cause synclines, anticlines, and faults to form?

Make a Model

② Use modeling clay of one color to form a long cylinder. Place the cylinder in the center of the glossy side of the poster-board strip.

③ Mold the clay to the strip. Try to make the clay layer the same thickness all along the strip; you can use the soup can or rolling pin to even the clay out. Pinch the sides of the clay so that it is the same width and length as the strip. Your strip should be at least 15 cm long and 5 cm wide.

Datasheets for LabBook

Daniel Bugenhagen
Yutan Jr.–Sr. High School
Yutan, Nebraska

4 Flip the strip over on the newspaper your teacher has placed across your desk. Carefully peel the strip from the modeling clay.

5 Repeat steps 2–4 with the other colors of modeling clay. Each member of your group should have a turn molding the clay. Each time you flip the strip over, stack the new clay layer on top of the previous one. When you are finished, you should have a block of clay made of four layers.

6 Lift the block of clay and hold it parallel to and just above the table top. Push gently on the block from opposite sides, as shown on the previous page.

7 Use the colored pencils to draw the results of step 6 in your ScienceLog. Use the terms *syncline* and *anticline* to label your diagram. Draw arrows to show the direction that each edge of the clay was pushed.

8 Repeat steps 2–5 to form a second block of clay.

9 Using the plastic knife, carefully cut the second block of clay in two at a 45° angle as seen from the side of the block.

10 Press one poster-board square on the angled end of each of the block's two pieces. The poster board represents a fault. The two angled ends represent a hanging wall and a footwall. The model should resemble the one in the photograph below.

11 Keeping the angled edges together, lift the blocks and hold them parallel to and just above the table top. Push gently on the two blocks until they move. Record your observations in your ScienceLog.

12 Now hold the two pieces of the clay block in their original position, and slowly pull them apart, allowing the two blocks to slide past each other. Record your observations.

Analyze the Results

13 What happened to the first block of clay in step 6? What force did you model?

14 What happened to the pieces of the second block of clay in step 11? What force did you model?

15 What happened to the pieces of the second block of clay in step 12? Describe the forces that acted on the block and how the pieces of the block reacted.

Draw Conclusions

16 Summarize how the forces you applied to the blocks of clay relate to the way tectonic forces affect rock layers. In communicating your results, be sure to use the terms *fold, fault, anticline, syncline, hanging wall, footwall, tension,* and *compression.*

111

Preparation Notes

Homemade Modeling Dough (optional) The night before the activity, prepare enough modeling dough for each class using the recipe below. The recipe provides enough dough for each group. Combine the following ingredients in a large saucepan over low heat in the order that they are listed:

- 2 cups cold water
- $\frac{1}{3}$ cup cooking oil
- 1 cup salt
- 4 teaspoons cream of tartar
- 2 cups flour
- Food coloring

Constantly stir the mixture until the modeling dough forms a ball. Turn the modeling dough out onto a floured surface. Use a ruler to divide the dough into fourths. When the dough cools slightly, add 15–20 drops of food coloring to each quarter. Fold and knead to evenly distribute the color throughout the dough. Place the dough in an airtight container, such as an 8 oz yogurt container. If you freeze it, the modeling dough will last for months.

Just before the activity, cover all workspaces with newspaper and secure the newspapers in place. If the dough gets dry, rinse your hands and continue to mold the dough.

Answers

13. The first block got shorter and taller. The layers of clay became folded due to compression.

14. One of the pieces (the hanging wall) slid above the other piece (the footwall) due to compression.

15. One of the pieces (the footwall) moved up relative to the other piece (the hanging wall) as tension was released.

16. The conclusion should be a complete summary of this activity, indicating the direction of pressure at each step. Any diagrams should be correctly labeled, and students should demonstrate a good understanding of the terms *fold, fault, anticline, syncline, hanging wall, footwall, tension,* and *compression.*

Chapter Highlights

Chapter Highlights

VOCABULARY DEFINITIONS

SECTION 1

crust the thin, outermost layer of the Earth, or the uppermost part of the lithosphere

mantle the layer of the Earth between the crust and the core

core the central, spherical part of the Earth below the mantle

lithosphere the outermost, rigid layer of the Earth that consists of the crust and the rigid upper part of the mantle

asthenosphere the soft layer of the mantle on which pieces of the lithosphere move

mesosphere literally, the "middle sphere"—the strong, lower part of the mantle between the asthenosphere and the outer core

outer core the liquid layer of the Earth's core that lies beneath the mantle and surrounds the inner core

inner core the solid, dense center of the Earth

tectonic plate a piece of the lithosphere that moves around on top of the asthenosphere

SECTION 2

continental drift the theory that continents can drift apart from one another and have done so in the past

sea-floor spreading the process by which new oceanic lithosphere is created at mid-ocean ridges as older materials are pulled away from the ridge

---

SECTION 1

Vocabulary

crust (p. 88)
mantle (p. 89)
core (p. 89)
lithosphere (p. 90)
asthenosphere (p. 90)
mesosphere (p. 91)
outer core (p. 91)
inner core (p. 91)
tectonic plate (p. 92)

Section Notes

- The Earth is made of three basic compositional layers—the crust, the mantle, and the core.

- The Earth is made of five main structural layers—lithosphere, asthenosphere, mesosphere, outer core, and inner core.

- Tectonic plates are large pieces of the lithosphere that move around on the Earth's surface.

- Knowledge about the structure of the Earth comes from the study of seismic waves caused by earthquakes.

SECTION 2

Vocabulary

continental drift (p. 95)
sea-floor spreading (p. 97)

Section Notes

- Wegener's theory of continental drift explained many puzzling facts, including the fit of the Atlantic coastlines of South America and Africa.

- Today's continents were originally joined together in the ancient continent Pangaea.

- Some of the most important evidence for sea-floor spreading comes from magnetic reversals recorded in the ocean floor.

☑ Skills Check

Math Concepts

MAKING MODELS Suppose you built a model of the Earth that had a radius of 100 cm (diameter of 200 cm). The radius of the real Earth is 6,378 km, and the thickness of its outer core is 2,200 km. What percentage of the Earth's radius is the outer core? How thick would the outer core be in your model?

$$\frac{2,200 \text{ km}}{6,378 \text{ km}} = 0.34 = 34\%$$

$$34\% \text{ of } 100 \text{ cm} = 0.34 \times 100 \text{ cm} = 34 \text{ cm}$$

Visual Understanding

SEA-FLOOR SPREADING This close-up view of a mid-ocean ridge shows how new oceanic lithosphere forms. As the two tectonic plates pull away from each other, magma fills in the cracks that open between them. When this magma solidifies, it becomes the newest part of the oceanic plate.

Lab and Activity Highlights

 Vocabulary Review Worksheet

Oh, the Pressure! **PG 110**

Datasheets for LabBook (blackline masters for these labs)

SECTION 3

Vocabulary

plate tectonics *(p. 99)*
convergent boundary *(p. 100)*
subduction zone *(p. 100)*
divergent boundary *(p. 101)*
transform boundary *(p. 101)*

Section Notes

- The processes of ridge push, convection, and slab pull provide some possible driving forces for plate tectonics.

- Tectonic plate boundaries are classified as convergent, divergent, or transform.

- Data from satellite tracking indicate that some tectonic plates move an average of 3 cm a year.

SECTION 4

Vocabulary

stress *(p. 103)*
compression *(p. 103)*
tension *(p. 103)*
folding *(p. 104)*
fault *(p. 105)*
normal fault *(p. 105)*
reverse fault *(p. 105)*
strike-slip fault *(p. 106)*

Section Notes

- As tectonic plates move next to and into each other, a great amount of stress is placed on the rocks at the boundary.

- Folding occurs when rock layers bend due to stress.

- Faulting occurs when rock layers break due to stress and then move on either side of the break.

- Mountains are classified as either folded, fault-block, or volcanic, depending on how they form.

- Mountain building is caused by the movement of tectonic plates. Different types of movement cause different types of mountains.

☐ internet**connect**

GO TO: go.hrw.com

Visit the **HRW** Web site for a variety of learning tools related to this chapter. Just type in the keyword:

KEYWORD: HSTTEC

*SCi*LINKS.™
N S T A
GO TO: www.scilinks.org

Visit the **National Science Teachers Association** on-line Web site for Internet resources related to this chapter. Just type in the *sci*LINKS number for more information about the topic:

TOPIC: Composition of the Earth	*sci***LINKS NUMBER:** HSTE155
TOPIC: Structure of the Earth	*sci***LINKS NUMBER:** HSTE160
TOPIC: Tectonic Plates	*sci***LINKS NUMBER:** HSTE165
TOPIC: Faults	*sci***LINKS NUMBER:** HSTE170
TOPIC: Mountain Building	*sci***LINKS NUMBER:** HSTE175

113

Lab and Activity Highlights

LabBank

Whiz-Bang Demonstrations, Thar She Blows!

Labs You Can Eat
- Rescue Near the Center of the Earth
- Cracks in the Hard-Boiled Earth
- Dough Fault of Your Own

Long-Term Projects & Research Ideas, Legend Has It

VOCABULARY DEFINITIONS, *continued*

SECTION 3

plate tectonics the theory that the Earth's lithosphere is divided into tectonic plates that move around on top of the asthenosphere

convergent boundary the boundary between two colliding tectonic plates

subduction zone the region where an oceanic plate sinks down into the asthenosphere at a convergent boundary, usually between continental and oceanic plates

divergent boundary the boundary between two tectonic plates that are moving away from each other

transform boundary the boundary between two tectonic plates that are sliding past each other horizontally

SECTION 4

stress the amount of force per unit area that is put on a given material

compression the type of stress that occurs when an object is squeezed

tension the type of stress that occurs when forces act to stretch an object

folding the bending of rock layers due to stress in the Earth's crust

fault a break in the Earth's crust along which two blocks of the crust slide relative to one another

normal fault a fault in which the hanging wall moves down relative to the footwall

reverse fault a fault in which the hanging wall moves up relative to the footwall

strike-slip fault a fault in which the two fault blocks move past each other horizontally

Blackline masters of these Chapter Highlights can be found in the **Study Guide.**

Chapter Review
Answers

Chapter Review

USING VOCABULARY

For each pair of terms, explain the difference in their meanings.

1. oceanic crust/continental crust

2. lithosphere/asthenosphere

3. convergent boundary/divergent boundary

4. folding/faulting

5. oceanic crust/oceanic lithosphere

6. normal fault/reverse fault

UNDERSTANDING CONCEPTS

Multiple Choice

7. The part of the Earth that is a liquid is the
   - a. crust.
   - b. mantle.
   - c. outer core.
   - d. inner core.

8. The part of the Earth on which the tectonic plates are able to move is the
   - a. lithosphere.
   - b. asthenosphere.
   - c. mesosphere.
   - d. subduction zone.

9. The ancient continent that contained all the landmasses is called
   - a. Pangaea.
   - b. Gondwana.
   - c. Laurasia.
   - d. Panthalassa.

10. The type of tectonic plate boundary involving a collision between two tectonic plates is
    - a. divergent.
    - b. transform.
    - c. convergent.
    - d. normal.

11. The type of tectonic plate boundary that sometimes has a subduction zone is
    - a. divergent.
    - b. transform.
    - c. convergent.
    - d. normal.

12. The San Andreas fault is an example of a
    - a. divergent boundary.
    - b. transform boundary.
    - c. convergent boundary.
    - d. normal boundary.

13. When a fold is shaped like an arch, with the fold in an upward direction, it is called a(n)
    - a. monocline.
    - b. anticline.
    - c. syncline.
    - d. decline.

14. The type of fault in which the hanging wall moves down relative to the footwall is called
    - a. strike-slip.
    - b. reverse.
    - c. normal.
    - d. fault-block.

15. The type of mountain involving huge sections of the Earth's crust being pushed up into anticlines and synclines is the
    - a. folded mountain.
    - b. fault-block mountain.
    - c. volcanic mountain.
    - d. strike-slip mountain.

16. Continental mountain ranges are usually associated with
    - a. divergent boundaries.
    - b. transform boundaries.
    - c. convergent boundaries.
    - d. normal boundaries.

17. Mid-ocean ridges are associated with
    - a. divergent boundaries.
    - b. transform boundaries.
    - c. convergent boundaries.
    - d. normal boundaries.

Short Answer

18. A tectonic plate is a large piece of the lithosphere that moves around on top of the asthenosphere.

19. Wegener's theory did not explain the driving force responsible for continental drift.

20. Stress occurs in the Earth's crust because the crust is a part of all tectonic plates, and tectonic plates are constantly colliding, pulling apart, and sliding past each other.

Short Answer

18. What is a tectonic plate?

19. What was the major problem with Wegener's theory of continental drift?

20. Why is there stress on the Earth's crust?

Concept Mapping

21. Use the following terms to create a concept map: sea-floor spreading, convergent boundary, divergent boundary, subduction zone, transform boundary, tectonic plates.

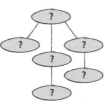

CRITICAL THINKING AND PROBLEM SOLVING

Write one or two sentences to answer each of the following questions:

22. Why is it necessary to think about the different layers of the Earth in terms of both their composition and their physical properties?

23. Folded mountains usually form at the edge of a tectonic plate. How can you explain old folded mountain ranges located in the middle of a tectonic plate?

24. New tectonic plate material continually forms at divergent boundaries. Tectonic plate material is also continually destroyed in subduction zones at convergent boundaries. Do you think the total amount of lithosphere formed on Earth is about equal to the amount destroyed? Why?

MATH IN SCIENCE

25. Assume that a very small oceanic plate is between a mid-ocean ridge to the west and a subduction zone to the east. At the ridge, the oceanic plate is growing at a rate of 5 km every million years. At the subduction zone, the oceanic plate is being destroyed at a rate of 10 km every million years. If the oceanic plate is 100 km across, in how many million years will the oceanic plate disappear?

INTERPRETING GRAPHICS

Imagine that you could travel to the center of the Earth. Use the diagram below to answer the questions that follow.

Composition	Structure
Crust (50 km)	Lithosphere (150 km)
Mantle (2,900 km)	Asthenosphere (250 km)
	Mesosphere (2,550 km)
Core (3,428 km)	Outer core (2,200 km)
	Inner core (1,228 km)

26. How far beneath Earth's surface would you have to go to find the liquid material in the Earth's core?

27. At what range of depth would you find mantle material but still be within the lithosphere?

Reading Check-up

Take a minute to review your answers to the Pre-Reading Questions found at the bottom of page 86. Have your answers changed? If necessary, revise your answers based on what you have learned since you began this chapter.

Concept Mapping

21.
An answer to this exercise can be found in the front of this book.

CRITICAL THINKING AND PROBLEM SOLVING

22. Some layers of the Earth (such as the inner and outer cores) have the same composition but different physical properties.

23. At the time they formed, the folded mountains must have been on the edge of a tectonic plate. New material was later added to the tectonic plate, causing the folded mountains to be located closer to the center of the plate.

24. Answers will vary. The amount of crust formed is roughly equal to the amount of crust destroyed globally. If this were not true, the Earth would be either expanding or shrinking.

MATH IN SCIENCE

25. In 1 million years, the tectonic plate grows 5 km on one side but shrinks by 10 km on the other side. Every 1 million years, the tectonic plate shrinks by 5 km. In 20 million years, the tectonic plate will disappear entirely.

Rate of tectonic plate destruction:
$5 \text{ km/y} - 10 \text{ km/y} = -5 \text{ km/y}$

The tectonic plate will completely disappear in:
$\frac{100 \text{ km}}{5 \text{ km/y}} = 20$ million years

INTERPRETING GRAPHICS

26. 150 km + 250 km + 2,550 km = 2,950 km

27. between 50 and 150 km

Concept Mapping Transparency 7

Blackline masters of this Chapter Review can be found in the **Study Guide.**

Background

Geothermal energy is a clean natural resource that is relatively easy to harness. Before converting to geothermal energy, Reykjavik, Iceland's capital, was one of the most polluted cities in the world. The city relied on imported fossil fuels, so heating costs were very high. Today Reykjavik has better air quality than any large city in Europe. Electricity costs in Iceland are among the lowest in the world and have attracted foreign investment projects in the power-intensive industries.

Science, Technology, and Society

Living on the Mid-Atlantic Ridge

Imagine living hundreds of kilometers from other people on an icy outcrop of volcanic rock surrounded by the cold North Atlantic Ocean. How would you stay warm? For the people of Iceland, this is an important question that affects their daily lives. Iceland is a volcanic island situated on the Mid-Atlantic Ridge, just south of the Arctic Circle. Sea-floor spreading produces active volcanoes, earthquakes, hot springs, and geysers that make life on this island seem a little unstable. However, the same volcanic force that threatens civilization provides the heat necessary for daily life. Icelanders use the geothermal energy supplied by their surroundings in ways that might surprise you.

▲ *The Blue Lagoon in Iceland is the result of producing energy from water power.*

Let's Go Geothermal!

Geothermal literally means "earth heat," *geo-* meaning "earth" and *therme* meaning "heat." Around the ninth century A.D., Iceland's earliest settlers took advantage of the Earth's heat by planting crops in naturally heated ground. This encouraged rapid plant growth and an early harvest of food. In 1928, Iceland built its first public geothermal utility project—a hole drilled into the Earth in order to pump water from a hot spring. After the oil crisis of the 1970s,

geothermal-energy projects were built on a grand scale in Iceland. Today 85 percent of all houses in Iceland are heated by geothermal energy. Hot water from underground pools is pumped directly to houses, where it is routed through radiators to provide heating.

Geothermal water is also pumped to homes to provide hot tap water. This natural source meets all the hot-water needs for the city of Reykjavik, with a population of about 150,000 people!

There are still other uses for this hot water. For example, it is used to heat 120 public swimming pools. Picture yourself swimming outside in naturally hot water during the dead of winter! Greenhouses, where fruits and vegetables are grown, are also warmed by this water. Even fish farming on Iceland's exposed coastline wouldn't be possible without geothermal energy to adjust the water temperature. In other industries, geothermal energy is used to dry timber, wool, and seaweed.

Power Production

Although hydropower (producing energy from water power) is the principal source of electricity in Iceland, geothermal energy is also used. Water ranging in temperature from 300–700°C is pumped into a reservoir, where the water turns into steam that forces turbines to turn. The spinning motion of these turbines generates electricity. Power generation from geothermal sources is only about 5–15 percent efficient and results in a very large amount of water runoff. At the Svartsengi power plant, this water runoff has created a beautiful pool that swimmers call the Blue Lagoon.

Going Further

▶ Can you think of other abundant clean-energy resources? How could we harness such sources?

116

Answers to Going Further

Answers will vary. It is important that students realize the consequences of rampant consumption of fossil fuels and learn from Iceland's model of using alternative, clean energy resources. Students should realize, however, that geothermal energy is not a practical option in most parts of the world.

Continental Drift

When Alfred Wegener proposed his theory of continental drift in the early 1900s, many scientists laughed at the idea of continents plowing across the ocean. In fact, many people found his theory so ridiculous that Wegener, a university professor, had difficulty getting a job! Wegener's theory jolted the very foundation of geology.

Alfred Wegener (1880–1930)

Wegener's Theory

Wegener used geologic, fossil, and glacial evidence gathered on opposite sides of the Atlantic Ocean to support his theory of continental drift. For example, Wegener recognized geologic similarities between the Appalachian Mountains, in eastern North America, and the Scottish Highlands, as well as similarities between rock strata in South Africa and Brazil. He believed that these striking similarities could be explained only if these geologic features were once part of the same continent.

Wegener proposed that because they are less dense, continents float on top of the denser rock of the ocean floor. Although continental drift explained many of Wegener's observations, he could not find scientific evidence to develop a complete explanation of how continents move.

The Critics

Most scientists were skeptical of Wegener's theory and dismissed it as foolishness. Some critics held fast to old theories that giant land bridges could explain similarities among fossils in South America and Africa. Others argued that Wegener's theory could not account for the tremendous forces that would have been required to move continents such great distances. Wegener, however, believed that these forces could be the same forces responsible for earthquakes and volcanic eruptions.

The Evidence

During the 1950s and 1960s, discoveries of sea-floor spreading and magnetic reversal provided the evidence that Wegener's theory needed and led to the theory of plate tectonics. The theory of plate tectonics describes how the continents move. Today geologists recognize that continents are actually parts of moving tectonic plates that float on the asthenosphere, a layer of partially molten rock.

Like the accomplishments of so many scientists, Wegener's accomplishments went unrecognized until years after his death. The next time you hear a scientific theory that sounds far out, don't underestimate it. It may be proven true!

Also an Astronomer and Meteorologist

Wegener had a very diverse background in the sciences. He earned a Ph.D. in astronomy from the University of Berlin. But he was always very interested in geophysics and meteorology. His interest in geophysics led to his theory on continental drift. His interest in meteorology eventually led to his death. He froze to death in Greenland while returning from a rescue mission to bring food to meteorologists camped on a glacier.

On Your Own

► Photocopy a world map. Carefully cut out the continents from the map. Be sure to cut along the line where the land meets the water. Slide the continents together like a jigsaw puzzle. How does this relate to the tectonic plates and continental drift?

117

Teaching Strategy

The formation of new hypotheses is an essential part of scientific inquiry. Yet scientists are often met with opposition when they challenge conventional theories. Encourage students to investigate other scientists whose theories were rejected during their lifetime but later were accepted. Students may want to explore the controversial theories of Copernicus, Mendel, or Darwin or explore some modern controversies in the scientific community.

Answers to On Your Own

The coastlines of most continents make a rough fit, especially those of South America and Africa. In the case of South America and Africa, this implies that the two continents were once joined. One would then look for other evidence of continental drift by looking for similarities in the rocks of each continent in the places where they would have been next to each other long ago.

Chapter Organizer

CHAPTER ORGANIZATION	TIME MINUTES	OBJECTIVES	LABS, INVESTIGATIONS, AND DEMONSTRATIONS
Chapter Opener pp. 118–119	45	National Standards: SAI 1, ST 1, SPSP 3, 4	**Start-Up Activity,** Bend, Break, or Shake, p. 119
Section 1 **What Are Earthquakes?**	90	▶ Determine where earthquakes come from and what causes them. ▶ Identify different types of earthquakes. ▶ Describe how earthquakes travel through the Earth. UCP 2, SAI 1, HNS 1, ES 1b	**Demonstration,** Faults and Earthquakes, p. 121 in ATE **QuickLab,** Modeling Seismic Waves, p. 125
Section 2 **Earthquake Measurement**	120	▶ Explain how earthquakes are detected. ▶ Demonstrate how to locate earthquakes. ▶ Describe how the strength of an earthquake is measured. UCP 3, SAI 1, 2, SPSP 3, 4, HNS 1, 3; Labs UCP 3, SAI 1	**Skill Builder,** Earthquake Waves, p. 184 **Datasheets for LabBook,** Earthquake Waves
Section 3 **Earthquakes and Society**	120	▶ Explain earthquake hazard. ▶ Compare methods of earthquake forecasting. ▶ List ways to safeguard buildings against earthquakes. ▶ Outline earthquake safety procedures. UCP 2, 3, SAI 1, SPSP 1, 3–5; Labs UCP 2, 5, SAI 1, ST 1, SPSP 5	**Design Your Own,** Quake Challenge, p. 138 **Datasheets for LabBook,** Quake Challenge **Whiz-Bang Demonstrations,** When Buildings Boogie
Section 4 **Earthquake Discoveries Near and Far**	90	▶ Describe how seismic studies reveal Earth's interior. ▶ Summarize seismic discoveries on other cosmic bodies. HNS 2, ES 1a	**Demonstration,** Mapping with Seismic Waves, p. 136 in ATE **Long-Term Projects & Research Ideas,** Whole Lotta Shakin'

---

*See page **T23** for a complete correlation of this book with the*

NATIONAL SCIENCE EDUCATION STANDARDS.

TECHNOLOGY RESOURCES

 Guided Reading Audio CD English or Spanish, Chapter 5

One-Stop Planner CD-ROM with Test Generator

 CNN **Scientists in Action,** Earthquake Architect, Segment 11

CLASSROOM WORKSHEETS, TRANSPARENCIES, AND RESOURCES	SCIENCE INTEGRATION AND CONNECTIONS	REVIEW AND ASSESSMENT
Directed Reading Worksheet **Science Puzzlers, Twisters & Teasers**		
Directed Reading Worksheet, Section 1 **Transparency 130,** Elastic Rebound **Transparency 280,** Transverse and Longitudinal Waves **Transparency 131,** Primary Wave **Transparency 131,** Secondary Wave **Transparency 131,** Surface Wave	**Cross-Disciplinary Focus,** p. 120 in ATE **Multicultural Connection,** p. 121 in ATE **Cross-Disciplinary Focus,** p. 123 in ATE **Multicultural Connection,** p. 123 in ATE **Physics Connection,** p. 124 **Connect to Physical Science,** p. 124 in ATE	**Homework,** pp. 121, 122 in ATE **Self-Check,** p. 123 **Section Review,** p. 125 **Quiz,** p. 125 in ATE **Alternative Assessment,** p. 125 in ATE
Transparency 132, Finding an Earthquake's Epicenter **Directed Reading Worksheet,** Section 2 **Math Skills for Science Worksheet,** Earthquake Power! **Reinforcement Worksheet,** Complete a Seismic Story	**Multicultural Connection,** p. 126 in ATE **MathBreak,** Moving Up the Scale, p. 128	**Section Review,** p. 128 **Quiz,** p. 128 in ATE **Alternative Assessment,** p. 128 in ATE
Directed Reading Worksheet, Section 3 **Math Skills for Science Worksheet,** Dividing Whole Numbers with Long Division	**Cross-Disciplinary Focus,** p. 130 in ATE **Math and More,** p. 130 in ATE **Connect to Life Science,** p. 131 in ATE **Apply,** p. 134 **Weird Science:** Can Animals Predict Earthquakes? p. 144 **Eye on the Environment:** What Causes Such Destruction? p. 145	**Self-Check,** p. 130 **Homework,** pp. 132, 133 in ATE **Section Review,** p. 134 **Quiz,** p. 134 in ATE **Alternative Assessment,** p. 134 in ATE
Transparency 133, Discoveries in the Earth's Interior **Directed Reading Worksheet,** Section 4 **Critical Thinking Worksheet,** Nearthlings Unite!		**Homework,** p. 136 in ATE **Section Review,** p. 137 **Quiz,** p. 137 in ATE **Alternative Assessment,** p. 137 in ATE

 Holt, Rinehart and Winston On-line Resources

go.hrw.com

For worksheets and other teaching aids related to this chapter, visit the HRW Web site and type in the keyword: **HSTEQK**

 National Science Teachers Association

www.scilinks.org

Encourage students to use the *sci*LINKS numbers listed in the internet connect boxes to access information and resources on the **NSTA** Web site.

END-OF-CHAPTER REVIEW AND ASSESSMENT

Chapter Review in Study Guide
Vocabulary and Notes in Study Guide
Chapter Tests with Performance-Based Assessment, Chapter 5 Test
Chapter Tests with Performance-Based Assessment, Performance-Based Assessment 5
Concept Mapping Transparency 8

Chapter Resources & Worksheets

Visual Resources

TEACHING TRANSPARENCIES

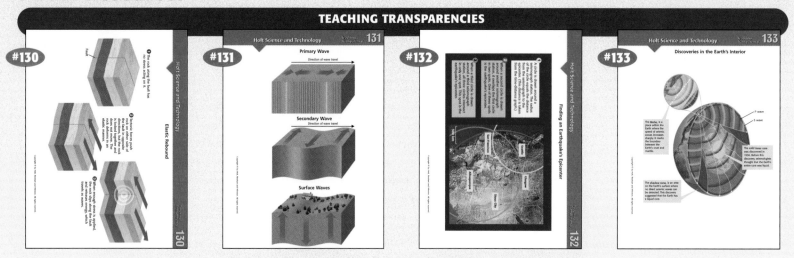

TEACHING TRANSPARENCIES

CONCEPT MAPPING TRANSPARENCY

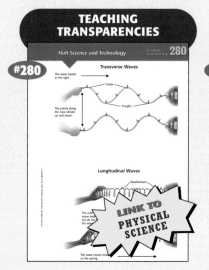

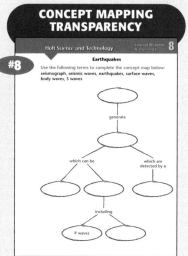

Meeting Individual Needs

DIRECTED READING

REINFORCEMENT & VOCABULARY REVIEW

SCIENCE PUZZLERS, TWISTERS & TEASERS

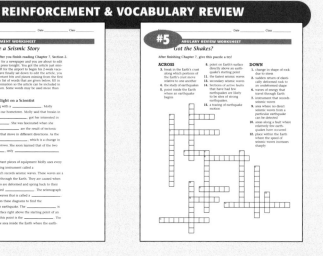

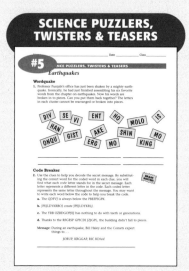

Chapter 5 • Earthquakes

Review & Assessment

STUDY GUIDE

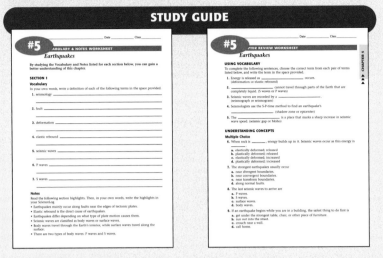

CHAPTER TESTS WITH PERFORMANCE-BASED ASSESSMENT

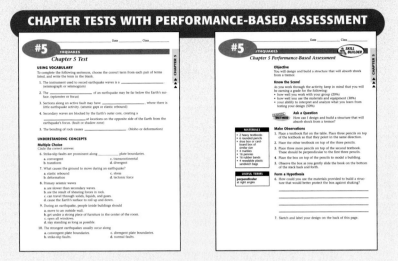

Lab Worksheets

WHIZ-BANG DEMONSTRATIONS

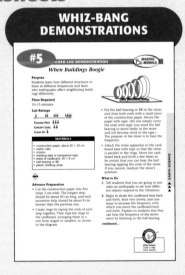

LONG-TERM PROJECTS & RESEARCH IDEAS

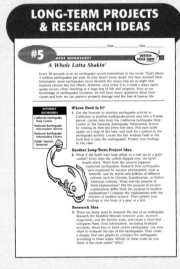

DATASHEETS FOR LABBOOK

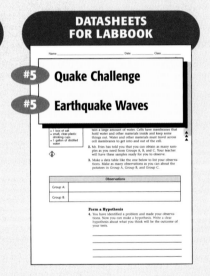

Applications & Extensions

CRITICAL THINKING & PROBLEM SOLVING

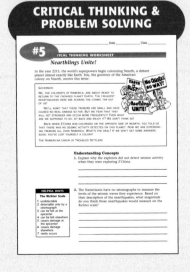

SCIENTISTS IN ACTION

SECTION 1

What Are Earthquakes?

▶ Earthquake Origins

Shallow earthquakes are those that originate within about 60 km of Earth's surface. Intermediate-depth earthquakes are those that originate between depths of about 60 km and 300 km. Deep earthquakes are those that originate below 300 km.

- Tectonic activity is not the only source of earthquakes. Earthquakes can also be caused by volcanic eruptions and by the impacts of cosmic bodies. These earthquakes, however, are less common than those occurring along faults.

▶ The New Madrid Earthquakes

Eyewitnesses to the 1811–1812 earthquakes in New Madrid, Missouri, reported seeing bright flashes of light and a dull glow in the sky over a wide area. Reeking sulfurous odors also accompanied the quakes. Many survivors were convinced that the quakes were a heavenly sign meant to frighten the local citizens back to church. As a result, church attendance in the area skyrocketed between 1811 and 1812!

▶ The Punishment of Loki

In Scandinavian mythology, earthquakes are believed to be caused by the clever prankster Loki. The gods decided to punish Loki when they discovered that he killed Balder, the god of light and joy. Loki was chained in a deep cave, and a huge, poisonous snake was hung above him. As the poison from the snake's fangs dripped down, Loki's sister tried to protect him by catching the poison in a cup. Sometimes, however, a drop of poison would splash Loki, causing him unbearable pain. At those times he would pull so violently on his chains that the ground above would tremble.

IS THAT A FACT!

- ☛ In 1755, in Lisbon, Portugal, an earthquake occurred that killed an estimated 60,000 people. It was this tragedy that resulted in an analytic and systematic approach to studying earthquakes, the basis of seismology.

SECTION 2

Earthquake Measurement

▶ Magnitude Versus Intensity

Earthquakes can be measured by magnitude or intensity. An earthquake's magnitude is a quantitative measurement of its strength. The Richter scale is used to measure magnitude. Intensity is a qualitative measurement of an earthquake's effect in a particular area. The Modified Mercalli Intensity scale is used to assess an earthquake's intensity. This scale incorporates observations of the earthquake's effects at a particular location. Although an earthquake may have different intensities at different locations, it has only one magnitude.

▶ Seismic Rock

In 1992, a British rock group caused some miniature earthquakes at one of their concerts! Scientists were at first mystified by the seismic events they recorded. Upon investigating the tremors, however, researchers at the Global Seismology Research Group, in Scotland, discovered that the energy patterns of the tremors matched those of certain hit songs and were generated by the foot stomping of the more than 30,000 fans at a nearby stadium!

IS THAT A FACT!

- ☛ One of the best structures for resisting damage from earthquakes is a wood-framed building. Wood-framed buildings are not very rigid and can therefore flex quite a bit without collapsing.

- ☛ The strongest earthquake recorded to date occurred in Chile in 1960. It measured 9.5 on the Richter scale. This is equivalent to detonating more than 1 billion tons of TNT!

SECTION 3
Earthquakes and Society

▶ **Magnetometers**

Magnetometers are devices that measure changes in the Earth's magnetic field, which can be indicative of an upcoming quake. Elastic strain can cause slight magnetic variations in the rock. Detecting these variations can help seismologists predict earthquakes.

▶ **Survival of Structures**

The ability of a structure to withstand a quake depends on a variety of factors, including the composition of the ground on which the structure stands. Structures built on waterlogged or unconsolidated sediment, such as sand, are more likely to suffer intense damage than structures built on bedrock.

IS THAT A FACT!

🖝 Sand boils are common during earthquakes that occur in areas with unconsolidated sediments. Loose, sandy sediments behave like a fluid as the ground moves. This condition can create a miniature "geyser" that spews buried debris from beneath the Earth's surface.

SECTION 4
Earthquake Discoveries Near and Far

▶ **Sunquakes**

The waves generated by "sunquakes" resemble those produced when an object is dropped into a standing body of water. Unlike water ripples, however, in which a series of waves travels at constant velocity, a single 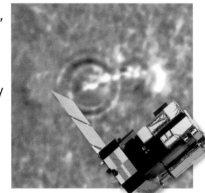 series of solar seismic waves may vary in velocity from 35,400 km/h to 402,300 km/h. "Sunquakes" release enormous amounts of energy. Scientists estimate that a "sunquake" observed in 1996 released an incredible amount of energy—equivalent to covering Earth's land masses with a meter-deep pile of dynamite and detonating it all at once!

▶ **The Passive Seismic Experiment**

The passive seismic experiment, conducted via the *Apollo 11–16* space missions, produced some significant information about the moon. The experiment suggested that the moon has three distinct layers—a crust, a mantle, and a small, dense core. The studies also suggest that most significant "moonquakes" originate within the moon's mantle; few start in the crust. On Earth, most significant quakes originate in the crust.

IS THAT A FACT!

🖝 The average "moonquake" is about one-millionth as strong as the average earthquake.

> **For background information about teaching strategies and issues, refer to the *Professional Reference for Teachers*.**

Earthquakes

CHAPTER 5

 Pre-Reading Questions

Students may not know the answers to these questions before reading the chapter, so accept any reasonable response.

Suggested Answers

1. Elastic rebound along active faults is the direct cause of most earthquakes. Answers that attribute earthquakes to tectonic-plate movement or the movement of rock along faults are acceptable. Less appropriate answers may attribute earthquakes to volcanic eruptions or explosions.

2. Earthquake strength varies according to the type of tectonic-plate motion that causes them. Also, some earthquakes are stronger than others because more elastic deformation builds up along certain faults or parts of faults than along others.

3. It depends on how they are built. Some buildings are reinforced to withstand earthquakes better than other buildings.

CHAPTER 5

Earthquakes

Sections

 **Pre-Reading Questions**

1. What causes earthquakes?
2. Why are some earthquakes stronger than others?
3. Why do some buildings remain standing during earthquakes while others fall down?

If You Build It, Will It Stand?

On September 21, 1999, the island of Taiwan was forever changed. At 1:47 A.M., an earthquake struck, toppling buildings and burying thousands of people in rubble. Why did this building collapse while those that surrounded it did not? The collapsed building was not built to be as strong as the other buildings. In this chapter, you will learn about what causes earthquakes and what you can do to prepare for one. You will also learn how buildings can be constructed to withstand the force of an earthquake.

Search and rescue dogs help save lives after an earthquake.

---

 internet connect

 HRW On-line Resources

go.hrw.com

For worksheets and other teaching aids, visit the HRW Web site and type in the keyword: **HSTEQK**

 NSTA

www.scilinks.com

Use the *sci*LINKS numbers at the end of each chapter for additional resources on the **NSTA** Web site.

 Smithsonian Institution®

www.si.edu/hrw

Visit the Smithsonian Institution Web site for related on-line resources.

 CNNfyi.com

www.cnnfyi.com

Visit the CNN Web site for current events coverage and classroom resources.

BEND, BREAK, OR SHAKE

If you were in a building during an earthquake, what would you want the building to be made of? To answer this question, you need to know how building materials react to stress.

Procedure

1. Gather a **small wooden stick**, a **wire clothes hanger**, and a **plastic clothes hanger.**

2. Draw a straight line on a **sheet of paper.** Use a **protractor** to measure and draw the following angles from the line: 20°, 45°, and 90°.

3. Put on your safety goggles. Using the angles that you drew as a guide, try bending each item 20° and then releasing it. What happens? Does it break? If it bends, does it return to its original shape? Write your observations in your ScienceLog.

4. Repeat step 3, but bend each item 45°. Repeat the test again, but bend each item 90°.

Analysis

5. How do the materials' responses to bending compare?

6. Where earthquakes happen, engineers use building materials that are flexible but do not break or stay bent. Which materials from this experiment would you want building materials to behave like? Explain your answer.

119

START-UP Activity

BEND, BREAK, OR SHAKE

MATERIALS
FOR EACH GROUP: • small wooden stick flexible enough to bend • wire clothes hanger • plastic clothes hanger • sheet of paper *(1 per student)* • protractor *(1 per student)*

Safety Caution

Remind students to review all safety cautions and icons before beginning this lab activity.

Teacher's Notes

Assist students who have difficulty manipulating the protractor or provide them with paper on which the angles have already been drawn.

Answers to START-UP Activity

5. Answers will vary depending on the materials used and on the strength of the materials.

6. Desirable building materials would behave like the materials that did not bend permanently or break.

Focus

What Are Earthquakes?

This section discusses the seismic events known as earthquakes. Students learn where earthquakes most commonly occur and what causes them. The section also covers different kinds of earthquakes and discusses how earthquakes travel as waves of energy through the Earth.

 **Bellringer**

Ask students to write a few sentences in their ScienceLog describing what they think an earthquake is. Ask volunteers to read their descriptions. Students can review what they wrote after completing this section.
Sheltered English

1 Motivate

DISCUSSION

Explain to students that *seismos* is a Greek word meaning "to shake." Have students make a list of all the words that contain the root *seis-*. (These include *seismology, seismologists, seismic, seismographs, Seismosaurus,* and *seismograms.*) Have students copy the words onto a sheet of paper and consult a dictionary to divide each word into its proper parts. Then have students define each word part and write a definition of each complete term using the meanings of its parts.
Sheltered English

 Directed Reading Worksheet Section 1

Terms to Learn

seismology	seismic waves
fault	P waves
deformation	S waves
elastic rebound	

What You'll Do

◆ Determine where earthquakes come from and what causes them.

◆ Identify different types of earthquakes.

◆ Describe how earthquakes travel through the Earth.

What Are Earthquakes?

The word *earthquake* defines itself fairly well. But there is more to an earthquake than just ground shaking. In fact, there is a branch of Earth science devoted to earthquakes called seismology (siez MAHL uh jee). **Seismology** is the study of earthquakes. Earthquakes are complex, and they present many questions for *seismologists,* the scientists who study earthquakes.

Where Do Earthquakes Occur?

Most earthquakes take place near the edges of tectonic plates. *Tectonic plates* are giant masses of solid rock that make up the outermost part of the Earth. **Figure 1** shows the Earth's tectonic plates and the locations of recent major earthquakes recorded by scientists.

Tectonic plates move in different directions and at different speeds. Two plates can push toward each other or pull away from each other. They can also slip past each other like slow-moving trains traveling in opposite directions.

As a result of these movements, numerous features called faults exist in the Earth's crust. A **fault** is a break in the Earth's crust along which blocks of the crust slide relative to one another. Earthquakes occur along faults due to this sliding.

Faults occur in many places, but they are especially common near the edges of tectonic plates where they form the boundaries along which the plates move. This is why earthquakes are so common near tectonic plate boundaries.

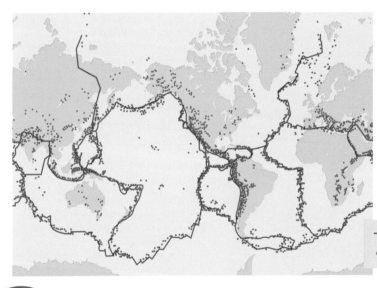

Figure 1 *The largest and most active earthquake zone lies along the plate boundaries surrounding the Pacific Ocean.*

— Plate boundary
• Recorded earthquake

CROSS-DISCIPLINARY FOCUS

History Aristotle was one of the first to attribute earthquakes to Earth processes. He hypothesized that earthquakes were caused by strong winds blowing through a myriad of caverns deep in the Earth's interior. Until the seventeenth century, many people believed that earthquakes were caused by large, restless creatures beneath the Earth's surface. It wasn't until the late 1700s that scientists began a systematic study of earthquakes. But as recently as the late 1800s, scientists did not know the true cause of earthquakes. Students can make a timeline illustrating the development of seismology from the ancient Greeks to the present.

What Causes Earthquakes?

As tectonic plates push, pull, or scrape against each other, stress builds up along faults near the plates' edges. In response to this stress, rock in the plates deforms. **Deformation** is the change in the shape of rock in response to stress. Rock along a fault deforms in mainly two ways—in a plastic manner, like a piece of molded clay, or in an elastic manner, like a rubber band. *Plastic deformation*, which is shown in **Figure 2,** does not lead to earthquakes.

Elastic deformation, however, does lead to earthquakes. While rock can stretch farther than steel without breaking, it will break at some point. Think of elastically deformed rock as a stretched rubber band. You can stretch a rubber band only so far before it breaks. When the rubber band breaks, it releases energy, and the broken pieces return to their unstretched shape.

Like the return of the broken rubber-band pieces to their unstretched shape, **elastic rebound** is the sudden return of elastically deformed rock to its original shape. Elastic rebound occurs when more stress is applied to rock than the rock can withstand. During elastic rebound, rock releases energy that causes an earthquake, as shown in **Figure 3.**

Figure 2 *This photograph, taken in Hollister, California, shows how plastic deformation along the Calaveras Fault permanently bent a wall.*

Figure 3 Elastic Rebound and Earthquakes

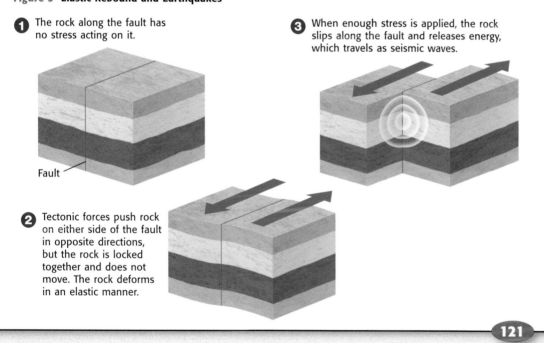

1 The rock along the fault has no stress acting on it.

Fault

2 Tectonic forces push rock on either side of the fault in opposite directions, but the rock is locked together and does not move. The rock deforms in an elastic manner.

3 When enough stress is applied, the rock slips along the fault and releases energy, which travels as seismic waves.

121

Multicultural CONNECTION

Many different cultures have myths about earthquakes. According to Japanese mythology, earthquakes are caused by the *namazu,* a giant catfish that lives in mud beneath the Earth. Kamisha, a brave warrior, protects Japan from earthquakes by using divine powers to trap the *namazu* under an enormous rock. Earthquakes occur when Kamisha lets his guard down and allows the *namazu* to thrash about. Encourage students to research other cultural myths about earthquakes and to share their research with the class. Students can also write their own legend about the origin of earthquakes.

2 Teach, continued

USING THE FIGURE

Each circle in the illustration is a magnified view of a fault at the edge of a tectonic plate. In fact, large systems of multiple faults define the boundaries between plates. The sliding of crust along these faults and the overall movement of crust along plate boundaries are similar. For example, the block of crust to the right of the reverse fault moves down relative to the block to the left of the fault. Similarly, the plate to the right of the convergent plate boundary moves down relative to the plate to the left of the boundary.

GROUP ACTIVITY

Forces and Faults For each pair of students, obtain a pair of wooden blocks cut at an angle. Ask students to demonstrate normal-fault movement by sliding the top block down relative to the bottom block. To show a reverse fault, students should slide the top block up relative to the bottom block. Have them slide the blocks horizontally to demonstrate a strike-slip fault. Make sure students see how divergent, convergent, and transform motion cause the different types of fault movement.

READING 📖 STRATEGY

Mnemonics A footwall is the rock beneath an inclined fault. Using these mnemonic devices, students can remember the difference between a normal fault and a reverse fault by noting the movement of the footwall.

FUN **F**ootwall **U**p is **N**ormal

FDR **F**ootwall **D**own is **R**everse

122 Chapter 5 • Earthquakes

Are All Earthquakes the Same?

Earthquakes differ in strength and in the depth at which they begin. These differences depend on the type of tectonic plate motion that produces the earthquake. Examine the chart and the diagram below to learn how earthquakes differ.

Plate motion	Prominent fault type	Earthquake characteristics
Transform	strike-slip fault	moderate, shallow
Convergent	reverse fault	strong, deep
Divergent	normal fault	weak, shallow

Transform motion occurs where two plates slip past each other.

Transform motion creates **strike-slip faults.** Blocks of crust slide horizontally past each other, causing moderate, shallow earthquakes.

122

Homework

Ask students to draw the three types of faults illustrated on these pages. Students should label each fault, state the type of plate motion that creates each fault, and write a brief description of the earthquakes associated with each type of fault. Encourage students to locate an example of each type of tectonic plate boundary on a map.

(An example of a transform plate boundary is the San Andreas Fault, in California; an example of a convergent plate boundary is off the west coast of South America—convergent motion created the Andes; an example of a divergent plate boundary is the Mid-Atlantic Ridge, on the bottom of the Atlantic Ocean.)

Sheltered English

Self-Check

Name two differences between the results of convergent motion and the results of divergent motion. *(See page 216 to check your answer.)*

Answers to Self-Check

Convergent motion creates reverse faults, while divergent motion creates normal faults. Convergent motion produces deep, strong earthquakes, while divergent motion produces shallow, weak earthquakes.

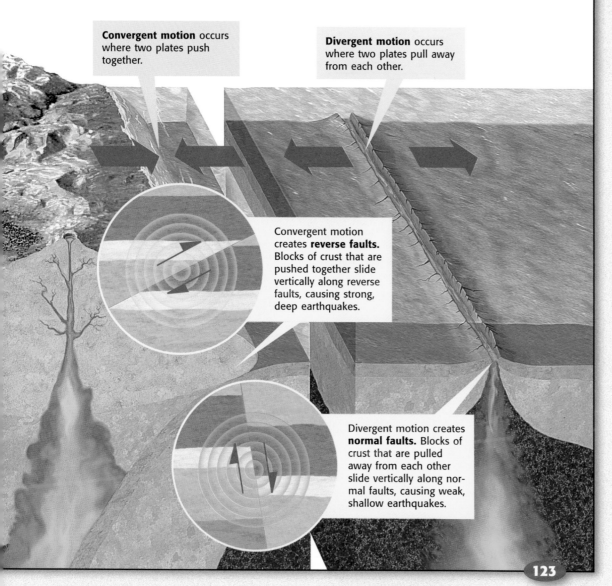

Convergent motion occurs where two plates push together.

Divergent motion occurs where two plates pull away from each other.

Convergent motion creates **reverse faults.** Blocks of crust that are pushed together slide vertically along reverse faults, causing strong, deep earthquakes.

Divergent motion creates **normal faults.** Blocks of crust that are pulled away from each other slide vertically along normal faults, causing weak, shallow earthquakes.

123

CROSS-DISCIPLINARY FOCUS

Writing **Language Arts** John James Audubon was in Kentucky during the New Madrid earthquakes. He wrote that "the ground rose and fell in successive furrows like the ruffled waters of a lake. The earth waved like a field of corn before a breeze." After sharing this quote with the class, ask students to use similes and metaphors to write their own description of an earthquake.

Multicultural CONNECTION

American Indian legends refer to the unstable crust in the New Madrid, Missouri, area. One story describes how Chief Reelfoot of the Chickasaw tribe kidnapped a bride from the Choctaw tribe. Just as the Chief and his bride were about to be married, a great earthquake caused the ground under them to collapse. The entire wedding party was drowned as a river flooded the area, forming Reelfoot Lake, in Tennessee. Geologists now know that the lake was indeed formed by the New Madrid earthquakes.

WEIRD SCIENCE

Many people assume that major earthquakes in the United States occur only on the West Coast. However, major quakes have occurred in South Carolina and Missouri—far from any active plate boundaries. The four major tremors of the 1811–1812 earthquakes in New Madrid, Missouri, were so intense that, according to reports, they altered the flow of the Mississippi River and rang church bells in Boston! The cause of these quakes baffled scientists until the late 1970s, when they found a series of faults deep beneath sediment deposited by the Mississippi River. The area is still seismically active, and large quakes may still occur.

MEETING INDIVIDUAL NEEDS

Learners Having Difficulty
Tell students that the *P* in *P waves* and the *S* in *S waves* stand for two descriptive words each. The letters describe how each type of wave affects rock; *P* stands for *pressure,* and *S* stands for *shear. P* also stands for *primary,* while *S* stands for *secondary.* This scheme describes the arrival times of each type of wave—P waves always arrive first, and S waves always arrive second.
Sheltered English

CONNECT TO PHYSICAL SCIENCE

Use Transparency 280 to discuss the differences between P waves (longitudinal) and S waves (transverse). Have students create a labeled poster of S waves and identify the trough, crest, wave period, wavelength, and wave height. Then have students make a list of the differences between P waves and S waves. Lists should include but are not limited to the following:

• P waves travel faster than S waves.

• P waves travel through solids, liquids, and gases; S waves cannot travel through materials that are completely liquid.

• P waves move rock back and forth between a squeezed and stretched position, while S waves shear rock back and forth.

Teaching Transparency 280
"Transverse and Longitudinal Waves"
LINK TO PHYSICAL SCIENCE

Physics CONNECTION

All types of waves share basic features. Understanding one type, such as seismic waves, can help you understand many other types. Other types of waves include light waves, sound waves, and water waves.

How Do Earthquakes Travel?

Remember that rock releases energy when it springs back after being deformed. This energy travels in the form of seismic waves. **Seismic waves** are waves of energy that travel through the Earth. Seismic waves that travel through the Earth's interior are called *body waves*. There are two types of body waves: P waves and S waves. Seismic waves that travel along the Earth's surface are called *surface waves*. Different types of seismic waves travel at different speeds and move the materials that they travel through differently.

P Is for Primary If you squeeze an elastic material into a smaller volume or stretch it into a larger volume, the pressure inside the material changes. When you suddenly stop squeezing or stretching the material, it springs briefly back and forth before returning to its original shape. This is how P waves (pressure waves) affect rock, as shown in **Figure 4. P waves,** which travel through solids, liquids, and gases, are the fastest seismic waves. Because they are the fastest seismic waves and because they can move through all parts of the Earth, P waves always travel ahead of other seismic waves. Because P waves are always the first seismic waves to be detected, they are also called *primary* waves.

S Is for Secondary Rock can also be deformed from side to side. When the rock springs back to its original position after being deformed, S waves are created. **S waves,** or shear waves, are the second-fastest seismic wave. S waves shear rock back and forth, as shown in **Figure 5.** *Shearing* stretches parts of rock sideways from other parts.

Direction of wave travel

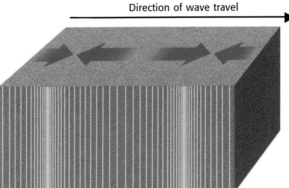

Figure 4 *P waves move rock back and forth between a squeezed position and a stretched position as they travel through it.*

Direction of wave travel

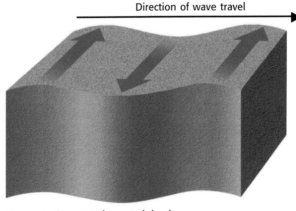

Figure 5 *S waves shear rock back and forth as they travel through it.*

124

---

internetconnect

SCiLINKS
NSTA

TOPIC: What Is an Earthquake?
GO TO: www.scilinks.org
*sci*LINKS NUMBER: HSTE180

Unlike P waves, S waves cannot travel through parts of the Earth that are completely liquid. Also, S waves are slower than P waves and always arrive second; thus, they are also called *secondary* waves.

Surface Waves Surface waves move the ground up and down in circles as the waves travel along the surface. This is shown in **Figure 6.** Many people have reported feeling like they were on a roller coaster during an earthquake. This feeling comes from surface waves passing along the Earth's surface. Surface waves travel more slowly than body waves but are more destructive. Most damage during an earthquake comes from surface waves, which can literally shake the ground out from under a building.

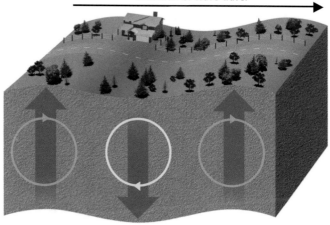

Direction of wave travel

Figure 6 *Surface waves move the ground much like ocean waves move water particles.*

SECTION REVIEW

1. Where do earthquakes occur?

2. What directly causes earthquakes?

3. Arrange the types of earthquakes caused by the three plate-motion types from weakest to strongest.

4. **Analyzing Relationships**   Why are surface waves more destructive to buildings than P waves or S waves?

internetconnect

SCI**LINKS**
NSTA

TOPIC: What Is an Earthquake?
GO TO: www.scilinks.org
*sci*LINKS NUMBER: HSTE180

125

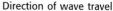

Focus

Earthquake Measurement

In this section students learn how seismographs are used to detect and locate earthquakes. This section explains the difference between an earthquake's focus and its epicenter. Students will also learn how the Richter scale is used to measure the strength of earthquakes.

Bellringer

Ask students to create a qualitative scale for gauging earthquake intensity. Students should use brief phrases to describe the effects of very minor to extreme earthquakes. Discuss the advantages and disadvantages of their finished scale. Tell them that they will learn about a quantitative scale for earthquake measurement in this chapter.

1) Motivate

ACTIVITY

Ask students to close their eyes. Tell them that you will move to some part of the room and snap your fingers. When they hear you snap, have them point to where they think you are standing. Have students keep their eyes closed while you return to the front of the room. Ask the class to locate where you were standing, and have a helper stand in that spot. Ask students how they were able to pinpoint your location. Explain that when an earthquake occurs, it is noted at seismic stations around the world. By comparing the time it took the tremors to reach each station, the earthquake's origin can be pinpointed.

Terms to Learn

seismograph   epicenter
seismogram   focus

What You'll Do

- ◆ Explain how earthquakes are detected.
- ◆ Demonstrate how to locate earthquakes.
- ◆ Describe how the strength of an earthquake is measured.

Figure 7 *The line in a seismogram traces the movement of the ground as it shakes. The more the ground moves, the farther back and forth the line traces.*

126

Earthquake Measurement

After an earthquake occurs, seismologists try to find out when and where it started. Earthquake-sensing devices enable seismologists to record and measure seismic waves. These measurements show how far the seismic waves traveled. The measurements also show how much the ground moved. Seismologists use this information to pinpoint where the earthquake started and to find out how strong the earthquake was.

Locating Earthquakes

How do seismologists know when and where earthquakes begin? They depend on earthquake-sensing instruments called seismographs. **Seismographs** are instruments located at or near the surface of the Earth that record seismic waves. When the waves reach a seismograph, the seismograph creates a seismogram, such as the one in **Figure 7**. A **seismogram** is a tracing of earthquake motion created by a seismograph.

When Did It Happen? Seismologists use seismograms to calculate when an earthquake started. An earthquake starts when rock slips suddenly enough along a fault to create seismic waves. Seismologists find an earthquake's start time by comparing seismograms and noting the difference in arrival times of P waves and S waves.

Where Did It Happen? Seismologists also use seismograms to find an earthquake's epicenter. An **epicenter** is the point on the Earth's surface directly above an earthquake's starting point. A **focus** is the point inside the Earth where an earthquake begins. **Figure 8** shows the relationship between an earthquake's epicenter and its focus.

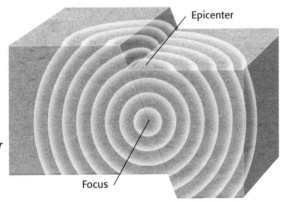

Epicenter

Focus

Figure 8 *An earthquake's epicenter is on the Earth's surface directly above the earthquake's focus.*

Multicultural CONNECTION

A Chinese man named Chang Heng designed the first known earthquake detector around A.D. 132. It was a bronze urn decorated with six dragons' heads. Each head held a bronze ball in its mouth. A pendulum was suspended inside the urn. During a tremor, the urn would strike the pendulum, causing one of the balls to drop into the open mouth of a bronze toad below. The ball would make a loud noise, signaling the occurrence of an earthquake. By noting which ball fell, people could determine the direction of the earthquake's epicenter. Have students design their own earthquake detector and share it with the class.

Putting It All Together Perhaps the most common method by which seismologists find an earthquake's epicenter is the *S-P-time method*. When using the S-P-time method, seismologists begin by collecting several seismograms of the same earthquake from different locations. Seismologists then place the seismograms on a time-distance graph so the first P waves line up with the P-wave curve and the first S waves line up with the S-wave curve. This is shown in **Figure 9**.

After the seismograms are placed on the graph, seismologists can see how far away from each station the earthquake was by reading the distance axis. After seismologists find out the distances, they can find the earthquake's epicenter as shown below.

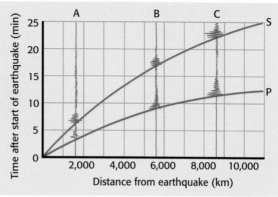

Plotting Seismograms on a Time-Distance Graph

Figure 9 *Seismologists subtract a wave's travel time (read from the vertical axis) from the time that the wave was recorded. This indicates when the earthquake started. The distance of the stations from the epicenter is read from the horizontal axis.*

Finding an Earthquake's Epicenter

1 A circle is drawn around a seismograph station. The radius of the circle equals the distance from the seismograph to the epicenter. (This distance is taken from the time-distance graph.)

2 When a second circle is drawn around another seismograph station, it overlaps the first circle in two spots. One of these spots is the earthquake's epicenter.

3 When a third circle is drawn around a third seismograph station, all three circles intersect in only one spot. This spot is the earthquake's epicenter.

Seattle

Glasgow

Sioux City

San Francisco

Albuquerque

500 km

127

SCIENTISTS AT ODDS

When Charles Richter was a 27-year-old graduate student, he was working on a catalog of earthquakes in southern California. He wanted to find an objective way to compare earthquakes. Up to that point, geologists used the Mercalli scale to classify earthquakes. Giuseppe Mercalli developed the scale in 1902 to describe the intensity of earthquakes. The Mercalli scale was based on the observations of people who witnessed an earthquake and on the damage it caused. Richter wanted to devise a more objective, quantitative measure of earthquake strength. This desire led him to develop the Richter scale in 1935, which is based on measurements from seismographs.

2 Teach

USING THE FIGURE

Explain to students that in **Figure 9** the seismograms are the blue, wavy lines that extend vertically. The seismograms read from bottom to top; seismic activity at the bottom of a seismogram was recorded before seismic activity at the top. The large "wiggles" that line up with the P-wave curve are P waves, and the large "wiggles" that line up with the S-wave curve are S waves. Ask students to note the difference in time between the moment P waves reached station A and the moment S waves reached the station. (3 minutes) Have students compare this time difference with the measurements recorded at station C. (The time difference at station C is 13 minutes.) Have students explain why the difference was greater at a station farther away from the epicenter. (P waves travel faster than S waves, so as the distance both waves travel increases, the difference in their arrival times also increases.)

Earthquake Waves PG 184

Teaching Transparency 132 "Finding an Earthquake's Epicenter"

Directed Reading Worksheet Section 2

internetconnect

SC*i*LINKS
NSTA

TOPIC: Earthquake Measurement
GO TO: www.scilinks.org
*sci*LINKS NUMBER: HSTE185

3 Close

Quiz

1. How is an earthquake's epicenter related to its focus? (The epicenter is the point on the Earth's surface directly above the focus, which is where the earthquake originates.)

2. As seismic waves travel farther, what happens to the difference in arrival times of P and S waves? (It increases.)

ALTERNATIVE ASSESSMENT

PORTFOLIO

Have students identify 10 recent earthquakes with a magnitude greater than 5.0 on the Richter scale. Students can compile their findings in a table that includes the epicenter and the magnitude of the quake, the damage it caused, and any other interesting information about the quake. Challenge students to find trends in the data.

Math Skills Worksheet
"Earthquake Power!"

Reinforcement Worksheet
"Complete a Seismic Story"

MATH BREAK

Moving Up the Scale

If the amount of energy released by an earthquake with a magnitude of 2.0 on the Richter scale is *n*, what are the amounts of energy released by earthquakes with the following magnitudes in terms of *n*: 3.0, 4.0, 5.0, and 6.0? (Hint: The energy released by an earthquake with a magnitude of 3.0 is 31.7n.)

internet connect

SCILINKS
NSTA

TOPIC: Earthquake Measurement
GO TO: www.scilinks.org
*sci*LINKS NUMBER: HSTE185

Measuring Earthquake Strength

"How strong was the earthquake?" is a common question asked of seismologists. This is not an easy question to answer. But it is an important question for public officials, safety organizations, and businesses as well as seismologists. Fortunately, seismograms can be used not only to determine an earthquake's epicenter and its start time but also to find out an earthquake's strength.

The Richter Scale The *Richter scale* is commonly used to measure earthquake strength. It is named after Charles Richter, an American seismologist who developed the scale in the 1930s. A modified version of the Richter scale is shown below.

Modified Richter Scale	
Magnitude	**Estimated effects**
2.0	can be detected only by seismograph
3.0	can be felt at epicenter
4.0	felt by most in area
5.0	causes damage at epicenter
6.0	causes widespread damage
7.0	causes great, widespread damage

Earthquake Energy There is a pattern in the Richter scale relating an earthquake's magnitude and the amount of energy released by the earthquake. Each time the magnitude increases by 1 unit, the amount of energy released becomes 31.7 times larger. For example, an earthquake with a magnitude of 5.0 on the Richter scale will release 31.7 times as much energy as an earthquake with a magnitude of 4.0 on the Richter scale.

SECTION REVIEW

1. What is the difference between a seismogram and a seismograph?

2. How many seismograph stations are needed to use the S-P-time method? Why?

3. **Doing Calculations** If the amount of energy released by an earthquake with a magnitude of 7.0 on the Richter scale is *x*, what is the amount of energy released by an earthquake with a magnitude of 6.0 in terms of *x*?

Earthquakes and Society

Terms to Learn

gap hypothesis
seismic gap

What You'll Do

◆ Explain earthquake hazard.
◆ Compare methods of earthquake forecasting.
◆ List ways to safeguard buildings against earthquakes.
◆ Outline earthquake safety procedures.

Earthquakes are a fascinating part of Earth science, but they are very dangerous. Seismologists have had some success in predicting earthquakes, but simply being aware of earthquakes is not enough. It is important for people in earthquake-prone areas to be prepared.

Earthquake Hazard

Earthquake hazard measures how prone an area is to experiencing earthquakes in the future. An area's earthquake-hazard level is determined by past and present seismic activity. Look carefully at the map in **Figure 10.** As you can see, some areas of the United States have a higher earthquake-hazard level than others. This is because some areas have more seismic activity than others. The West Coast, for example, has a very high earthquake-hazard level because it has a lot of seismic activity. Areas such as the Gulf Coast or the Midwest have much lower earthquake-hazard levels because they do not have as much seismic activity.

Can you find the area where you live on the map? What level or levels of earthquake hazard are shown for your area? Look at the hazard levels in nearby areas. How do their hazard levels compare with your area's hazard level? What could explain the earthquake-hazard levels in your area and nearby areas?

Figure 10 *This is an earthquake-hazard map of the continental United States. It shows various levels of earthquake hazard for different areas of the country.*

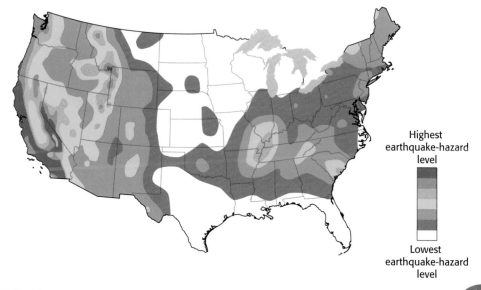

Highest earthquake-hazard level

Lowest earthquake-hazard level

129

IS THAT A FACT!

On March 27, 1964, an earthquake with a magnitude of 9.1 occurred in southern Alaska. The earthquake, which is the strongest recorded earthquake in North America, lasted for about 4 minutes. When it was over, about 215,000 km² of land had been either raised or lowered. The port on Montague Island was raised 10 m, stranding ships that had been docked in the port. After the earthquake, four tsunamis swept the coastline, adding to the destruction.

Focus

Earthquakes and Society

In this section students learn how earthquake hazard is determined. The section explores the methods seismologists use to predict when and where earthquakes will occur. Students learn about the technologies used to reinforce buildings against earthquakes. The section concludes with a discussion of earthquake safety procedures.

🔔 Bellringer

If any of your students have experienced an earthquake, have them write a short paragraph in their ScienceLog describing how they felt and what they did to protect themselves during the quake. Have students who have not experienced a quake write a paragraph describing what they *think* they would do during a moderate earthquake.

1 Motivate

DISCUSSION

Have students examine **Figure 10.** Challenge them to explain why the West Coast has such high levels of earthquake hazard. If they need a hint, have them look again at **Figure 1,** in Section 1. (The correct explanation is that there is a tectonic plate boundary along the western coast of the United States.)

 Directed Reading Worksheet Section 3

Prediction Guide Have students determine whether the following statements are true or false before they read the rest of this section:

- Hundreds of thousands of earthquakes that occur each year are not felt by people. (true)
- During an earthquake, rigid pipelines for natural gas and water are more resistant to damage than flexible pipelines are. (false)
- Because earthquakes are unpredictable, people cannot prepare for them. (false)

CROSS-DISCIPLINARY FOCUS

Art Have students find out what has been done to protect sculptures from earthquake damage at the J. Paul Getty Museum, in Malibu, California, or at another museum in an earthquake-prone area.

MATH and MORE

Have students use **Figure 11** to convert the average number of minor earthquakes that occur each year to the number that occur each day. (49,000 quakes a year ÷ 365 days a year = 134 quakes a day)

Math Skills Worksheet
"Dividing Whole Numbers with Long Division"

✓ **Self-Check**

According to the chart below, about how many earthquakes with a magnitude between 6.0 and 6.9 occur annually?

(See page 216 to check your answer.)

Earthquake Forecasting

Predicting when and where earthquakes will occur and how strong they will be is a difficult task. However, by closely monitoring active faults and other areas of seismic activity, seismologists have discovered some patterns in earthquakes that allow them to make some broad predictions.

Strength and Frequency As you learned earlier, earthquakes vary in strength. And you can probably guess that earthquakes don't occur on a set schedule. But what you may not know is that the strength of earthquakes is related to how often they occur. The chart in **Figure 11** provides more detail on this relationship.

Figure 11 *Generally, with each step down in earthquake magnitude, the number of earthquakes per year is about 10 times greater.*

Worldwide Earthquake Frequency (Based on Observations Since 1900)		
Descriptor	**Magnitude**	**Average occurring annually**
Great	8.0 and higher	1
Major	7.0–7.9	18
Strong	6.0–6.9	120
Moderate	5.0–5.9	800
Light	4.0–4.9	about 6,200
Minor	3.0–3.9	about 49,000
Very minor	2.0–2.9	about 365,000

This relationship between earthquake strength and frequency is also observed on a local scale. For example, each year approximately 10 earthquakes occur in the Puget Sound area of Washington with a magnitude of 4 on the Richter scale. Over this same time period, approximately 10 times as many earthquakes with a magnitude of 3 occur in this area. Scientists use these statistics to make predictions about the strength, location, and frequency of future earthquakes.

Can animals predict earthquakes? To decide for yourself, turn to page 144 to read about links between animal behavior and earthquakes.

Science Bloopers

In 1989, Iben Browning, a self-taught climatologist, predicted that a large earthquake would occur near New Madrid, Missouri. He based his prediction on the fact that the gravitational pull of the sun and the moon on the area would be very strong on December 3, 1990. Seismologists dismissed his prediction, but after the story made the news, public interest increased. As the date approached, schools in New Madrid were dismissed and emergency personnel were prepared. Some residents left town, while other people flocked to New Madrid to experience a major earthquake. The much-awaited day passed without the slightest tremor.

The Gap Hypothesis Another method of predicting an earthquake's strength, location, and frequency is based on the gap hypothesis. The **gap hypothesis** states that sections of active faults that have had relatively few earthquakes are likely to be the sites of strong earthquakes in the future. The areas along a fault where relatively few earthquakes have occurred are called **seismic gaps. Figure 12** below shows an example of a seismic gap.

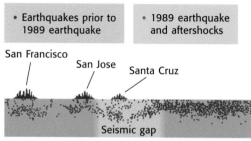

Figure 12 *This diagram shows a cross section of the San Andreas Fault. Note how the seismic gap was filled by the 1989 earthquake and its aftershocks, which are weaker earthquakes that follow a stronger earthquake.*

The gap hypothesis helped seismologists forecast the approximate time, strength, and location of the 1989 Loma Prieta earthquake in the San Francisco Bay area. The seismic gap that they identified is illustrated in Figure 12. In 1988, seismologists predicted that over the next 30 years there was a 30 percent chance that an earthquake with a magnitude of at least 6.5 would fill this seismic gap. Were they correct? The Loma Prieta earthquake, which filled in the seismic gap in 1989, measured 7.1 on the Richter scale. That's very close, considering how complicated the forecasting of earthquakes is.

Earthquakes and Buildings

Much like a judo master knocks the feet out from under his or her opponent, earthquakes shake the ground out from under buildings and bridges. Once the center of gravity of a structure has been displaced far enough off the structure's supporting base, most structures simply collapse.

Figure 13 shows what can happen to buildings during an earthquake. These buildings were not designed or constructed to withstand the forces of an earthquake.

Figure 13 *An earthquake shook the ground floor out from under the second story of this apartment building, which then collapsed.*

131

Answers to Activity

Accept all reasonable responses.

USING THE FIGURE

Have students answer the following questions using the illustrations on this page:

- How are the mass damper system and the active tendon system alike? (In both systems, motion sensors detect movement and send this information to a computer. The computer signals devices that counteract the movement of the structure.)

- What is a base isolator? (a shock absorber that prevents seismic waves from traveling through a structure)

- What advantage do flexible pipes have over rigid metal pipes during an earthquake? (Flexible pipes twist and bend more readily than metal pipes, which tend to snap when subjected to significant seismic tremors.)

DEBATE

Nuclear Waste: Is Any Area Seismically Stable? Scientists must consider the geologic stability of potential sites for nuclear waste facilities. Have students research and debate the issue of nuclear waste disposal. Have them consider that there are few viable options for the disposal of the world's nuclear waste. Remind them that no one can be sure that an area will be stable over the thousands of years it takes for nuclear waste to decay.

Activity

Research a tall building to find out how its structure is reinforced. Would any of the building's reinforcements safeguard it against earthquakes? Has an earthquake occurred in the building's area since the building was constructed? If so, how well did the building withstand the shaking?

TRY at HOME

Earthquake Resistant Buildings People have learned a lot from building failure during earthquakes. Architects and engineers use the newest technology to design and construct buildings and bridges to better withstand earthquakes. Study this diagram carefully to learn about some of this modern technology.

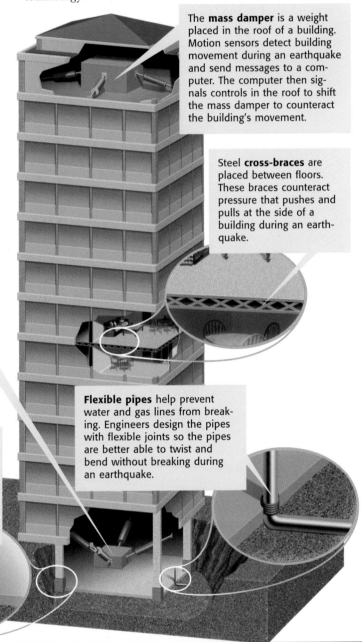

The **mass damper** is a weight placed in the roof of a building. Motion sensors detect building movement during an earthquake and send messages to a computer. The computer then signals controls in the roof to shift the mass damper to counteract the building's movement.

Steel **cross-braces** are placed between floors. These braces counteract pressure that pushes and pulls at the side of a building during an earthquake.

The **active tendon system** works much like the mass damper system in the roof. Sensors notify a computer that the building is moving. Then the computer activates devices to shift a large weight to counteract the movement.

Flexible pipes help prevent water and gas lines from breaking. Engineers design the pipes with flexible joints so the pipes are better able to twist and bend without breaking during an earthquake.

Base isolators act as shock absorbers during an earthquake. They are made of layers of rubber and steel wrapped around a lead core. Base isolators absorb seismic waves, preventing them from traveling through the building.

132

Homework

Investigate Your Area Have students conduct a survey of their home and make a list of at least five things that should be altered to ensure minimal damage in the event of an earthquake. Changes might include reinforcing the foundation, adding steel support bars to unsupported areas of the building, bolting refrigerators and tall bookshelves to the walls, reinforcing old walls with plywood, securing water heaters, and replacing rigid pipes with flexible pipes. Suggest that students also include a floor plan that shows safe and unsafe places and possible escape routes.

Are You Prepared for an Earthquake?

If you live in an earthquake-prone area or ever plan to visit one, there are many things you can do to protect yourself and your property from earthquakes. Plan ahead so you will know what to do before, during, and after an earthquake. Stick to your plan as closely as possible.

Before the Shaking Starts The first thing you should do is safeguard your house against earthquakes. For example, put heavier objects on lower shelves so they do not fall on anyone during the earthquake. You can also talk to adults about having your home reinforced. Make a plan with others (your family, neighbors, or friends) to meet somewhere after the earthquake is over. This way someone will know you are safe. During the earthquake, waterlines, power lines, and roadways may be damaged. Therefore, you should store nonperishable food, water, a fire extinguisher, a flashlight with batteries, and a first-aid kit in a place you can access after the earthquake.

When the Shaking Starts The best thing to do if you are indoors is to crouch or lie face down under a table or desk in the center of a room, as shown in **Figure 15**. If you are outside, lie face down away from buildings, power lines, and trees, and cover your head with your hands. If you are in a car on an open road, you should stop the car and remain inside.

Figure 14 *Simple precautions can greatly reduce the chance of injury during an earthquake.*

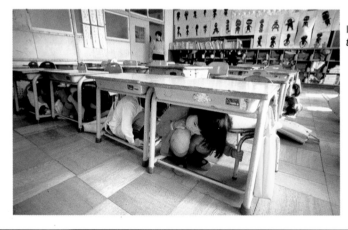

Figure 15 *These students are participating in an earthquake drill.*

133

internet**connect**

SCILINKS.
NSTA

TOPIC: Earthquakes and Society
GO TO: www.scilinks.org
*sci*LINKS **NUMBER:** HSTE190

4 Close

Quiz

1. What is the gap hypothesis?
(The gap hypothesis states that sections of active faults that have had relatively few earthquakes are likely to be the sites of strong earthquakes in the future.)

2. Why should you lie under a table or desk during an earthquake? (The table or desk might prevent falling objects from hitting you and causing injury.)

3. What are aftershocks? (They are weaker earthquakes that follow stronger earthquakes.)

ALTERNATIVE ASSESSMENT

Ask students to write a description of the hazards they might face if an earthquake occurred when they were in each of the following situations:

• **asleep in bed** (collapsing building)

• **at the beach** (tsunamis)

• **snow skiing** (avalanche)

GROUP ACTIVITY

Have small groups research how to make a building earthquake-proof. They should consider the site for the building and brainstorm about ways to protect the building. They can illustrate their best ideas and use descriptive labels to show how their building works. Have groups present their ideas to the class.

Answer to APPLY

Answers will vary but should reflect some precautions and procedures mentioned in this section.

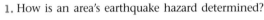
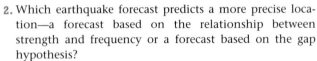

TOPIC: Earthquakes and Society
GO TO: www.scilinks.org
*sci***LINKS NUMBER:** HSTE190

After the Shaking Stops Being in an earthquake is a startling experience. Afterward, you should not be surprised to find yourself and others puzzled about what happened. You should try to calm down, get your bearings, and remove yourself from immediate danger, such as downed power lines, broken glass, and fire hazards. Be aware that there may be aftershocks. Recall your earthquake plan, and follow it through.

SECTION REVIEW

1. How is an area's earthquake hazard determined?

2. Which earthquake forecast predicts a more precise location—a forecast based on the relationship between strength and frequency or a forecast based on the gap hypothesis?

3. Describe two ways that buildings are reinforced against earthquakes.

4. Name four items that you should store in case of an earthquake.

5. **Using Graphics** Would the street shown in the photo at left be a safe place during an earthquake? Why or why not?

APPLY

Earthquake Safety Plan

You are at home reading the evening news. On the front page you read a report from the local seismology station. Scientists predict an earthquake in your area sometime in the near future. You realize that you are not prepared.

Make a detailed outline of how you would prepare yourself and your home for an earthquake. Then write a list of safety procedures to follow during an earthquake. When you are done, exchange your work with a classmate. How do your plans differ from your classmate's? How might you work together to improve your earthquake safety plans?

Answers to Section Review

1. It is determined by past and present seismic activity.

2. A forecast based on the gap hypothesis would predict a more precise location.

3. Describing any two features from this section (mass damper, cross braces, active tendon system, flexible pipes, and base isolators) is acceptable. Students may also describe features they learn about through additional research.

4. Answers will vary. Students may list some items not mentioned in the textbook. Items mentioned in this section include nonperishable food, water, a fire extinguisher, a flashlight with batteries, and a first-aid kit.

5. No; you would be very close to tall buildings that could collapse during the earthquake.

Terms to Learn

Moho
shadow zone

What You'll Do

◆ Describe how seismic studies reveal Earth's interior.
◆ Summarize seismic discoveries on other cosmic bodies.

Earthquake Discoveries Near and Far

The study of earthquakes has led to many important discoveries about the Earth's interior. Seismologists learn about the Earth's interior by observing how seismic waves travel through the Earth. Likewise, seismic waves on other cosmic bodies allow seismologists to study the interiors of those bodies.

Discoveries in Earth's Interior

Have you ever noticed how light bends in water? If you poke part of a pencil into water and look at it from a certain angle, the pencil looks bent. This is because the light waves that bounce off the pencil bend as they pass through the water's surface toward your eye. Seismic waves bend in much the same way as they travel through rock. Seismologists have learned a lot about the Earth's interior by studying how seismic waves bend.

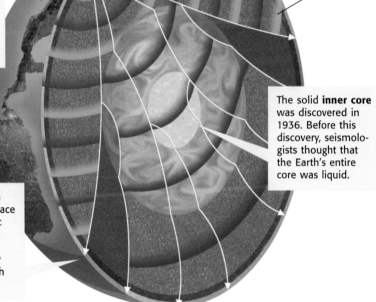

P wave

S wave

The **Moho** is a place within the Earth where the speed of seismic waves increases sharply. It marks the boundary between the Earth's crust and mantle.

The solid **inner core** was discovered in 1936. Before this discovery, seismologists thought that the Earth's entire core was liquid.

The **shadow zone** is an area on the Earth's surface where no direct seismic waves from a particular earthquake can be detected. This discovery suggested that the Earth has a liquid core.

135

SCIENTISTS AT ODDS

Until Inge Lehmann published her paper titled "P[1]" in 1936, most seismologists thought that the Earth's core was entirely liquid. Lehmann's work proved that the Earth's core had two parts—an outer, liquid part and an inner, solid part. She came up with her idea partly by calculating the time it took waves to pass through the Earth's core. Her discovery was based on observations of the reflection and refraction of seismic waves generated by deep-focus earthquakes.

Focus

Earthquake Discoveries Near and Far

In this section students learn how seismic evidence led to important discoveries about the Earth's interior. Students also learn about seismic activity on the moon, Mars, and the sun.

Bellringer

Ask students to brainstorm about what activities in their town might cause seismic "noise" that interferes with studying earthquakes in the same way that wind on Mars interfered with studying "marsquakes." (Traffic, trains, and construction all cause vibrations in the ground.)

1 Motivate

USING THE FIGURE

Use the figure on this page and Teaching Transparency 133 to help students understand why it took scientists so long to discover the cause of some earthquakes and to understand how the structure of the Earth's interior affects the way seismic waves travel.

 Teaching Transparency 133 "Discoveries in the Earth's Interior"

 Directed Reading Worksheet Section 4

DEMONSTRATION

Mapping with Seismic Waves

Place a clear, shallow glass pan containing 3 to 5 cm of water on an overhead projector. Turn on the projector, and produce waves by touching the surface of the water with your finger. Students will see the waves radiate from the point where you touched the water. Tell students that these waves simulate those that radiate out from an earthquake's epicenter. Next place a solid object, such as a coffee cup, in the pan. Repeat the demonstration, and ask students to describe what happens to the waves when they encounter the object. (Students should see that the solid object deflects the waves.)

Explain that this is similar to what happens to seismic waves as they pass through the Earth. As seismic waves encounter different zones of Earth's interior, their paths change.

3 Extend

RESEARCH

The seismic experiments on the moon helped scientists learn a great deal about the moon's structure and formation. Have students find out about different hypotheses regarding the origin of the moon. Have students make written evaluations of the strengths and weaknesses of these hypotheses. Tell them to base their evaluations on their understanding of the scientific method.

BRAIN FOOD

Many scientists think part of the moon was once part of the Earth. It is thought that when the Earth was almost entirely molten, a Mars-sized object collided with the Earth, knocking off part of Earth's mantle. The mantle material and material from the impacting body then began orbiting the Earth. Eventually, the orbiting material joined to form the moon.

Quakes and Shakes on Other Cosmic Bodies

Seismologists have taken what they have learned from earthquakes and applied it to studies of other cosmic bodies, such as planets, moons, and stars. They have been able to learn about the interiors of these cosmic bodies by studying how seismic waves behave within them. The first and perhaps most successful seismic test on another cosmic body was on Earth's moon.

The Moon In July 1969, humans set foot on the moon for the first time. They brought with them a seismograph. Not knowing if the moon was seismically active, they left nothing to chance—they purposely crashed their landing vehicle back into the moon's surface after they left to create artificial seismic waves. What happened after that left seismologists astonished.

If the lander had crashed into the Earth, the equivalent seismograms would have lasted 20–30 seconds at most. The surface of the moon, however, vibrated for more than an hour and a half! At first scientists thought the equipment was not working properly. But the seismograph recorded similar signals produced by meteoroid impacts and "moonquakes" long after the astronauts had left the moon. **Figure 16** shows the nature of these seismic events, which were observed remotely from Earth.

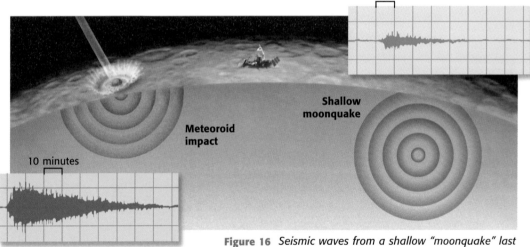

Figure 16 *Seismic waves from a shallow "moonquake" last 50 minutes. Seismic waves from a meteoroid impact last an hour and a half. Similar disturbances on Earth last less than a minute.*

Homework

Research Have students find out more about "moonquakes" and the research conducted by the Apollo space missions, such as the passive seismic experiment. Students could learn more about other cosmic bodies to find out if there are new discoveries about their seismic activity.

IS THAT A FACT!

"Moonquakes" fall into three categories: deep quakes, which might result from the gravitational pull of Earth; shallow quakes, which may be caused by the heating and cooling of the moon's surface; and quakes caused by the collision of objects with the moon's surface.

Mars In 1976, a space probe called *Viking 1* allowed seismologists to learn about seismic activity on Mars. The probe, which was controlled remotely from Earth, landed on Mars and conducted several experiments. A seismograph was placed on top of the spacecraft to measure seismic waves on Mars. However, as soon as the craft landed, *Viking 1*'s seismograph began to shake. Scientists immediately discovered that Mars is a very windy planet and that the seismograph was working mainly as a wind gauge!

Although the wind on Mars interfered with the seismograph, the seismograph recorded seismograms for months. During that time, only one possible "marsquake" shook the seismograph harder than the wind did.

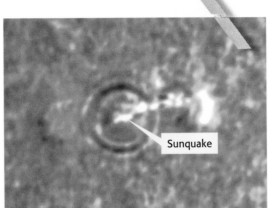

The Sun Seismologists have also studied seismic waves on the sun. Because humans cannot directly access the sun, scientists study it remotely by using a satellite called *SOHO*. Information gathered by *SOHO* has shown that solar flares produce seismic waves. *Solar flares* are powerful magnetic disturbances in the sun. The seismic waves that result cause "sunquakes," which are similar to earthquakes but are generally much stronger. For example, a moderate sunquake, shown in **Figure 17** beneath an image of *SOHO*, released more than 1 million times as much energy as the Great Hanshin earthquake mentioned at the beginning of this chapter!

Sunquake

Figure 17 *SOHO detects "sunquakes" that dwarf the greatest earthquakes in history.*

SECTION REVIEW

1. What observation of seismic-wave travel led to the discovery of the Moho?

2. Briefly describe one discovery seismologists have made about each of the following cosmic bodies: the moon, Mars, and the sun.

3. **Interpreting Graphics** Take another look at the figure on the first page of Section 4. Why don't S waves enter the Earth's outer core?

internetconnect

SCi**LINKS**
NSTA

TOPIC: Earthquake Discoveries Near and Far
GO TO: www.scilinks.org
*sci***LINKS NUMBER:** HSTE195

Answers to Section Review

1. Seismologists found a sharp increase in the speed of seismic waves and the bending of seismic waves at the Moho boundary.

2. Answers will vary. Possible answers include:
   • Seismic waves last a lot longer on the moon than they do on Earth.

   • Mars is not very seismically active.

   • "Sunquakes" are generally a lot stronger than earthquakes.

3. S waves do not enter the outer core because they cannot travel through parts of the Earth that are completely liquid.

Quake Challenge
Teacher's Notes

Time Required

One 45-minute class period

Lab Ratings

TEACHER PREP   ▲▲
STUDENT SET-UP   ▲
CONCEPT LEVEL   ▲▲
CLEAN UP   ▲▲

MATERIALS

The materials listed on the student page are enough for two students.

Safety Caution

Remind students to review all safety cautions and icons before beginning this lab activity.

Preparation Notes

Make the gelatin 24 hours in advance to ensure that it has set sufficiently. Cut the gelatin squares ahead of time, and place each square on a piece of wax paper. For steps 8 and 9, you will need to create a gelatin square large enough to place all the student structures on it. This allows each group's structure to be evaluated on its own merit. Keep the gelatin refrigerated until it's ready to be used.

Design Your Own Lab

USING SCIENTIFIC METHODS

Quake Challenge

In many parts of the world, it is important that buildings be built with earthquakes in mind. Each building must be planned so that the structure is protected during an earthquake. Architects have improved the design of buildings greatly since 1906, when an earthquake destroyed much of San Francisco. In this activity, you will use marshmallows and toothpicks to build a structure that can withstand a simulated earthquake. In the process, you will discover some of the ways that a building can be built to withstand an earthquake.

MATERIALS

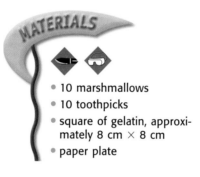

- 10 marshmallows
- 10 toothpicks
- square of gelatin, approximately 8 cm × 8 cm
- paper plate

Ask a Question

1 What features help a building withstand an earthquake? How can I use this information to build my structure?

Form a Hypothesis

2 Brainstorm with a classmate to design a structure that will resist a simulated earthquake. Sketch your design in your ScienceLog. Write two or three sentences to describe your design. Explain why you think your design will be able to withstand a simulated earthquake.

Test the Hypothesis

3 Follow your design to build a structure using the toothpicks and marshmallows.

4 Place the gelatin square on the paper plate and set your structure on the gelatin.

5 Shake the square of gelatin to test whether your building will remain standing during an earthquake. Do not pick up the gelatin.

6 If your first design does not work well, change it until you find a design that does. Each time, try to determine why your building falls so that you can improve your design.

7 Sketch your final design in your ScienceLog.

8 After you have tested your final design, place your structure on the gelatin square on your teacher's desk.

138

 Datasheets for LabBook

Helen Schiller
Northwood Middle School
Taylors, South Carolina

9 When every group has added a structure to the teacher's gelatin, your teacher will simulate an earthquake by shaking the gelatin. Watch to see which buildings withstand the most severe earthquake.

Analyze the Results

10 Which buildings were still standing after the final earthquake? What features made them more stable?

11 How would you change your design to make your structure more stable?

Communicate Results

12 Based on this activity, what advice would you give to architects who design buildings in earthquake zones?

13 What are some limitations of your earthquake model?

14 How could your research have an impact on society?

Answers

10. Answers will vary. Sample answer: Structures that had a wide base generally withstood the earthquake. Structures that incorporated triangles into the design also were successful.

11. Answers will vary. Accept all reasonable answers.

12. Buildings designed in earthquake-prone areas should have wide and flexible foundations. The building should also be reinforced to prevent collapsing.

13. Answers will vary.

14. Answers will vary.

139

Chapter Highlights

Chapter Highlights

VOCABULARY DEFINITIONS

SECTION 1

seismology the study of earthquakes

fault a break in the Earth's crust along which blocks of the crust slide relative to one another due to tectonic forces

deformation the change in the shape of rock in response to stress

elastic rebound the sudden return of elastically deformed rock to its undeformed shape

seismic waves waves of energy that travel through the Earth

P waves the fastest type of seismic wave; can travel through solids, liquids, and gases; also known as pressure waves and primary waves

S waves the second-fastest type of seismic wave; cannot travel through materials that are completely liquid; also known as shear waves and secondary waves

SECTION 2

seismograph an instrument located at or near the surface of the Earth that records seismic waves

seismogram a tracing of earthquake motion created by a seismograph

epicenter the point on the Earth's surface directly above an earthquake's starting point

focus the point inside the Earth where an earthquake begins

SECTION 1

Vocabulary

seismology (p. 120)
fault (p. 120)
deformation (p. 121)
elastic rebound (p. 121)
seismic waves (p. 124)
P waves (p. 124)
S waves (p. 124)

Section Notes

- Earthquakes mainly occur along faults near the edges of tectonic plates.

- Elastic rebound is the direct cause of earthquakes.

- Earthquakes differ depending on what type of plate motion causes them.

- Seismic waves are classified as body waves or surface waves.

- Body waves travel through the Earth's interior, while surface waves travel along the surface.

- There are two types of body waves: P waves and S waves.

SECTION 2

Vocabulary

seismograph (p. 126)
seismogram (p. 126)
epicenter (p. 126)
focus (p. 126)

Section Notes

- Seismographs detect seismic waves and record them as seismograms.

- An earthquake's focus is the underground location where seismic waves begin. The earthquake's epicenter is on the surface directly above the focus.

- Seismologists use the S-P-time method to find an earthquake's epicenter.

- Seismologists use the Richter scale to measure an earthquake's strength.

Labs

Earthquake Waves (p. 184)

☑ Skills Check

Math Concepts

EARTHQUAKE STRENGTH The energy released by an earthquake increases by a factor of 31.7 with each increase in magnitude. The energy released decreases by a factor of 31.7 with each decrease in magnitude. All you have to do is multiply or divide.

If magnitude 4 releases energy y, then:

- magnitude 5 releases energy $31.7y$

- magnitude 3 releases energy $\dfrac{y}{31.7}$

Visual Understanding

TIME-DISTANCE GRAPH Note on the time-distance graph in Figure 9 that the difference in arrival times between P waves and S waves increases with distance from the epicenter.

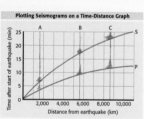

Lab and Activity Highlights

Quake Challenge PG 138

Earthquake Waves PG 184

 Datasheets for LabBook (blackline masters for these labs)

SECTION 3

Vocabulary

gap hypothesis (p. 131)

seismic gap (p. 131)

Section Notes

- Earthquake hazard measures how prone an area is to experiencing earthquakes in the future.

- Some earthquake predictions are based on the relationship between earthquake strength and earthquake frequency. As earthquake frequency decreases, earthquake strength increases.

- Predictions based on the gap hypothesis target seismically inactive areas along faults for strong earthquakes in the future.

- An earthquake usually collapses a structure by displacing the structure's center of gravity off the structure's supporting base.

- Buildings and bridges can be reinforced to minimize earthquake damage.

- People in earthquake-prone areas should plan ahead for earthquakes.

SECTION 4

Vocabulary

Moho (p. 135)

shadow zone (p. 135)

Section Notes

- The Moho, shadow zone, and inner core are features discovered on and inside Earth by observing seismic waves.

- Seismology has been used to study other cosmic bodies.

- Seismic waves last much longer on the moon than they do on Earth.

- Based on early seismic studies, Mars appears much less active seismically than the Earth.

- "Sunquakes" produce energy far greater than any earthquakes we know of.

VOCABULARY DEFINITIONS, continued

SECTION 3

gap hypothesis states that sections of active faults that have had relatively few earthquakes are likely to be the sites of strong earthquakes in the future

seismic gap an area along a fault where relatively few earthquakes have occurred

SECTION 4

Moho a place within the Earth where the speed of seismic waves increases sharply; marks the boundary between the Earth's crust and mantle

shadow zone an area on the Earth's surface where no direct seismic waves from a particular earthquake can be detected

 Vocabulary Review Worksheet

 Blackline masters of these Chapter Highlights can be found in the **Study Guide.**

---

internetconnect

GO TO: go.hrw.com

Visit the **HRW** Web site for a variety of learning tools related to this chapter. Just type in the keyword:

KEYWORD: HSTEQK

SCI LINKS
NSTA

GO TO: www.scilinks.org

Visit the **National Science Teachers Association** on-line Web site for Internet resources related to this chapter. Just type in the *sci*LINKS number for more information about the topic:

TOPIC: What Is an Earthquake?   *sci*LINKS NUMBER: HSTE180
TOPIC: Earthquake Measurement   *sci*LINKS NUMBER: HSTE185
TOPIC: Earthquakes and Society   *sci*LINKS NUMBER: HSTE190
TOPIC: Earthquake Discoveries   *sci*LINKS NUMBER: HSTE195
          Near and Far

141

Lab and Activity Highlights

LabBank

 Whiz-Bang Demonstrations, When Buildings Boogie

Long-Term Projects & Research Ideas, Whole Lotta Shakin'

Chapter Review

USING VOCABULARY

To complete the following sentences, choose the correct term from each pair of terms listed below:

1. Energy is released as ___?___ occurs. *(deformation* or *elastic rebound)*

2. ___?___ cannot travel through parts of the Earth that are completely liquid. *(S waves* or *P waves)*

3. Seismic waves are recorded by a ___?___. *(seismograph* or *seismogram)*

4. Seismologists use the S-P-time method to find an earthquake's ___?___. *(shadow zone* or *epicenter)*

5. The ___?___ is a place that marks a sharp increase in seismic wave speed. *(seismic gap* or *Moho)*

UNDERSTANDING CONCEPTS

Multiple Choice

6. When rock is ___?___ , energy builds up in it. Seismic waves occur as this energy is ___?___.
   a. elastically deformed; released
   b. plastically deformed; released
   c. elastically deformed; increased
   d. plastically deformed; increased

7. The strongest earthquakes usually occur
   a. near divergent boundaries.
   b. near convergent boundaries.
   c. near transform boundaries.
   d. along normal faults.

8. The last seismic waves to arrive are
   a. P waves.
   b. S waves.
   c. surface waves.
   d. body waves.

9. If an earthquake begins while you are in a building, the safest thing to do first is
   a. get under the strongest table, chair, or other piece of furniture.
   b. run out into the street.
   c. crouch near a wall.
   d. call home.

10. Studying earthquake waves currently allows seismologists to do all of the following *except*
    a. determine when an earthquake started.
    b. learn about the Earth's interior.
    c. decrease an earthquake's strength.
    d. determine where an earthquake started.

11. If a planet has a liquid core, then S waves
    a. speed up as they travel through the core.
    b. maintain their speed as they travel through the core.
    c. change direction as they travel through the core.
    d. cannot pass through the core.

Short Answer

12. What is the relationship between the strength of earthquakes and earthquake frequency?

13. You learned earlier that if you are in a car during an earthquake and are out in the open, it is best to stay in the car. Briefly describe a situation in which you might want to leave a car during an earthquake.

14. How did seismologists determine that the outer core of the Earth is liquid?

Concept Mapping

15. Use the following terms to create a concept map: focus, epicenter, earthquake start time, seismic waves, P waves, S waves.

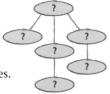

The graph below illustrates the relationship between earthquake magnitude and the height of the tracings on a seismogram. Charles Richter initially formed his magnitude scale by comparing the heights of seismogram readings for different earthquakes. Study the graph, and then answer the questions that follow.

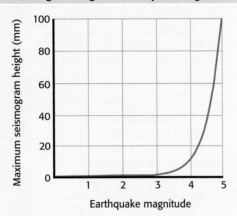

Seismogram Height Vs. Earthquake Magnitude

CRITICAL THINKING AND PROBLEM SOLVING

Write one or two sentences to answer the following questions:

16. How might the wall in Figure 2 appear if it had deformed elastically instead of plastically?

17. Why do strong earthquakes occur where there have not been many recent earthquakes? (Hint: Think about what gradually happens to rock before an earthquake occurs.)

18. What could be done to solve the wind problem with the seismograph on Mars? Explain how you would set up the seismograph.

MATH IN SCIENCE

19. Based on the relationship between earthquake magnitude and frequency, if 150 earthquakes with a magnitude of 2 occur in your area this year, about how many earthquakes with a magnitude of 4 should occur in your area this year?

20. What would the magnitude of an earthquake be if the height of its seismogram readings were 10 mm?

21. Look at the shape of the curve on the graph. What does this tell you about the relationship between seismogram heights and earthquake magnitudes? Explain.

Reading Check-up

Take a minute to review your answers to the Pre-Reading Questions found at the bottom of page 118. Have your answers changed? If necessary, revise your answers based on what you have learned since you began this chapter.

143

Concept Mapping

15. 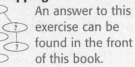 An answer to this exercise can be found in the front of this book.

CRITICAL THINKING AND PROBLEM SOLVING

16. If the wall in Figure 2 had deformed elastically instead of plastically, it might appear broken or cracked.

17. Strong earthquakes occur where there have not been many recent earthquakes because a lot of elastic deformation builds up along active faults where rock has not moved for awhile. The more deformation that builds up, the more energy the rock releases when it finally slips along the fault.

18. Answers will vary. One solution might be to place the seismograph in a hole or depression that is shielded from wind.

MATH IN SCIENCE

19. one or two

INTERPRETING GRAPHICS

20. 4
21. Answers will vary slightly. The relationship is logarithmic, not linear. Students should recognize that seismogram heights increase at a larger rate with each increase in earthquake magnitude.

 Concept Mapping Transparency 8

 Blackline masters of this Chapter Review can be found in the **Study Guide.**

Background

There have been many studies on the different types of animal responses to the geophysical environment. Most of these studies illustrated that the behavior of living organisms is affected by electromagnetic fields. Studies have been performed on how migrating birds find their way and how fish navigate. Fish such as catfish and sharks utilize electroreceptors to detect objects around them and to communicate. Even earthworms respond to changes in Earth's magnetic field.

An American geologist named Jim Berkland has been a strong proponent of using animals to predict earthquakes. It is likely that students pursuing further research in this area will encounter his name often. Berkland has successfully predicted a few earthquakes by observing animal behavior. However, he does not always correctly predict the magnitude of the earthquakes.

WEIRD SCIENCE

CAN ANIMALS PREDICT EARTHQUAKES?

It Could Happen to You!

One day you come home from visiting a friend for the weekend and learn that your dog Pepper is hiding under your bed. Your father explains that he has been trying to get Pepper out from under the bed for the last 6 hours. Just then your mother enters the room and says that she has found two snakes in the backyard—and that makes a total of five in 2 days! This is very odd because you usually don't find more than one each year.

All the animals seem to be acting very strange. Your goldfish is even hiding behind a rock. You wonder if there is some explanation.

What's Going On?

So what's your guess? What do you think is happening? Did you guess that an earthquake is about to occur? Well, if you did, you are probably right!

Publications from as far back as 1784 record unusual animal behavior prior to earthquakes. Some examples included zoo animals refusing to go into their shelters at night and domestic cattle seeking high ground. Other animals, like lizards, snakes, and small mammals, evacuate their underground burrows, and wild birds leave their usual habitats. All of these events occurred a few days, several hours, or a few minutes before the earthquakes happened.

Animals on Call?

Today the majority of scientists look to physical instruments in order to help them predict earthquakes. Yet the fact remains that none of the geophysical instruments we have allow scientists to predict exactly when an earthquake will occur. Could animals know the answer?

▼ *Goldfish or earthquake sensor?*

There are changes in the Earth's crust that occur prior to an earthquake, such as magnetic field changes, subsidence (sinking), tilting, and bulging of the surface. These things can be monitored by modern instruments. Many studies have shown that electromagnetic fields affect the behavior of living organisms. Is it possible that animals close to the epicenter of an earthquake are able to sense changes in their environment? Should we pay attention?

You Decide

▶ Currently, the United States government does not fund research that investigates whether animals can predict earthquakes. Have a debate with your classmates about whether the government should fund such research.

144

Answer to You Decide

Encourage students to understand both sides of this debate. Because government funding is limited, using these funds for one area of study could result in a reduction in the funding for other areas. Would students be willing to fund a study about animals predicting earthquakes if it meant decreasing the funding toward protecting the environment? Would it be better to require states in seismically active areas to fund this research themselves, either publicly or privately? Ask students to come up with solutions.

EYE ON THE ENVIRONMENT

What Causes Such Destruction?

At 5:04 P.M. on October 14, 1989, life in California's San Francisco Bay Area seemed as normal as ever. The third game of the World Series was underway in Candlestick Park, now called 3Com Park. While 62,000 fans filled the park, other people were rushing home from a day's work. By 5:05 P.M., however, things had changed drastically. The fact sheet of destruction looks like this:

Injuries:	3,757
Deaths:	68
Damaged homes:	23,408
Destroyed homes:	1,018
Damaged businesses:	3,530
Destroyed businesses:	366
Financial loss:	over $6 billion

The Culprit

The cause of such destruction was a 7.1 magnitude earthquake that lasted for 20 seconds. Its epicenter was 97 km south of San Francisco in an area called Loma Prieta. The earthquake was so strong that people in San Diego and western Nevada (740 km away) felt it too. Considering the earthquake's high magnitude and the fact that it occurred during rush hour, it is amazing that more people did not die. However, the damage to buildings was widespread—it covered an area of 7,770 km². And by October 1, 1990, there had been more than 7,000 aftershocks of this quake.

Take Heed

Engineers and seismologists had expected a major earthquake, so the amount of damage they saw from this earthquake was no surprise. But experts agree that if the earthquake were of a higher magnitude or centered closer to Oakland, San Jose, or San Francisco, the damage would have been much worse. They are concerned that people who live in these areas aren't paying attention to the warning this earthquake represents.

Many people have a false sense of security because their buildings withstood the quake with little or no damage. But engineers and seismologists agree that the only reason the buildings survived was because the ground motion in those areas was fairly low.

Tomorrow May Be Too Late

Many buildings that withstood this earthquake were poorly constructed and would not withstand another earthquake. Experts say there is a 50 percent chance that one or more 7.0 magnitude earthquakes will occur in the San Francisco Bay Area in the next 30 years. And the results of the next quake could be much more devastating if people don't reinforce their buildings before it's too late.

▲ *Notice the different levels of destruction for various buildings on the same street.*

On Your Own

▶ Research the engineering innovations for constructing bridges and buildings in areas with seismic activity. Share your information with the class.

Answers to On Your Own

Students' answers will vary. However, some of the design features that engineers and architects use to make buildings that better withstand earthquakes are as follows: the mass damper, the active tendon system, base isolators, cross-braces, and flexible pipes.

- **Mass Damper:** The mass damper is a 6-ton weight built into the top of the building. Motion sensors detect swaying and send a message to a computer system. The computer system then directs hydraulic actuators to shift the weight of the mass damper in order to counteract the building's movement during an earthquake or high winds.

- **Active Tendon System:** Similar to the mass damper system, but the damper is located at the base of the building.

- **Base Isolators:** Base isolators act as shock absorbers against the force of an earthquake. Each base isolator (approximately 60 cm tall and 60 cm wide) consists of layers of rubber and steel wrapped around a lead core. This arrangement of materials absorbs the energy of seismic waves that would otherwise travel up through the building.

- **Cross-Braces:** Cross-braces lend strength by counteracting the push-and-pull pressures that occur at the sides of a building during an earthquake. These cross-braces are made of steel, which is strong but flexible enough to stretch considerably before breaking.

- **Flexible Pipes:** The swaying and rocking of a building during an earthquake can cause pipes to break. Pipes with flexible joints are better able to bend without breaking during an earthquake.

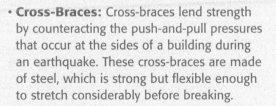

Chapter Organizer

CHAPTER ORGANIZATION	TIME MINUTES	OBJECTIVES	LABS, INVESTIGATIONS, AND DEMONSTRATIONS
Chapter Opener pp. 146–147	45	National Standards: SAI 1, ST 1, SPSP 3, 4	**Start-Up Activity,** Anticipation, p. 147
Section 1 Volcanic Eruptions	90	▶ Distinguish between nonexplosive and explosive volcanic eruptions. ▶ Explain how the composition of magma determines the type of volcanic eruption that will occur. ▶ Classify the main types of lava and volcanic debris. SAI 1, HNS 2, ES 1c	**QuickLab,** Bubble, Bubble, Toil and Trouble, p. 150
Section 2 Volcanoes' Effects on Earth	90	▶ Describe the effects that volcanoes have on Earth. ▶ Compare the different types of volcanoes. ST 2, SPSP 3–5, HNS 1, 3, ES 1c; Labs SAI 1	**Discovery Lab,** Some Go "Pop," Some Do Not, p. 162 **Datasheets for LabBook,** Some Go "Pop," Some Do Not **Whiz-Bang Demonstrations,** How's Your Lava Life?
Section 3 What Causes Volcanoes?	135	▶ Describe the formation and movement of magma. ▶ Explain the relationship between volcanoes and plate tectonics. ▶ Summarize the methods scientists use to predict volcanic eruptions. UCP 3, SAI 1, ST 2, SPSP 5, ES 1b, 1c; Labs SAI 1, ST 2	**QuickLab,** Reaction to Stress, p. 156 **Interactive Explorations CD-ROM,** What's the Matter? A **Worksheet** is also available in the **Interactive Explorations Teacher's Edition.** **Skill Builder,** Volcano Verdict, p. 186 **Datasheets for LabBook,** Volcano Verdict **Labs You Can Eat,** Hot Spots **Whiz-Bang Demonstrations,** What Makes a Vent Event? **Long-Term Projects & Research Ideas,** A City Lost and Found

See page **T23** *for a complete correlation of this book with the*

NATIONAL SCIENCE EDUCATION STANDARDS.

TECHNOLOGY RESOURCES

 Guided Reading Audio CD English or Spanish, Chapter 6

 One-Stop Planner CD-ROM with Test Generator

 Interactive Explorations CD-ROM CD 1, Exploration 4, What's the Matter?

 Scientists in Action, Volcano Hunters, Segment 13

 Earth Science Videodisc Volcanoes: 28244–32232

CLASSROOM WORKSHEETS, TRANSPARENCIES, AND RESOURCES	SCIENCE INTEGRATION AND CONNECTIONS	REVIEW AND ASSESSMENT
Directed Reading Worksheet **Science Puzzlers, Twisters & Teasers**		
Directed Reading Worksheet, Section 1 **Transparency 208,** Summarizing the Changes of State	**Connect to Life Science,** p. 149 in ATE **Multicultural Connection,** p. 149 in ATE **Connect to Physical Science,** p. 150 in ATE **Biology Connection,** p. 152 **Across the Sciences:** Europa: Life on a Moon? p. 169	**Section Review,** p. 152 **Quiz,** p. 152 in ATE **Alternative Assessment,** p. 152 in ATE
Directed Reading Worksheet, Section 2 **Transparency 134,** Three Types of Volcanoes **Problem Solving Worksheet,** Eruption Disruption **Transparency 135,** The Formation of a Caldera **Reinforcement Worksheet,** A Variety of Volcanoes	**Connect to Astronomy,** p. 153 in ATE **Cross-Disciplinary Focus,** p. 154 in ATE **Science, Technology, and Society:** Robot in the Hot Seat, p. 168	**Section Review,** p. 155 **Quiz,** p. 155 in ATE **Alternative Assessment,** p. 155 in ATE
Transparency 136, The Formation of Magma **Directed Reading Worksheet,** Section 3 **Math Skills for Science Worksheet,** Using Temperature Scales **Transparency 137,** How a Hot Spot Forms Volcanoes **Reinforcement Worksheet,** Tectonic Plate Movement	**Cross-Disciplinary Focus,** p. 157 in ATE **MathBreak,** How Hot Is Hot? p. 158 **Real-World Connection,** p. 158 in ATE **Apply,** p. 161	**Self-Check,** p. 157 **Homework,** pp. 158, 160 in ATE **Section Review,** p. 161 **Quiz,** p. 161 in ATE **Alternative Assessment,** p. 161 in ATE

 Holt, Rinehart and Winston On-line Resources
go.hrw.com

For worksheets and other teaching aids related to this chapter, visit the HRW Web site and type in the keyword: **HSTVOL**

 National Science Teachers Association
www.scilinks.org

Encourage students to use the *sci*LINKS numbers listed in the internet connect boxes to access information and resources on the **NSTA** Web site.

END-OF-CHAPTER REVIEW AND ASSESSMENT

Chapter Review in Study Guide
Vocabulary and Notes in Study Guide
Chapter Tests with Performance-Based Assessment, Chapter 6 Test
Chapter Tests with Performance-Based Assessment, Performance-Based Assessment 6
Concept Mapping Transparency 9

Chapter Resources & Worksheets

Visual Resources

TEACHING TRANSPARENCIES

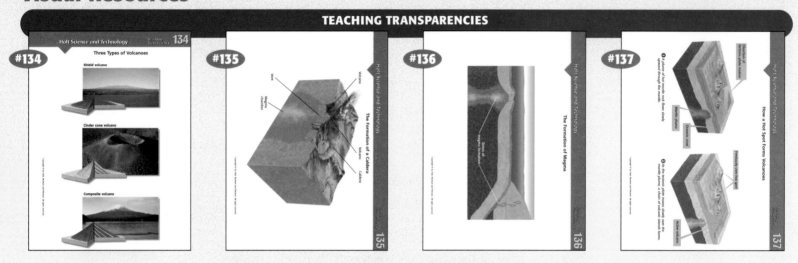

TEACHING TRANSPARENCIES

CONCEPT MAPPING TRANSPARENCY

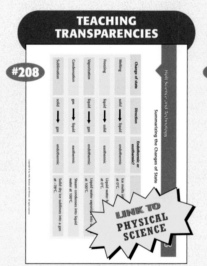

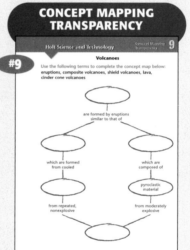

Meeting Individual Needs

DIRECTED READING

REINFORCEMENT & VOCABULARY REVIEW

SCIENCE PUZZLERS, TWISTERS & TEASERS

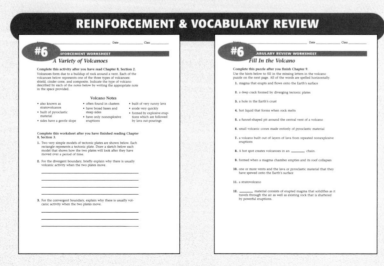

Review & Assessment

STUDY GUIDE

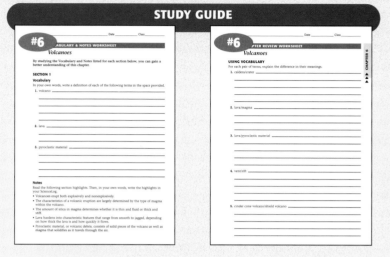

CHAPTER TESTS WITH PERFORMANCE-BASED ASSESSMENT

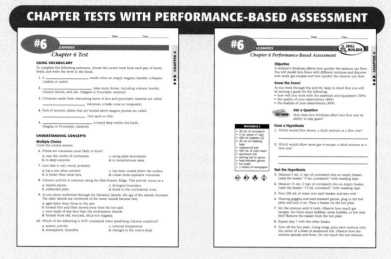

Lab Worksheets

LABS YOU CAN EAT

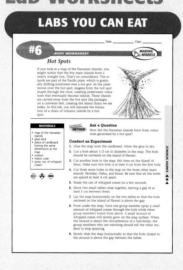

WHIZ-BANG DEMONSTRATIONS

LONG-TERM PROJECTS & RESEARCH IDEAS

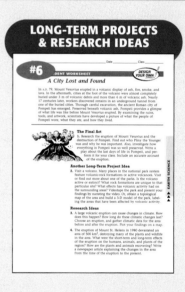

DATASHEETS FOR LABBOOK

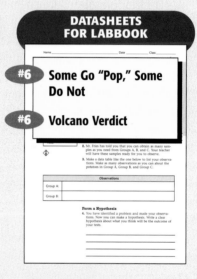

Applications & Extensions

CRITICAL THINKING & PROBLEM SOLVING

SCIENTISTS IN ACTION

INTERACTIVE EXPLORATIONS

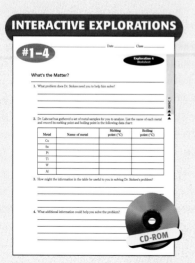

SECTION 1

Volcanic Eruptions

▶ Mineral Formation in Subduction Zones

The formation of commercially valuable minerals is common in areas where subduction creates volcanoes. As magma formed from subducted crust rises, it heats the surrounding rocks, causing the fluids they contain to circulate near the point of intrusion. The hot fluids react with the magma and surrounding rocks, dissolving some metals (including iron, lead, silver, and gold). As the fluid rises through the Earth's crust, mineral precipitation occurs at points where it cools. This process can result in the formation of rich mineral veins.

▶ The Origin of Volcanic Terms

Many terms for nonviolent eruptions are Hawaiian. Drops of liquid lava that blow into fine spiky strands are called *Pele's hair,* after the Hawaiian goddess of fire. *Limu o Pele,* or "Pele's seaweed," is the term for delicate, translucent sheets of spatter filled with tiny glass bubbles.

- The terms for violent eruptions, however, are generally not Hawaiian. *Nuée ardente,* French for "burning cloud," is a hot mass of volcanic gases, ash, and debris that is expelled explosively and then travels at hurricane speeds down a mountainside.

IS THAT A FACT!

- The Tambora volcano eruption in Indonesia is the largest in the last 200 years. The volcano erupted on April 10 and 11, 1815. The eruption and the resulting tsunamis killed more than 10,000 people. Ash covered so much land that farmland was devastated; disease and famine killed 82,000 more.

- During the Tambora eruption, so much ash was thrown into the atmosphere that weather patterns were affected worldwide. Scholars believe the eruption caused the "Year Without a Summer" in 1816, when snow fell in New England in July.

SECTION 2

Volcanoes' Effects on Earth

▶ The Krakatau Explosion

When the island of Krakatau, in Indonesia, exploded in 1883, it caused a shockwave that sped around the world seven times. The volcano ejected about 18 km³ of volcanic material into the air. One ash cloud reached 80 km high, and the explosion was heard on islands in the Indian Ocean nearly 4,600 km away. The ash clouds blocked out the sun and everything within 80 km of the volcano was plunged into complete darkness for more than two days. The volcano collapsed and the island lost 21 km² of land. All that was left was a caldera lying as deep as 275 m beneath the ocean!

- In 1927, a cloud of sulfur and ash rose from the water above the volcano—Krakatau's magma chamber was not gone. It was the beginning of Anak Krakatau, or "Child of Krakatau," which rose from the original volcano's crater. By 1990, Anak Krakatau was 300 m high, and it continues to grow.

▶ Fighting Lava with Water

Most attempts to divert lava away from homes and towns have failed. However, when lava flows in Iceland threatened to engulf a seaport and its harbor, the townspeople decided on a unique approach. Using ocean-going firefighting boats, they pumped icy water from the bay onto the oncoming lava. The water cooled the lava fast enough to divert the flow. Hawaiians have tried to divert lava flows this way but with little success.

IS THAT A FACT!

☛ When lava flows in a defined channel, a crust forms on the surface. If the crust remains stationary while the lava below is still flowing, a lava tube or a lava cave several kilometers long can result.

SECTION 3

What Causes Volcanoes?

▶ Merapi, "Mountain of Fire"

There are more active volcanoes in Indonesia than anywhere else on Earth—130! Perhaps the most dangerous volcano is called Merapi, or "Mountain of Fire," on the island of Java. Since 1548, Merapi has erupted violently 68 times. In 1998, it became active again, and people began to evacuate the area. Scientists are worried about the city of Yogyakarta, which lies just 70 km north of the volcano and is home to about 500,000 people. A large eruption could completely destroy the city.

Ring of Fire

▶ Predicting the Mount Pinatubo Eruptions

Perhaps the most successful prediction of a volcanic eruption was on Mount Pinatubo, in the Philippine Islands. When Pinatubo became active in March and April 1991, scientists rushed to the area and quickly established monitoring systems. Groups of scientists from the Philippines and the United States distributed a five-level alert system to civil defense and local officials. Evacuations began when an eruption appeared imminent (Level 4 alert); ultimately, more than 100,000 people evacuated the area. There were enormous losses of land, housing, and crops, but because of the preparations and warnings, there were only 700 deaths.

● Pinatubo was what geologists call a well-behaved volcano. It behaved as the geologists predicted, becoming increasingly active and then exploding. Most volcanoes are not so well behaved. For example, the same monitoring methods have been much less successful on Montserrat, in the Caribbean.

IS THAT A FACT!

☛ The youngest Hawaiian "island," Loihi, is 3,500 m above the ocean floor, but it must grow almost 1 km before coming out of the ocean. That, scientists say, could take more than 20,000 years.

☛ Native Hawaiians believed that Pele, the fire goddess, was responsible for volcanic activity on the islands. According to their tradition, Pele lives in the active crater of Kilauea. When angered, she stamps her feet, causing earthquakes and sending forth lava. Legend maintains that she appears as an old woman just before an eruption.

> **For background information about teaching strategies and issues, refer to the *Professional Reference for Teachers.***

Volcanoes

 Pre-Reading Questions

Students may not know the answers to these questions before reading the chapter, so accept any reasonable response.

Suggested Answers

1. A volcanic eruption is caused when pressure forces magma to rise toward the Earth's surface. If there is a vent or opening for the magma to escape through, it is extruded as lava in a volcanic eruption.

2. Lava is magma that has been extruded on the Earth's surface. Magma forms when rock melts due to changes in the composition of the rock, a decrease in pressure, or an increase in temperature.

CHAPTER **6**

Sections

Volcanoes

HOT LAVA, QUIET ERUPTION

Volcanic eruptions come in all sizes. In places like Hawaii, most eruptions are nonviolent. Lava flows in Hawaii are made of rock called basalt, which flows easily. Basaltic lava flows travel slowly but can reach a temperature of nearly 1,200°C! The lava flow shown here is slowly creeping across a road. As you can see, calm eruptions of lava can threaten property more than human life. In this chapter you will learn about nonexplosive eruptions, explosive eruptions, the formation of magma, and the ways that scientists are trying to predict volcanic eruptions.

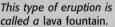
This type of eruption is called a lava fountain.

Pre-Reading Questions

1. What causes a volcanic eruption?
2. What is lava, and how does it form?

---

internet connect

 HRW On-line Resources

go.hrw.com

For worksheets and other teaching aids, visit the HRW Web site and type in the keyword: **HSTVOL**

SCiLINKS NSTA

www.scilinks.com

Use the *sci*LINKS numbers at the end of each chapter for additional resources on the **NSTA** Web site.

 Smithsonian Institution

www.si.edu/hrw

Visit the Smithsonian Institution Web site for related on-line resources.

 CNNfyi.com

www.cnnfyi.com

Visit the CNN Web site for current events coverage and classroom resources.

ANTICIPATION

As you will see in this activity, volcanic eruptions are very difficult to predict.

Procedure

1. Place **10 mL of baking soda** in the center of a sheet of **bathroom tissue.** Fold the corners over the baking soda and crease the edges so that they stay in place. Place the tissue packet in the middle of a **large pan.**

2. Put **modeling clay** around the top edge of a **funnel.** Turn the funnel upside down over the tissue packet. Press down to make a tight seal.

3. Put your safety goggles on and add **50 mL of vinegar** and **several drops of liquid dish soap** to a 200 mL **beaker,** and stir.

4. Predict how much time will elapse before your volcano erupts.

5. Pour the liquid into the upturned funnel. Using a **stopwatch,** record the time you began to pour and the time your volcano erupts. How close was your prediction?

Analysis

6. How does your model represent the natural world?

7. What are some limitations of your model?

8. Based on the predictions of the entire class, what can you conclude about the accuracy of predicting volcanic eruptions?

147

ANTICIPATION

MATERIALS

FOR EACH GROUP:
- 10 mL baking soda
- bathroom tissue
- large pan
- modeling clay
- funnel
- 50 mL vinegar
- liquid dishwashing soap
- 200 mL beaker
- stopwatch

Safety Caution

Students should wear safety goggles during this activity.

Answers to START-UP Activity

6. The model simulates the buildup of pressure below the surface that causes an eruption. Magma and the vinegar/soap mixture are both liquids. The sides of a volcano and the funnel and modeling clay are solids.

7. The materials used for the model are different. Also the temperature and pressure in a real volcano are much higher than those produced in the model.

8. Eruptions are very difficult to predict. As in the experiment, you can know that an eruption will occur in the near future, but it may be impossible to predict the exact moment of eruption.

Focus

Volcanic Eruptions

In this section, students learn about explosive and nonexplosive eruptions and about how the composition of magma affects these eruptions. Students learn to identify the internal structure of a volcano and the types of lava and pyroclastic material produced in an eruption.

Bellringer

Ask students to create a labeled drawing in their ScienceLog that illustrates what happens when a volcano erupts. Then have students describe the photographs shown on this page. Ask them to think about what causes lava to have such different characteristics. Have students share their ideas with the class. **Sheltered English**

1) Motivate

ACTIVITY

Writing Have students write a letter to a friend from a fictional survivor of the St. Pierre eruption described at the beginning of this chapter. Have students describe what the volcano was like hours before the eruption, the eruption itself, and the aftermath. Students can then exchange letters.

Directed Reading Worksheet Section 1

Terms to Learn

volcano
lava
pyroclastic material

What You'll Do

◆ Distinguish between nonexplosive and explosive volcanic eruptions.
◆ Explain how the composition of magma determines the type of volcanic eruption that will occur.
◆ Classify the main types of lava and volcanic debris.

▲ Sometimes nonexplosive eruptions can spray lava into the air. Lava fountains, such as this one, rarely exceed a few hundred meters in height.

148

Volcanic Eruptions

Think about the force of the explosion produced by the first atomic bomb used in World War II. Now imagine an explosion 10,000 times stronger, and you get an idea of how powerful a volcanic eruption can be. As you may know, volcanic eruptions give rise to volcanoes. A **volcano** is a mountain that forms when molten rock, called *magma,* is forced to the Earth's surface.

Fortunately, few volcanoes give rise to explosive eruptions. Most eruptions are of a nonexplosive variety. You can compare these two types of eruptions by looking at the photographs on this and the next page.

Nonexplosive Eruptions

When people think of volcanic eruptions, they often imagine rivers of red-hot lava, called *lava flows.* Lava flows come from nonexplosive eruptions. **Lava** is magma that flows onto the Earth's surface. Relatively calm outpourings of lava, like the ones shown below, can release a huge amount of molten rock. Some of the largest mountains on Earth grew from repeated lava flows over hundreds of thousands of years.

In this nonexplosive ▶ eruption, a continuous stream of lava pours quietly from the crater of Kilauea, in Hawaii.

◀ Lava can flow many kilometers before it finally cools and hardens. As you can see in this photograph, lava flows often pose a greater threat to property than to human life.

Although explosive volcanoes get the most attention, nonexplosive extrusions play a much more significant role in shaping our world. For instance, much of the ocean floor is covered by basaltic pillow lava, and nonexplosive volcanoes formed many of the Pacific islands.

IS THAT A FACT!

The volcano Mauna Kea is the tallest mountain in the world. It rises 4 km above sea level, and its slopes descend 5 km below the ocean. Hawaii's mass depresses the ocean floor another 8 km. This makes the volcano 17 km tall, almost twice the height of Mount Everest!

Explosive Eruptions

Take a look at **Figure 1.** In an explosive volcanic eruption, clouds of hot debris and gases shoot out from the volcano, often at supersonic speeds. Instead of producing lava flows, molten rock is blown into millions of pieces that harden in the air. The dust-sized particles can circle the globe for years in the upper atmosphere, while larger pieces of debris fall closer to the volcano.

In addition to shooting molten rock into the air, an explosive eruption can blast millions of tons of solid rock from a volcano. In a matter of minutes, an explosive eruption can demolish rock formations that took thousands of years to accumulate. Thus, as shown in **Figure 2,** a volcano may actually shrink in size rather than grow from repeated eruptions.

Figure 1 *In what resembles a nuclear explosion, volcanic debris rockets skyward during an eruption of Mount Redoubt, in Alaska.*

Figure 2 *Within minutes, the 1980 eruption of Mount St. Helens, in Washington, blasted away a whole side of the mountain, flattening and scorching 600 km² of forest.*

149

Multicultural CONNECTION

The Klickitat tribe of the Pacific Northwest had two names for Mount St. Helens. The first name was Loo-Wit, which referred to a lovely maiden who changed into a beautiful white mountain. Their other name was Tah-one-lat-clah, or "fire mountain," indicating their knowledge that the volcano was prone to eruptions. Ask students why they think the tribe had two very different names for Mount St. Helens. Have students research other American Indian names and legends for volcanic peaks in North America.

QuickLab

- 2 small drinking cups
- water
- honey
- 2 straws

Answers to QuickLab

3. Answers will vary.

4. The honey is thicker, so the air bubbles move much more slowly than in water.

5. Because the honey is thicker than water, it traps more air bubbles. Magma that is thicker will trap more gases, which creates a buildup of pressure. The more pressure that builds up, the more violent the volcanic eruption will be.

CONNECT TO PHYSICAL SCIENCE

Use Teaching Transparency 208 to discuss changes of state in magma. When water or carbon dioxide are part of minerals in a rock, they are in the solid state. When rock melts to form magma, it changes to liquid. When this happens, the water and carbon dioxide dissolved in the magma are also liquid. When temperature and pressure conditions allow, water and carbon dioxide in the magma solution exsolve, or vaporize, changing from liquid to gas. This greatly increases the volume of the magma and often results in violent eruptions. When the magma erupts on the surface, it cools and solidifies, changing from a liquid to a solid state.

Teaching Transparency 208
"Summarizing the Changes of State" *LINK TO PHYSICAL SCIENCE*

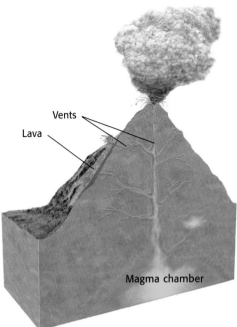

Vents

Lava

Magma chamber

Figure 3 *Volcanoes form around vents that release magma onto the Earth's surface.*

Cross Section of a Volcano

Whether they produce explosive or nonexplosive eruptions, all volcanoes share the same basic features. **Figure 3** shows some of the features that you might see if you could look inside an erupting volcano. Deep underground, the driving force that creates volcanoes is hot liquid material known as magma. Magma rises through holes in the Earth's crust called *vents*. Vents can channel magma all the way up to the Earth's surface during an eruption.

QuickLab

Bubble, Bubble, Toil and Trouble

With a few simple items, you can easily discover how the consistency of a liquid affects the flow of gases.

1. Fill a **drinking cup** halfway with **water** and another cup halfway with **honey.**
2. Using a **straw,** blow into the water and observe the bubbles.
3. Take another straw and blow into the honey. What happens?
4. How does the honey behave differently from the water?
5. How do you think this difference relates to volcanic eruptions?

TRY at HOME

Magma

By comparing the composition of magma from different types of eruptions, scientists have made an important discovery—the composition of the magma determines whether a volcanic eruption is nonexplosive, explosive, or somewhere in between.

Water A volcano is more likely to erupt explosively if its magma has a high water content. The effect water has on magma is similar to the effect carbon dioxide gas has in a can of soda. When you shake the can up, the carbon dioxide that was dissolved in the soda is released, and because gases need much more room than liquids, a great amount of pressure builds up. When you open the can, soda comes shooting out. The same phenomenon occurs with explosive volcanic eruptions.

Silica Explosive eruptions are also caused by magma that contains a large percentage of silica (a basic building block of most minerals). Silica-rich magma has a thick, stiff consistency. It flows slowly and tends to harden in the volcano's vent. This plugs the vent, resulting in a buildup of pressure as magma pushes up from below. If enough pressure builds up, an explosive eruption results. Thick magma also prevents water vapor and other gases from easily escaping. Magma that contains a smaller percentage of silica has a thinner, runnier consistency. Gases escape this type of magma more easily, making it less likely that explosive pressure will build up.

MISCONCEPTION ALERT

It may seem illogical that water makes magma more likely to explode. Explain that magma contains water and that the water is dissolved in the magma. When the water changes from a liquid to a gas, its volume increases dramatically. This change causes a pressure increase that can generate a great deal of explosive force. Discuss what would happen if students boiled water in a pot with a tight lid. Then have them think of other examples where water can be an explosive force, such as in a car's radiator or in popcorn.

What Erupts from a Volcano?

Depending on how explosive a volcanic eruption is, magma erupts as either *lava* or *pyroclastic material*. **Pyroclastic material** consists of the rock fragments created by explosive volcanic eruptions. Nonexplosive eruptions produce mostly lava. Explosive eruptions produce mostly pyroclastic material. Over many years, a volcano may alternate between eruptions of lava and eruptions of pyroclastic material. Eruptions of lava and pyroclastic material may also occur as separate stages of a single eruption event.

Fire and ice! A phrase to describe volcanoes? That depends on where they are. Turn to page 169 to find out more.

Lava Like magma, lava ranges in consistency from thick to thin. *Blocky lava* is so thick in consistency that it barely creeps along the ground. Other types of lava, such as *pahoehoe* (pah HOY нoy), *aa* (AH ah), and *pillow lava,* are thinner in consistency and produce faster lava flows. These types of lava are shown in the photographs below.

Blocky lava *is cool, stiff ▶ lava that cannot travel far from the erupting vent. Blocky lava usually oozes from a volcano, forming jumbled heaps of sharp-edged chunks.*

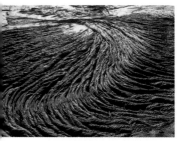

▲ **Pahoehoe** *lava flows slowly, like wax dripping from a candle, forming a glassy surface with rounded wrinkles.*

▲ **Aa** *is a Hawaiian word that refers to a type of lava that has a jagged surface. This slightly stiffer lava pours out quickly and forms a brittle crust. The crust is torn into jagged pieces as the molten lava underneath continues to move.*

▲ **Pillow lava** *forms when lava erupts underwater. As you can see here, it forms rounded lumps that are the size and shape of pillows.*

151

DISCUSSION

Discuss with students the differences between a *direct relationship* and an *inverse relationship*. Explain that when they push a swing, it goes higher and faster. This is a direct relationship. To illustrate an inverse relationship, explain that when they push down on one end of a seesaw, the other end rises. Then ask students to think about the role of water and silica in magma. Discuss them in terms of how they have a *direct relationship* with an explosion: as the amount of water or silica increases, the possibility of explosion also increases. Then discuss the way that silica affects lava's speed and consistency in terms of their *inverse relationship:* as the amount of silica increases, the speed of the lava decreases, and vice versa. Sheltered English

GROUP ACTIVITY

Introduce the concept of viscosity by having students describe the observable differences in flow rate as you pour molasses or honey, water, and vegetable oil down a gently sloping cookie sheet. (They should observe that the molasses or honey flows slowest, oil flows somewhat faster, and water flows very fast.)

Explain to students that viscosity is a liquid's resistance to flow. Honey has a high viscosity, so it flows very slowly. Water has a low viscosity, so it flows easily. Ask the students how magma's composition affects its viscosity. (The more silica that is present in magma, the greater its viscosity.)

TOPIC: Volcanic Eruptions
GO TO: www.scilinks.org
*sci*LINKS NUMBER: HSTE205

WEIRD SCIENCE

Lava cools very slowly not only because it is very hot to start with but also because it is a good insulator. When a Mexican lava flow in 1952 stopped, it was 10 m thick. In 1956, four years later, the lava still steamed when it rained.

READING 📖 STRATEGY

Mnemonics The word *pyroclastic* has two parts: *pyro,* Greek for "fire," and *clastic,* Greek for "broken." Other words that include *pyro-* are *pyrotechnics,* which describes "fire art," or fireworks, and *pyrometer,* a thermometer that measures temperatures too high for a mercury thermometer. Have students invent other words that include the prefix *pyro-*. Sheltered English

GOING FURTHER

Writing *Lahar* is an Indonesian term for a particularly deadly kind of pyroclastic flow. A lahar is a flow of water-saturated volcanic debris that races down the slope of a volcano with the consistency of wet cement. Lahars generally occur when a volcano's snowcap is suddenly melted by an eruption. When Nevada del Ruiz erupted in Colombia, its lahar killed more than 25,000 people. Have students research and report on lahars from two eruptions.

4) Close

Quiz

1. Describe the lava flow from a nonexplosive eruption. (a calm stream that can flow for hundreds of kilometers)

2. Describe an explosive eruption. (Ash, hot debris, gases, and chunks of rock spew from a volcano.)

3. Define *blocky* lava, *pahoehoe* lava, and *aa* lava. (*blocky* lava: cool, stiff lava that doesn't travel very fast; *pahoehoe* lava: flows quickly and forms a wrinkled surface, looks like coiled rope; *aa* lava: flows slowly and forms a brittle, jagged crust.)

ALTERNATIVE ASSESSMENT

Provide cornstarch, salt, and water to make a paste. Then have students experiment with the ingredients to create representations of the types of lava discussed in this section. Have students work independently to describe the eruptions that would produce each lava type.

Biology
CONNECTION

Volcanoes provide some of the most productive farmland in the world. It can take thousands of years for volcanic rock to break down into usable soil nutrients. On the other hand, the ash from a single explosive eruption can greatly increase the fertility of soil in only a few years and can keep the soil fertile for centuries.

internetconnect

SCLINKS
NSTA

TOPIC: Volcanic Eruptions
GO TO: www.scilinks.org
*sci*LINKS NUMBER: HSTE205

Pyroclastic Material Pyroclastic material is produced when magma explodes from a volcano and solidifies in the air. It is also produced when existing rock is shattered by powerful eruptions. It comes in a variety of sizes, from boulders the size of houses to particles so small they can remain suspended in the atmosphere for years. The photographs on this page show four major kinds of pyroclastic material: volcanic bombs, volcanic blocks, lapilli (luh PILL ee), and volcanic ash.

Volcanic blocks *are the largest pieces of pyroclastic material. They consist of solid rock blasted out of the volcano.*

Volcanic bombs *are large blobs of magma that harden in the air. The shape of the bomb shown here resulted from the magma's spinning through the air as it cooled.*

Lapilli, *which means "little stones" in Italian, are pebble-like bits of magma that became solid before they hit the ground.*

Volcanic ash *forms when the gases in stiff magma expand rapidly and the walls of the gas bubbles explode into tiny glasslike slivers.*

SECTION REVIEW

1. Is a nonexplosive volcanic eruption more likely to produce lava or pyroclastic material? Explain.

2. If a volcano contained magma with small proportions of water and silica, would you predict a nonexplosive eruption or an explosive one? Why?

3. **Making Inferences** Pyroclastic material is classified primarily by the size of the particles. What is the basis for classifying lava?

▼ **Answers to Section Review**

1. A nonexplosive eruption is more likely to produce lava than pyroclastic material because lava is thin and runny compared with pyroclastic material.

2. A nonexplosive eruption should result. Water turns to steam, which builds up a great amount of pressure, leading to explosive eruptions. Silica-rich magma is thick, allowing it to trap volcanic gases, such as steam, causing explosive eruptions.

3. Lava is classified according to how it flows. Blocky lava is thickest and flows very slowly because it is mostly solidified. *Aa* lava is still thick but is made of smaller blocks and thus flows faster than blocky lava. *Pahoehoe* lava is thin and runny, and it flows quickly, forming a ropy texture. Pillow lava forms under water.

Volcanoes' Effects on Earth

Terms to Learn

shield volcano   crater
cinder cone volcano   caldera
composite volcano

What You'll Do

- Describe the effects that volcanoes have on Earth.
- Compare the different types of volcanoes.

The effects of volcanic eruptions can be seen both on land and in the air. Heavier pyroclastic materials fall to the ground, causing great destruction, while ash and escaping gases affect global climatic patterns. Volcanoes also build mountains and plateaus that become lasting additions to the landscape.

An Explosive Impact

Because it is thrown high into the air, ash ejected during explosive volcanic eruptions can have widespread effects. The ash can block out the sun for days over thousands of square kilometers. Volcanic ash can blow down trees and buildings and can blanket nearby towns with a fine powder.

Flows and Fallout As shown in **Figure 4,** clouds of hot ash can flow rapidly downhill like an avalanche, choking and searing every living thing in their path. Sometimes large deposits of ash mix with rainwater or the water from melted glaciers during an eruption. With the consistency of wet cement, the mixture flows downhill, picking up boulders, trees, and buildings along the way. As volcanic ash falls to the ground, the effects can be devastating. Buildings may collapse under the weight of so much ash. Ash can also dam up river valleys, resulting in massive floods. And although ash is an effective plant fertilizer, too much ash can smother crops, causing food shortages and loss of livestock.

Figure 4 *During the 1991 eruption of Mount Pinatubo, in the Philippines, clouds of volcanic gases and ash sped downhill at up to 250 km/h.*

Climatic Changes In large-scale eruptions, volcanic ash, along with sulfur-rich gases, can reach the upper atmosphere. As the ash and gases spread around the globe, they can block out enough sunlight to cause the average global surface temperature to drop noticeably. The eruption of Mount Pinatubo in 1991 caused average global temperatures to drop by as much as 0.5°C. Although this may not seem like a large change in temperature, such a shift can disrupt climates all over the world. The lower average temperatures may last for several years, bringing wetter, milder summers and longer, harsher winters.

153

SCIENTISTS AT ODDS

Today most scientists think that dinosaurs became extinct 65 million years ago when a large asteroid struck Earth. But a small group of volcanologists have a controversial hypothesis that the gases and ash released from a series of large volcanic eruptions may have caused the extinction. Encourage students to find out more about these theories.

CONNECT TO ASTRONOMY

Early astronomers thought that the dark patches on the moon were lunar seas, but today we know that they are basins filled with solidified lava that erupted after the moon's formation. Have students research volcanism on another planet or moon in our solar system.

MEETING INDIVIDUAL NEEDS

Writing **Learners Having Difficulty** Have students copy descriptive phrases about the three types of volcanoes in their ScienceLog. Beside the entries, have them draw a cross section of each type of volcano. Students should find an example of each volcano type and write three paragraphs about it. The paragraphs should describe how the volcano fits its category, detail its last eruption, and explain how the volcano's shape is linked to the way it erupted.

Sheltered English

MEETING INDIVIDUAL NEEDS

Advanced Learners In 1943, Dominic Pulido, a farmer in central Mexico, was working in his cornfield when the ground began to tremble and a noise like thunder filled the air. Pulido discovered a fissure in the field about 0.5 m deep. The ground began to swell and formed a mound 2.5 m high! A volcano named Paricutín was being born. In one year, the cinder cone volcano grew to 334 m high! Encourage students to read *Hill of Fire*, by Thomas P. Lewis, and write a book report about it.

Teaching Transparency 134 "Three Types of Volcanoes"

Problem Solving Worksheet "Eruption Disruption"

Different Types of Volcanoes

The lava and pyroclastic material that erupt from volcanoes create a variety of landforms. Perhaps the best known of all volcanic landforms are the volcanoes themselves. Volcanoes result from the buildup of rock around a vent. Three basic types of volcanoes are illustrated in **Figure 5.**

Figure 5   Three Types of Volcanoes

Shield volcano

Cinder cone volcano

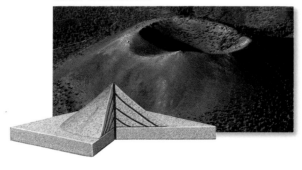

Composite volcano

Shield volcanoes are built out of layers of lava from repeated nonexplosive eruptions. Because the lava is very runny, it spreads out over a wide area. Over time, the layers of lava create a volcano with gently sloping sides. Although their sides are not very steep, shield volcanoes can be enormous. Hawaii's Mauna Kea, the shield volcano shown here, is the largest mountain on Earth. Measured from its base on the sea floor, Mauna Kea is taller than Mount Everest, the tallest mountain on land.

Cinder cone volcanoes are small volcanic cones made entirely of pyroclastic material from moderately explosive eruptions. The pyroclastic material forms steeper slopes with a narrower base than the lava flows of shield volcanoes, as you can see in this photo of the volcano Paricutín, in Mexico. Cinder cone volcanoes usually erupt for only a short time and often occur in clusters, commonly on the sides of shield and composite volcanoes. They erode quickly because the pyroclastic particles are not cemented together by lava.

Composite volcanoes, sometimes referred to as *stratovolcanoes,* are one of the most common types of volcanoes. They form by explosive eruptions of pyroclastic material followed by quieter outpourings of lava. The combination of both types of eruptions forms alternating layers of pyroclastic material and lava. Composite volcanoes, such as Japan's Mount Fuji, shown here, have broad bases and sides that get steeper toward the summit.

154

CROSS-DISCIPLINARY FOCUS

History One of World War II's fiercest battles was fought on the volcanic island of Iwo Jima. More than 6,000 Allied soldiers and 20,000 Japanese soldiers died fighting for an island about 8 km long and 4 km wide. Have students research the battle of Iwo Jima and prepare a map to show why this volcanic island was difficult to capture.

IS THAT A FACT!

The fastest lava flow recorded moved at a speed of 60 km/h—about the same speed as a champion thoroughbred racehorse.

Craters and Calderas

At the top of the central vent in most volcanoes is a funnel-shaped pit called a **crater.** (Craters are also the circular pits made by meteorite impacts.) The photograph of the cinder cone on the previous page shows a well-defined crater. A crater's funnel shape results from explosions of material out of the vent as well as the collapse of material from the crater's rim back into the vent. A **caldera** forms when a magma chamber that supplies material to a volcano empties and its roof collapses. This causes the ground to sink, leaving a large, circular depression, as shown in **Figure 6.**

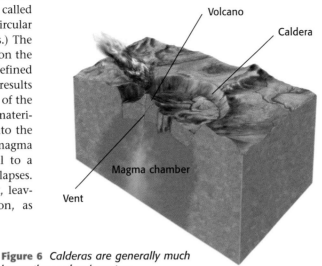

Volcano

Caldera

Magma chamber

Vent

Figure 6 *Calderas are generally much larger than volcanic craters.*

Lava Plateaus

The most massive outpourings of lava do not come from individual volcanoes. Most of the lava on Earth's continents erupts from long cracks, or *fissures,* in the crust. In this non-explosive type of eruption, runny lava pours from a series of fissures and may spread evenly over thousands of square kilometers. The resulting landform is known as a *lava plateau.* The Columbia River Plateau, a lava plateau that formed about 15 million years ago, can be found in the northwestern United States.

SECTION REVIEW

1. Briefly explain why the ash from a volcanic eruption can be hazardous.

2. Why do cinder cone volcanoes have narrower bases and steeper sides than shield volcanoes?

3. **Comparing Concepts** Briefly describe the difference between a crater and a caldera.

internetconnect

SC/LINKS
NSTA

TOPIC: Volcanic Effects
GO TO: www.scilinks.org
*sci*LINKS NUMBER: HSTE210

▼ *Answers to Section Review*

1. Answers will vary. Volcanic ash is hazardous when it dams rivers, causing floods, and when it smothers crops, resulting in food shortages.

2. Shield volcanoes are made of lava flows, which are thin and runny, and spread out over large areas. Cinder cone volcanoes are made of pyroclastic material, which is thick and piles up around the volcano.

3. A crater forms when the rock around the main vent of a volcano is blasted out in an explosive eruption, forming an inverted cone-shaped depression. Most volcanoes have craters at their summits. A caldera forms when the magma chamber that feeds a volcano empties. When this happens, the roof of the magma chamber collapses, forming a circular depression. Calderas are usually much larger than craters.

Have students form pairs and search books, magazines, or Internet sites for pictures of craters, calderas, and lava plateaus. Have pairs use their findings to make a model of one of these features. **Sheltered English**

3) Close

Quiz

1. Describe the shapes of shield, cinder cone, and composite volcanoes. (shield volcano: broad area with gentle shallow slopes; cinder cone volcano: generally smaller, steeper, more angled sides; composite volcano: high, covers less area than shield volcanoes, has sides that become steeper as they near the crater)

2. What causes a caldera? (A volcano's magma chamber empties, causing the ground above it to collapse.)

3. What is a lava plateau? (a layered formation caused when lava erupts from long cracks, or fissures, and covers a wide area)

ALTERNATIVE ASSESSMENT

 Have students draw a poster of an explosive volcano. Have them illustrate flows, fallout, and a crater or caldera. Students must label and write a caption for all the volcano's parts.

 Teaching Transparency 135 "The Formation of a Caldera"

Reinforcement Worksheet "A Variety of Volcanoes"

Section 2 • Volcanoes' Effects on Earth   **155**

SECTION 3

Focus

What Causes Volcanoes?

In this section, students learn how magma forms and how pressure and heat affect the temperature at which rocks melt. The section draws a connection between volcanic activity and tectonic movement and concludes with a discussion of the challenges involved in predicting eruptions.

Bellringer

Ask students to imagine they live on a volcanic island. Have them list in their ScienceLog the signals that would tell them the volcano was about to erupt.

1) Motivate

DISCUSSION

Have students brainstorm about measures a community could take to protect citizens from a volcanic eruption and then write their ideas in their ScienceLog. Have them compare their suggestions with the information they learn in the chapter.
Sheltered English

Teaching Transparency 135
"The Formation of Magma"

Directed Reading Worksheet Section 3

Terms to Learn
rift   hot spot

What You'll Do
- Describe the formation and movement of magma.
- Explain the relationship between volcanoes and plate tectonics.
- Summarize the methods scientists use to predict volcanic eruptions.

QuickLab

Reaction to Stress

1. Make a pliable "rock" by pouring 60 mL (¼ cup) of **water** into a **plastic cup** and adding 150 mL of **cornstarch,** 15 mL (1 tbsp) at a time. Stir well after each addition.
2. Pour half of the cornstarch mixture into a **clear bowl.** Carefully observe how the "rock" flows. Be patient—this is a slow process!
3. Scrape the rest of the "rock" out of the cup with a **spoon.** Observe the behavior of the "rock" as you scrape.
4. What happened to the "rock" when you let it flow by itself? What happened when you put stress on the "rock"?
5. How is this pliable "rock" similar to the rock of the upper part of the mantle?

TRY at HOME

156

QuickLab

MATERIALS
- water
- plastic cup
- cornstarch
- stirring stick
- clear bowl
- spoon

What Causes Volcanoes?

Scientists have learned a great deal over the years about what happens when a volcano erupts. Many of the results are dramatic and immediately visible. Unfortunately, understanding what causes a volcano to erupt in the first place is much more difficult. Scientists must rely on models based on rock samples and other data that provide insight into volcanic processes. Because it is so difficult to "see" what is going on deep inside the Earth, there are many uncertainties about why volcanoes form.

The Formation of Magma

You learned in the previous section that volcanoes form by the eruption of lava and pyroclastic material onto the Earth's surface. But the key to understanding why volcanoes erupt is understanding how magma forms. As you can see in **Figure 7,** volcanoes begin when magma collects in the deeper regions of the Earth's crust and in the uppermost layers of the mantle, the zone of intensely hot and pliable rock beneath the Earth's crust.

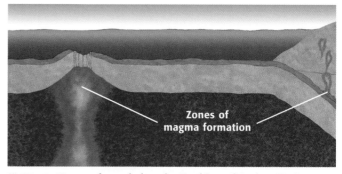
Zones of magma formation

Figure 7 *Magma forms below the Earth's surface in a region that includes the lower crust and part of the upper mantle.*

Pressure and Temperature Although hot and pliable, the rock of the mantle is considered a solid. But the temperature of the mantle is high enough to melt almost any rock, so why doesn't it melt? The answer has to do with pressure. The weight of the rock above the mantle exerts a tremendous amount of pressure. This pressure keeps the atoms of mantle rock tightly packed, preventing the rock from changing into a liquid state. An increase in pressure raises the melting point of most materials.

Answers to QuickLab

4. When left alone, the "rock" flowed like a liquid but very slowly. When pressure was applied by the spoon, the "rock" broke, acting like a solid.

5. Because of the high pressure, the mantle is a solid. But over long periods of time, the mantle flows, acting more like a liquid.

As you can see in **Figure 8,** rock melts and forms magma when the temperature of the rock increases or when the pressure on the rock decreases. Because the temperature of the mantle is relatively constant, a decrease in pressure is usually what causes magma to form.

Density Once formed, the magma rises toward the surface of the Earth because it is less dense than the surrounding rock. Magma is commonly a mixture of liquid and solid mineral crystals and is therefore normally less dense than the completely solid rock that surrounds it. Like air bubbles that form on the bottom of a pan of boiling water, magma will rise toward the surface.

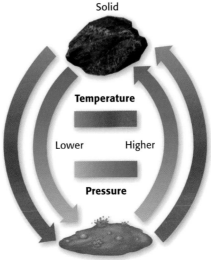

Solid

Temperature

Lower   Higher

Pressure

Liquid

Figure 8 *This diagram shows how both pressure and temperature affect the formation of magma within the mantle.*

> ✔ **Self-Check**
>
> What two factors may cause solid rock to become magma? *(See page 216 to check your answer.)*

Where Volcanoes Form

The locations of volcanoes around the globe provide clues to how volcanoes form. The world map in **Figure 9** shows the location of the world's active volcanoes on land. It also shows tectonic plate boundaries. As you can see, a large number of the volcanoes lie directly on tectonic plate boundaries. In fact, the plate boundaries surrounding the Pacific Ocean have so many volcanoes that these boundaries together are called the *Ring of Fire.*

Why are most volcanoes on tectonic plate boundaries? These boundaries are where the plates either collide with one another or separate from one another. At these boundaries, it is easier for magma to travel upward through the crust. In other words, the boundaries are where the action is!

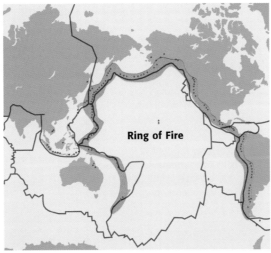

Ring of Fire

Figure 9 *Tectonic plate boundaries are likely places for volcanoes to form. The Ring of Fire contains nearly 75 percent of the world's active volcanoes on land.*

157

Answers to Self-Check

Solid rock may become magma when pressure is released, when the temperature rises above its melting point, or when its composition changes.

② Teach

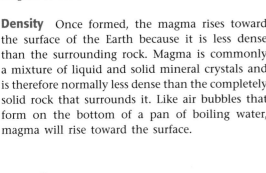

BRAIN FOOD

Igneous rocks form when either magma or lava cools and solidifies. If they are from the same source, often the only difference between the two is the rate at which they cool. Because magma is underground, it cools much more slowly than lava. A molten rock that cools slowly generally has larger crystals than one that cools faster.

How could scientists use this information to study an igneous outcrop? (By studying mineral crystal size and type, scientists can determine the origin of igneous rock.)

CROSS-DISCIPLINARY FOCUS

Geography Point out to students that most volcanic activity takes place on the ocean floor, where vast amounts of lava rise through rifts or volcanoes at diverging plate boundaries. Ask students to identify a spot where plates are diverging. (Sample answer: the Mid-Atlantic Ridge)

What plates are diverging along the Mid-Atlantic Ridge? (the North American and Eurasian plates)

What landmass formed by volcanic activity along this diverging plate boundary? (the island of Iceland)

Then point out to students that Iceland is merely a visible part of the Mid-Atlantic Ridge. Also explain that volcanic eruptions along diverging tectonic plates are generally much less violent than volcanoes typical of convergent boundaries.

REAL-WORLD CONNECTION

 Earthquake tremors are often a warning signal that a volcano is about to erupt. In the months before the explosive eruption of Mount St. Helens, small earthquakes, which grew in number and intensity, shook the area. On March 27, 1980, the volcano began venting steam and ash. Geologists had set up seismometers to record the frequency, location, and magnitude of the quakes. Electronic surveying equipment employed laser beams to measure ground swelling as the lava dome rose. Tiltmeters measured changes in the mountain's slope. Steam gauges recorded water temperatures, pH levels, and amounts of suspended minerals in the waters around the volcano. Gas sensors on the ground and in aircraft monitored hydrogen, carbon dioxide, and sulfur dioxide levels that might signal the movement of magma toward the surface. Have students write a report about the prediction of the Mount St. Helens eruption and the eruption itself.

Answer to MATHBREAK

$°F = \frac{9}{5} \times 1,400°C + 32 = 2,552°F$

Math Skills Worksheet
"Using Temperature Scales"

internetconnect

SCILINKS.
NSTA

TOPIC: What Causes Volcanoes?
GO TO: www.scilinks.org
*sci*LINKS NUMBER: HSTE215

TOPIC: The Ring of Fire
GO TO: www.scilinks.org
*sci*LINKS NUMBER: HSTE220

MATH**BREAK**

How Hot Is Hot?

Inside the Earth, magma can reach a burning-hot 1,400°C! You are probably more familiar with Fahrenheit temperatures, so convert 1,400°C to degrees Fahrenheit by using the formula below.

$$°F = \frac{9}{5}°C + 32$$

What is the magma's temperature in degrees Fahrenheit?

When Tectonic Plates Separate When two tectonic plates separate and move away from each other, a *divergent boundary* forms. As the tectonic plates separate, a deep crack, or **rift,** forms between the plates. Mantle material then rises to fill in the gap. Because the mantle material is now closer to the surface, the pressure on it decreases. This decrease in pressure causes the mantle rock to partially melt and become magma.

Because magma is less dense than the surrounding rock, it rises up through the rift. As the magma rises, it cools down, and the pressure on it decreases. So even though it becomes cooler as it rises, it remains molten because of the reduced pressure.

Magma continuously rises up through the rift between the separating plates and creates new crust. Although a few divergent boundaries exist on land, most are located on the ocean floor. There they produce long mountain chains called mid-ocean spreading centers, or *mid-ocean ridges.* **Figure 10** shows the process of forming such an underwater mountain range at a divergent boundary.

Figure 10 How Magma Forms at a Divergent Boundary

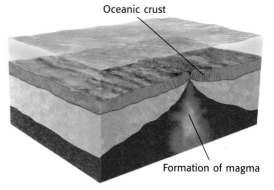

1 *Mantle material rises to fill the space opened by separating tectonic plates. As the pressure decreases, the mantle begins to melt.*

Oceanic crust

Formation of magma

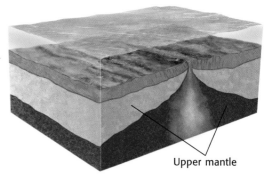

2 *Because magma is less dense than the surrounding rock, it rises toward the surface, where it forms new crust on the ocean floor.*

Upper mantle

Homework

Debate How reliable are volcano warnings? An estimated 500 million people around the world live either on or near a volcano, and each year more than 100 volcanoes erupt on Earth. The potential for an eruption to affect a large number of people is great. Scientists are using tools such as seismographs, laser range finders, and satellites to learn more about volcanoes and volcanic eruptions, but they are still not able to accurately predict volcanic eruptions. Encourage students to research the recent advances in volcano-eruption prediction and debate whether scientists will ever be able to make accurate predictions, and what kinds of technology would make this possible.

When Tectonic Plates Collide

If you slide two pieces of notebook paper into one another on a flat desktop, the papers will either buckle upward or one piece of paper will move under the other. This gives you an idea of what happens when tectonic plates collide. The place where two tectonic plates collide is called a *convergent boundary*.

Convergent boundaries are commonly located where oceanic plates collide with continental plates. The oceanic crust is denser and thinner and therefore moves underneath the continental crust. The movement of one tectonic plate under another is called *subduction*, shown in **Figure 11.**

As the descending oceanic crust scrapes past the continental crust, it sinks deeper into the mantle, getting hotter. As it does so, the pressure on the oceanic crust increases as well. The combination of increased heat and pressure causes the water contained in the oceanic crust to be released. The water then mixes with the mantle rock, which lowers the rock's melting point, causing it to melt.

Hot Spots

Not all magma develops along tectonic plate boundaries. For example, the Hawaiian Islands, some of the most well-known volcanoes on Earth, are nowhere near a plate boundary. The volcanoes of Hawaii and several other places on Earth are known as *hot spots*. **Hot spots** are places on the Earth's surface that are directly above columns of rising magma, called *mantle plumes*. Mantle plumes begin deep in the Earth, possibly at the boundary between the mantle and the core. Scientists are not sure what causes these plumes, but some think that a combination of heat conducted upward from the core and heat from radioactive elements keeps the plumes rising.

Figure 11 How Magma Forms at a Convergent Boundary

1 *As the oceanic plate moves downward, some of the rock melts and forms magma.*

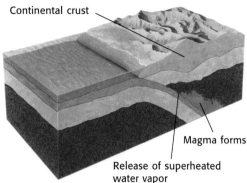

Continental crust

Magma forms

Release of superheated water vapor

2 *When magma is less dense than the surrounding rock, it rises toward the surface.*

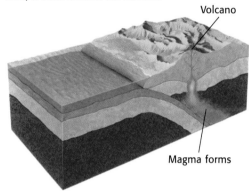

Volcano

Magma forms

159

3) Extend

COOPERATIVE LEARNING

More than 30 earthquakes a year are caused by the movement of magma beneath Mount Rainier, in Washington State. It is the second most seismically active volcano in the Cascade Range, after Mount St. Helens. Because the area around Mount Rainier is so heavily populated, an eruption would endanger thousands of people and destroy property worth millions of dollars. Many groups of people are studying Mount Rainier and preparing for a possible eruption.

Divide the class into groups and give the following assignments:

- **Research Group** Members investigate the volcano's history to determine why it has been ranked as a "decade volcano."

- **Early-Warning Group** Members research how the volcano's activity is being monitored with scientific equipment and other methods.

- **Washington State Emergency Management Agency (WaSEMA) Group** Members find out how this state organization plans to help people in case of an eruption.

- **Schools, Police, and Fire Group** This group investigates how local agencies would design a plan for warning and a plan for the aftermath of an eruption.

After the groups research their areas, have them make presentations using posters, models, maps, and graphs.

 **PG 186**
Volcano Verdict

A hot spot often produces a long chain of volcanoes. This is because the mantle plume stays in the same spot, while the tectonic plate above moves over it. The Hawaiian Islands, for example, are riding on the Pacific plate, which is moving slowly to the northwest. **Figure 12** shows how a hot spot can form a chain of volcanic islands.

Figure 12 How a Hot Spot Forms Volcanoes

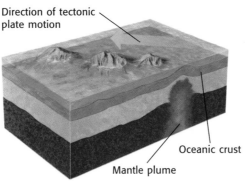
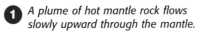
Direction of tectonic plate motion

Oceanic crust

Mantle plume

1 *A plume of hot mantle rock flows slowly upward through the mantle.*

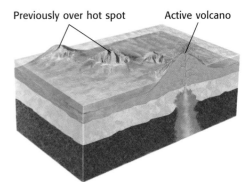
Previously over hot spot   Active volcano

2 *As the tectonic plate moves slowly over the mantle plume, a chain of volcanic islands forms.*

Predicting Volcanic Eruptions

To help predict volcanic eruptions, scientists classify volcanoes based on their eruption histories and on how likely it is that they will erupt again. *Extinct* volcanoes are those that have not erupted in recorded history and probably never will again. *Dormant* volcanoes are those that are not currently erupting but have erupted at some time in recorded history. *Active* volcanoes are those that are in the process of erupting or that show signs of erupting in the very near future.

Measuring Small Quakes Most active volcanoes produce small earthquakes as the magma within them moves upward and causes the surrounding rock to shift. Just before an eruption, the number and intensity of the small earthquakes increase, and the occurrence of quakes may be continuous. These earthquakes are measured with a *seismograph*, as shown in **Figure 13.**

Figure 13 *Seismographs help scientists determine when magma is moving beneath a volcano.*

Measuring Slope Measurements of a volcano's slope also give scientists clues with which to predict eruptions. For example, bulges in the volcano's slope may form as magma pushes against the inside of the volcano. By attaching an instrument called a *tiltmeter* to the surface of the volcano, scientists can detect small changes in the angle of the slope.

160

 Teaching Transparency 137 "How a Hot Spot Forms Volcanoes"

 Reinforcement Worksheet "Tectonic Plate Movement"

Homework

 PORTFOLIO There are volcanic hot spots in Yellowstone Park, Easter Island, Baja California, Hawaii, the Marquesas, the Canary Islands, Cameroon, Iceland, the Galápagos Islands, and the Samoan Islands. Have each student prepare a report on a hot spot, using maps, models, and details of the hot spot's history.

Measuring Volcanic Gases The outflow of volcanic gases from a volcano can also help scientists predict eruptions. Some scientists think that the ratio of certain gases, especially that of sulfur dioxide (SO_2) to carbon dioxide (CO_2), is important in predicting eruptions. They know that when this ratio changes, it is an indication that things are changing in the magma chamber down below! As you can see in **Figure 14,** collecting this type of data is often dangerous.

Measuring Temperature from Orbit Some of the newest methods scientists are using to predict volcanic eruptions rely on satellite images. Many of these images record infrared radiation, which allows scientists to measure changes in temperature over time. They are taken from satellites orbiting more than 700 km above the Earth. By analyzing images taken at different times, scientists can determine if the site is getting hotter as magma pushes closer to the surface.

Figure 14 *As if getting this close to an active volcano is not dangerous enough, the gases that are being collected here are extremely poisonous.*

SECTION REVIEW

1. How does pressure determine whether the mantle is solid or liquid?

2. Describe a technology scientists use to predict volcanic eruptions.

3. **Interpreting Illustrations** Figure 9, shown earlier in this chapter, shows the locations of active volcanoes on land. Describe where on the map you would plot the location of underwater volcanoes and why. (Do not write in this book.)

internetconnect

SCI*LINKS*
NSTA

TOPIC: What Causes Volcanoes?
GO TO: www.scilinks.org
*sci***LINKS NUMBER:** HSTE215

Calling an Evacuation?

Although scientists have learned a lot about volcanoes, they cannot predict eruptions with total accuracy. Sometimes there are warning signs before an eruption, but often there are none. Imagine that you are the mayor of a town near a large volcano, and a geologist

warns you that an eruption is probable. You realize that ordering an evacuation of your town could be an expensive embarrassment if the volcano doesn't erupt. But if you decide to keep quiet, people could be in serious danger if the volcano does erupt. Considering the social and economic consequences of your decision, your job is perhaps even more difficult. What would you do?

161

RESEARCH

The International Association of Volcanology and Chemistry of the Earth's Interior (IAVCEI) has declared 15 volcanoes to be "decade volcanoes," or volcanoes that pose enough danger that they warrant focused scientific attention. Have students prepare reports on the decade-volcano program. They may research IAVCEI's criteria, the designated volcanoes, a particular volcano's history, and monitoring and research of the volcano.

4) Close

Quiz

1. What conditions make magma rise? (when magma is less dense than the surrounding rock and when it has a conduit to move up through)

2. Define a rift. (a series of deep cracks that occur where tectonic plates separate)

ALTERNATIVE ASSESSMENT

Post a map of the world on the bulletin board that shows the location of tectonic plates. Have volunteers use pins and string to outline the plates on the map. Have other students use flagged pins to mark the location of the volcanoes they learned about in this chapter. Then pair students, and have partners explain how tectonic plate boundaries and volcanoes are related. Each partner should evaluate the other's understanding by assessing their descriptions of rifts, converging tectonic plates, diverging tectonic plates, subduction, hot spots, and magma formation.

▼ *Answers to Section Review*

1. Where there is enough pressure on the mantle, the atoms in the rock are forced to stay close together, keeping it solid. Where this pressure is released, mantle rock melts.

2. Answers will vary but should include a discussion of one of the following: measuring changes in the frequency of small earthquakes near the volcano; measuring changes in the slope of the volcano; measuring changes in the ratios of different volcanic gases over time; and measuring changes in how much thermal energy escapes a volcano by using infrared satellite images.

3. Underwater volcanoes should appear along the margins of all tectonic plates. Most volcanic activity happens at tectonic plate boundaries.

Some Go "Pop," Some Do Not
Teacher's Notes

Time Required

One or two 45-minute class periods

Lab Ratings

EASY ————————→ HARD

TEACHER PREP 🧪🧪
STUDENT SET-UP 🧪
CONCEPT LEVEL 🧪🧪🧪
CLEAN UP 🧪

MATERIALS

The materials listed on the student page are enough for one student. Students may wish to use tracing paper in step 1.

Preparation Notes

From the unit, students should be aware that volcanoes with a high water and silica content tend to erupt explosively. They should use this information to analyze the data in this activity. You may also wish to inform students that, in general, quietly erupting volcanoes are derived from basaltic crust, while explosively erupting volcanoes are derived from granitic crust. Oceanic crust is basaltic and low in silica. Continental crust is granitic and high in silica.

Students may need some practice finding locations using latitude and longitude. If necessary, guide them through the steps needed to locate the first volcano on the chart.

Discovery Lab

Some Go "Pop," Some Do Not

Volcanic eruptions range from mild to violent. When volcanoes erupt, the rocks left behind provide information to scientists studying Earth's crust. Mild, or nonexplosive, eruptions produce lava that is low in silica and has a low viscosity. In nonexplosive eruptions, lava simply flows down the side of the volcano. Explosive eruptions, on the other hand, do not produce much lava. Instead, the explosions hurl ash and debris into the air. The rocks left behind are light in color, are high in silica, and have a high viscosity. These rocks help geologists find out what the crust below the volcanoes is made of.

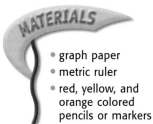
MATERIALS

- graph paper
- metric ruler
- red, yellow, and orange colored pencils or markers

Procedure

1. Copy the map on the next page onto graph paper or recreate it using a computer. Be sure to line the grid up properly.

2. Locate each volcano from the list by drawing a circle with a diameter of about 1 cm in the proper location on your copy of the map. Use the latitude and longitude grids to help you.

3. Review all the eruptions for each volcano. For each explosive eruption, color the circle red. For each quiet volcano, color the circle yellow. For volcanoes that have erupted in both ways, color the circle orange.

Analysis

4. According to your map, where are volcanoes that always have nonexplosive eruptions located?

5. Where are volcanoes that always erupt explosively located? Where are volcanoes that erupt in both ways located?

6. If volcanoes get their magma from the crust below them, what can you infer about the silica content of Earth's crust under the oceans?

7. What is the composition of the crust under the continents? How do we know?

8. What is the source of rocks for volcanoes that erupt in both ways? How do you know?

9. Do the locations of volcanoes that erupt in both ways make sense based on your answers to items 7 and 8? Explain.

162

Datasheets for LabBook

C. John Graves
Monforton Middle School
Bozeman, Montana

Volcanic Activity Chart

Volcano name	Location	Description
Mount St. Helens	46°N 122°W	An explosive eruption blew the top off the mountain. Light-colored ash covered thousands of square kilometers. Another eruption sent a lava flow down the southeast side of the mountain.
Kilauea	19°N 155°W	One small eruption sent a lava flow along 12 km of highway.
Rabaul caldera	4°S 152°E	Explosive eruptions have caused tsunamis and have left 1–2 m of ash on nearby buildings.
Popocatépetl	19°N 98°W	During one explosion, Mexico City closed the airport for 14 hours because huge columns of ash made it too difficult for pilots to see. Eruptions from this volcano have also caused damaging avalanches.
Soufriere Hills	16°N 62°W	Small eruptions have sent lava flows down the hills. Other explosive eruptions have sent large columns of ash into the air.
Long Valley caldera	37°N 119°W	Explosive eruptions have sent ash into the air.
Okmok	53°N 168°W	Recently, there have been slow lava flows from this volcano. Twenty-five hundred years ago, ash and debris exploded from the top of this volcano.
Pavlof	55°N 161°W	Eruption clouds have been sent 200 m above the summit. Eruptions have sent ash columns 10 km into the air. Occasionally, small eruptions have caused lava flows.
Fernandina	42°N 12°E	Eruptions have ejected large blocks of rock from this volcano.
Mount Pinatubo	15°N 120°E	Ash and debris from an explosive eruption destroyed homes, crops, and roads within 52,000 km^2 around the volcano.

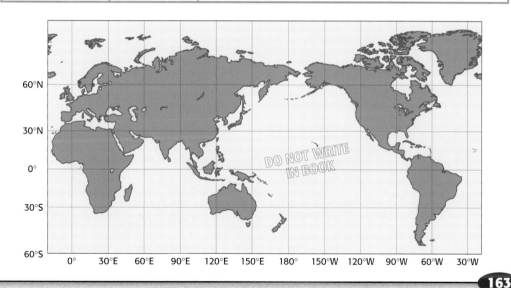

DO NOT WRITE IN BOOK

163

Lab Notes

In a very simple way, this lab models how the composition of magma can evolve. For example, basaltic (mafic) magma can evolve into granitic (felsic) magma through chemical differentiation processes. Scientists often use measurements of trace elements in the resulting rock to "fingerprint" the source of magma from which volcanic rocks formed.

Answers

4. Nonexplosive volcanoes are usually located on oceanic crust.

5. Explosive volcanoes are usually located on continental crust. Volcanoes that erupt in both ways are usually located near boundaries between oceanic and continental crust.

6. The crust under the oceans must be low in silica. Students may also know that the crust is likely to be made of basalt.

7. Continental crust is generally high in silica. Students may also know that the crust is likely to be made of granite.

8. The volcanoes that erupt in both ways must be near the boundary between the oceanic crusts and the continental crusts. The crust must have both basalt and granite.

9. The volcanoes that erupt in both ways are located near the boundaries between continents and oceans. Students should understand that two different crusts must meet in these areas and that both granitic (felsic) and basaltic (mafic) magma is generated.

Chapter Highlights

Chapter Highlights

VOCABULARY DEFINITIONS

SECTION 1

volcano a mountain that forms when molten rock, called magma, is forced to the Earth's surface

lava magma that flows onto the Earth's surface

pyroclastic material fragments of rock that are created by explosive volcanic eruptions

SECTION 2

shield volcano a large, gently sloped volcano that forms from repeated, nonexplosive eruptions of lava

cinder cone volcano a small, steeply sloped volcano that forms from moderately explosive eruptions of pyroclastic material

composite volcano a volcano made of alternating layers of lava and pyroclastic material; also called *stratovolcano*

crater a funnel-shaped pit around the central vent of a volcano

caldera a circular depression that forms when a magma chamber empties and causes the ground above to sink

---

SECTION 1

Vocabulary
volcano (p. 148)
lava (p. 148)
pyroclastic material (p. 151)

Section Notes

- Volcanoes erupt both explosively and nonexplosively.
- The characteristics of a volcanic eruption are largely determined by the type of magma within the volcano.
- The amount of silica in magma determines whether it is thin and fluid or thick and stiff.
- Lava hardens into characteristic features that range from smooth to jagged, depending on how thick the lava is and how quickly it flows.

- Pyroclastic material, or volcanic debris, consists of solid pieces of the volcano as well as magma that solidifies as it travels through the air.

SECTION 2

Vocabulary
shield volcano (p. 154)
cinder cone volcano (p. 154)
composite volcano (p. 154)
crater (p. 155)
caldera (p. 155)

Section Notes

- The effects of volcanic eruptions are felt both locally and around the world.
- Volcanic mountains can be classified according to their composition and overall shape.
- Craters are funnel-shaped pits that form around the central vent of a volcano. Calderas are large bowl-shaped depressions formed by a collapsed magma chamber.

☑ Skills Check

Math Concepts

CONVERTING TEMPERATURE SCALES So-called low-temperature magmas can be 1,100°C. Just how hot is such a magma? If you are used to measuring temperature in degrees Fahrenheit, you can use a simple formula to find out.

$$°F = \frac{9}{5}°C + 32$$

$$°F = \frac{9}{5}(1,100) + 32$$

$$°F = 1,980 + 32 = 2,012$$

$$2,012°F = 1,100°C$$

Visual Understanding

CALDERAS Calderas are caused by the release of massive amounts of magma from beneath the Earth's surface. When the volume of magma decreases, it no longer exerts pressure to hold the ground up. As a result, the ground sinks, forming a caldera.

Lab and Activity Highlights

Some Go "Pop," Some Do Not `PG 162`

Volcano Verdict `PG 186`

Datasheets for LabBook
(blackline masters for these labs)

VOCABULARY DEFINITIONS, *continued*

SECTION 3

rift a deep crack that forms between tectonic plates as they separate

hot spot a place on Earth's surface that is directly above a column of rising magma called a mantle plume

SECTION 2

- In the largest type of volcanic eruption, lava simply pours from long fissures in the Earth's crust to form lava plateaus.

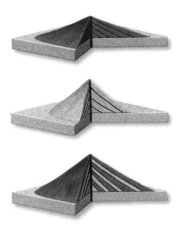

SECTION 3

Vocabulary
rift *(p. 158)*
hot spot *(p. 159)*

Section Notes

- Volcanoes result from magma formed in the mantle.

- When pressure is reduced, some of the solid rock of the already hot mantle melts to form magma.

- Because it is less dense than the surrounding rock, magma rises to the Earth's surface. It either erupts as lava or solidifies in the crust.

- Most volcanic activity takes place along tectonic plate boundaries, where plates either separate or collide.

- Volcanoes also occur at hot spots. Chains of volcanic islands can form when tectonic plates move relative to the hot spot.

- Volcanic eruptions cannot be predicted with complete accuracy. But scientists now have several methods of forecasting future eruptions.

Labs
Volcano Verdict *(p. 186)*

 Vocabulary Review Worksheet

 Blackline masters of these Chapter Highlights can be found in the **Study Guide.**

---

 internetconnect

GO TO: go.hrw.com

Visit the **HRW** Web site for a variety of learning tools related to this chapter. Just type in the keyword:

KEYWORD: HSTVOL

SCiLINKS
NSTA

GO TO: www.scilinks.org

Visit the **National Science Teachers Association** on-line Web site for Internet resources related to this chapter. Just type in the *sci*LINKS number for more information about the topic:

TOPIC: Volcanic Eruptions	*sci*LINKS NUMBER: HSTE205
TOPIC: Volcanic Effects	*sci*LINKS NUMBER: HSTE210
TOPIC: What Causes Volcanoes?	*sci*LINKS NUMBER: HSTE215
TOPIC: The Ring of Fire	*sci*LINKS NUMBER: HSTE220

165

Lab and Activity Highlights

LabBank

 **Whiz-Bang Demonstrations**
- How's Your Lava Life?
- What Makes a Vent Event?

Labs You Can Eat, Hot Spots

Long-Term Projects & Research Ideas,
A City Lost and Found

Interactive Explorations CD-ROM

CD 1, Exploration 4, "What's the Matter?"

Chapter Review Answers

Using Vocabulary

1. A caldera forms when the roof of a magma chamber collapses. A crater forms when the material above the main vent of a volcano is blasted out.

2. Magma is hot, liquid rock material beneath the Earth's surface. Lava is magma that flows out onto the Earth's surface.

3. Lava is mostly liquid and is thin and runny. Lava flows out of a volcanic vent onto the ground. Pyroclastic material is mostly solid rock and is blasted into the air in a violent volcanic eruption.

4. A vent is a hole in the Earth's surface that allows lava or pyroclastic material to erupt. A rift is a long, deep crack in the Earth's surface that forms when tectonic plates separate.

5. A cinder cone volcano forms when pyroclastic material erupts and piles up around the volcanic vent. A shield volcano forms when lava erupts and spreads out over large areas.

Understanding Concepts

Multiple Choice

6. b
7. b
8. b
9. d
10. b
11. c
12. b

Short Answer

13. Answers will vary but should include two of the following: measuring changes in the frequency of small earthquakes near the volcano; measuring changes in the slope of the volcano; measuring changes in the ratios of different volcanic gases over time; and measuring changes in how much thermal energy escapes a volcano by using infrared satellite images.

Chapter Review

USING VOCABULARY

For each pair of terms listed below, explain the difference in their meanings.

1. caldera/crater

2. lava/magma

3. lava/pyroclastic material

4. vent/rift

5. cinder cone volcano/shield volcano

UNDERSTANDING CONCEPTS

Multiple Choice

6. The type of magma that often produces a violent eruption can be described as
   a. thin due to high silica content.
   b. thick due to high silica content.
   c. thin due to low silica content.
   d. thick due to low silica content.

7. When lava hardens quickly to form ropy formations, it is called

   a. aa lava.
   b. pahoehoe lava.
   c. pillow lava.
   d. blocky lava.

8. Volcanic dust and ash can remain in the atmosphere for months or years, causing
   a. decreased solar reflection and higher temperatures.
   b. increased solar reflection and lower temperatures.
   c. decreased solar reflection and lower temperatures.
   d. increased solar reflection and higher temperatures.

9. Mount St. Helens, in Washington, covered the city of Spokane with tons of ash. Its eruption would most likely be described as
   a. nonexplosive, producing lava.
   b. explosive, producing lava.
   c. nonexplosive, producing pyroclastic material.
   d. explosive, producing pyroclastic material.

10. Magma forms within the mantle most often as a result of
    a. high temperature and high pressure.
    b. high temperature and low pressure.
    c. low temperature and high pressure.
    d. low temperature and low pressure.

11. At divergent plate boundaries,
    a. heat from the Earth's core produces mantle plumes.
    b. oceanic plates sink, causing magma to form.
    c. tectonic plates move apart.
    d. hot spots produce volcanoes.

12. A theory that helps to explain the causes of both earthquakes and volcanoes is the theory of
    a. pyroclastics.
    b. plate tectonics.
    c. climatic fluctuation.
    d. mantle plumes.

Short Answer

13. Briefly describe two methods that scientists use to predict volcanic eruptions.

14. Describe how differences in magma affect volcanic eruptions.

15. Along what types of tectonic plate boundaries are volcanoes generally found? Why?

16. Describe the characteristics of the three types of volcanic mountains.

14. Magma that has a high water and silica content will more likely produce a violent volcanic eruption than magma that has a low water and silica content. Water turns to steam, which builds up a great amount of pressure, which leads to explosive eruptions. Silica makes magma thick, allowing it to trap volcanic gases such as water (steam).

15. Volcanoes are generally found along convergent boundaries because in a subduction zone, oceanic crust is forced downward, which adds water to the mantle. The addition of water lowers the mantle rock's melting point. This melted mantle becomes magma that rises to the surface to form volcanoes.

16. Cinder cones are made from a pyroclastic eruption, are small, and have steep sides. Shield volcanoes are made of lava that runs over great distances before it solidifies, making very large, gently sloped volcanoes. Composite volcanoes are made of both

Concept Mapping

17. Use any of the terms from the vocabulary lists in Chapter Highlights to construct a concept map that illustrates the relationship between types of magma, the eruptions they produce, and the shapes of the volcanoes that result.

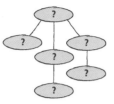

CRITICAL THINKING AND PROBLEM SOLVING

Write one or two sentences to answer the following questions:

18. Imagine that you are exploring a volcano that has been dormant for some time. You begin to keep notes on the types of volcanic debris you encounter as you walk. Your first notes describe volcanic ash, and later your notes describe lapilli. In what direction would you most likely be traveling—toward or away from the crater? Explain.

19. Loihi is a future Hawaiian island in the process of forming on the ocean floor. Considering how this island chain formed, tell where you think the new volcanic island will be located and why.

20. What do you think would happen to the Earth's climate if volcanic activity increased to 10 times its current level?

MATH IN SCIENCE

21. Midway Island is 1,935 km northwest of Hawaii. If the Pacific plate is moving to the northwest at 9 cm/yr, how long ago was Midway Island located over the hot spot that formed it?

INTERPRETING GRAPHICS

The following graph illustrates the average change in temperature above or below normal for a community over several years.

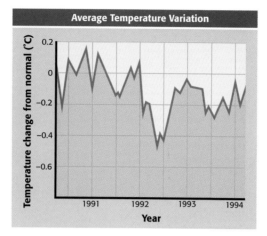

Average Temperature Variation

22. If the variation in temperature over the years was influenced by a major volcanic eruption, when did the eruption most likely take place? Explain.

23. If the temperature were plotted only in yearly intervals rather than several times per year, how might your interpretation be different?

Reading Check-up

Take a minute to review your answers to the Pre-Reading Questions found at the bottom of page 146. Have your answers changed? If necessary, revise your answers based on what you have learned since you began this chapter.

167

lava and pyroclastic material. Composite volcanoes have large, gently sloping bases and steep sides.

Concept Mapping

17. An answer to this exercise can be found in the front of this book.

CRITICAL THINKING AND PROBLEM SOLVING

18. You would be traveling toward the volcano because the larger the pyroclastic material is, the closer it will be to the vent. It takes more energy to move larger particles than it does to move smaller particles.

19. The new island will be located southeast of Hawaii because the Pacific plate is moving toward the northwest.

20. The overall surface temperature of the Earth would decrease because the volcanic ash in the atmosphere would block out much of the sun's energy. (Students may also note that volcanic eruptions release large amounts of CO_2, which could cause longer-term global warming.)

MATH IN SCIENCE

21. 1 km = 1,000 m = 100,000 cm
1,935 km = 193,500,000 cm
193,500,000/9 cm per year = **21,500,000 years**

INTERPRETING GRAPHICS

22. The eruption probably happened in 1992 because that year had the lowest temperature below normal. The volcanic ash that was erupted into the atmosphere blocked the sunlight and lowered the temperature.

23. If the temperature was measured once a year, the graph would indicate that 1991 had the lowest temperature. This would indicate that the eruptions happened in 1991 instead of 1992.

Teaching Strategy

After its mission was completed, the *Dante II* robot was put on display at the Carnegie Science Center in Pittsburgh. The exhibit included information on *Dante II*'s expedition as well as general information on robotics. Have students construct an exhibit for the classroom that serves the same purpose.

You may wish to have students investigate other current applications of robotic technology. For instance, robots are used extensively in industry to perform repetitive or dangerous tasks.

Science, Technology, and Society

Robot in the Hot Seat

Scientists have to be calm, cool, and collected to study active volcanoes. But the recently cooled magma in a volcanic crater isn't the most hospitable location for scientific study. What kind of daredevil would run the risk of creeping along a crater floor? A volcanologist like *Dante II*, that's who!

Hot Stuff

A volcano crater may seem empty after a volcano erupts, but it is in no way devoid of volcanic information. Gases hissing up through the crater floor

▲ *Dante II*

give scientists clues about the molten rock underneath, which may help them understand how and why volcanoes erupt repeatedly. But these gases may be poisonous or scalding hot, and the crater's floor can crack or shift at any time. Over the years, dozens of scientists have been seriously injured or killed while trying to explore volcano craters. Obviously, volcanologists needed some help studying the steamy abyss.

Getting a Robot to Take the Heat

Enter *Dante II*, an eight-legged robot with cameras for eyes and computers for a brain. In 1994, led by a team of scientists from NASA, Carnegie Mellon University, and the Alaskan Volcano Observatory, *Dante II* embarked on its first mission. It climbed into a breach called Crater Peak on the side of Mount Spurr, an active volcano in Alaska. Anchored at the crater's rim by a strong cable, *Dante II* was

controlled partly by internal computers and partly by a team of scientists. The team communicated with the robot through a satellite link and Internet connections. *Dante II* moved very slowly, taking pictures and collecting scientific data. It was equipped with gas sensors that provided continuous readings of the crater gases. It performed the tasks human scientists could not, letting the humans keep their cool.

Mission Accomplished?

During its expedition, *Dante II* encountered large rocks, some of which were as big as the robot itself. In addition, while climbing out of the volcano, *Dante II* slipped and fell, damaging one of its legs. Eventually *Dante II* had to be rescued by helicopter because its support cable broke. Despite these obstacles, *Dante II* was able to gather valuable data from the volcano's crater.

Dante II's mission also met one of NASA's objectives: to prove that robots could be used successfully to explore extreme terrain, such as that found on planetary surfaces. *Dante II* paved the way for later robotic projects, such as the exploration of the surface of Mars by the *Sojourner* rover in 1997.

Write About It

▶ Write a proposal for a project in which a robot is used to explore a dangerous place. Don't forget to include what types of data the robot would be collecting.

168

Answers to Write About It

Accept all reasonable responses. Students may propose that a robot be used to explore a mine, a site contaminated with hazardous waste, or an extraterrestrial environment.

ACROSS THE SCIENCES

EARTH SCIENCE • LIFE SCIENCE

Europa: Life on a Moon?

Smooth and brownish white, one of Jupiter's moons, Europa, has fascinated scientists and science-fiction writers for decades. More recently, scientists were excited by tantalizing images from the Galileo Europa Mission. Could it be that life is lurking (or sloshing) beneath Europa's surface?

An Active History

Slightly smaller than Earth's moon, Europa is the fourth largest of Jupiter's moons. It is unusual among other bodies in the solar system because of its extraordinarily smooth surface. The ridges and brownish channels that criss-cross Europa's smooth surface may tell a unique story—the surface appears to be a slushy combination of ice and water. Some scientists think that the icy ridges and channels are ice floes left over from ancient volcanoes that erupted water! The water flowed over Europa's surface and froze, like lava flows and cools on Earth's surface.

A Slushy Situation

Scientists speculate that Europa's surface consists of thin tectonic plates of ice floating on a layer of slush or water. These plates, which would look like icy rafts floating in an ocean of slush, have been compared to giant glaciers floating in polar regions on Earth.

◀ *Europa looks like a cracked cue ball.*

Where plates push together, the material of the plates may crumple, forming an icy ridge. Where plates pull apart, warmer liquid mixed with darker silicates may erupt toward the surface and freeze, forming the brownish icy channels that create Europa's cracked cue-ball appearance.

Life on Europa?

These discoveries have led scientists to consider an exciting possibility: Does Europa have an environment that could support primitive life-forms? In general, at least three things are necessary for life as we know it to develop—water, organic compounds (substances that contain carbon), and heat. Europa has water, and organic compounds are fairly common in the solar system. But is it hot enough? Europa's slushy nature suggests a warm interior. One theory is that the warmth is the result of Jupiter's strong gravitational pull on Europa. Another theory is that warmth is brought to Europa's surface by convection heating.

So does Europa truly satisfy the three requirements for life? The answer is still unknown, but the sloshing beneath Europa's surface has sure heightened some scientists' curiosity!

If You Were in Charge . . .

▶ If you were in charge of NASA's space-exploration program, would you send a space-craft to look for life on Europa? (Remember that this would cost millions of dollars and would mean sacrificing other important projects!) Explain your answer.

169

Teaching Strategy

The latest information about Europa can be found at the NASA Web site. You could ask students to compare Europa with Callisto or Ganymede, which some scientists believe could also support life.

Answers to If You Were in Charge . . .

Accept all reasonable answers. Factors that students should consider are the tremendous costs associated with sending astronauts on long-term space travel. Even if the spaceship did not carry astronauts, the cost of sending a probe would be more than a hundred million dollars. To pay for a project of that nature, taxes would have to be raised or money would have to be taken from other government programs, such as health care, defense spending, environmental protection, or law enforcement.

SAFETY FIRST!

Exploring, inventing, and investigating are essential to the study of science. However, these activities can also be dangerous. To make sure that your experiments and explorations are safe, you must be aware of a variety of safety guidelines.

You have probably heard of the saying, "It is better to be safe than sorry." This is particularly true in a science classroom where experiments and explorations are being performed. Being uninformed and careless can result in serious injuries. Don't take chances with your own safety or with anyone else's.

Following are important guidelines for staying safe in the science classroom. Your teacher may also have safety guidelines and tips that are specific to your classroom and laboratory. Take the time to be safe.

Safety Rules!

Start Out Right

Always get your teacher's permission before attempting any laboratory exploration. Read the procedures carefully, and pay particular attention to safety information and caution statements. If you are unsure about what a safety symbol means, look it up or ask your teacher. You cannot be too careful when it comes to safety. If an accident does occur, inform your teacher immediately, regardless of how minor you think the accident is.

Safety Symbols

All of the experiments and investigations in this book and their related worksheets include important safety symbols to alert you to particular safety concerns. Become familiar with these symbols so that when you see them, you will know what they mean and what to do. It is important that you read this entire safety section to learn about specific dangers in the laboratory.

If you are instructed to note the odor of a substance, wave the fumes toward your nose with your hand. Never put your nose close to the source.

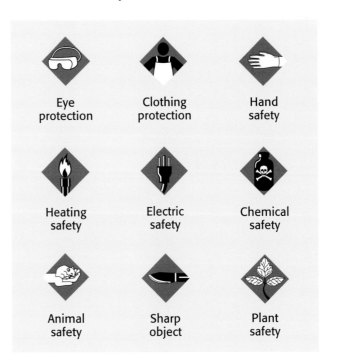

Eye protection

Clothing protection

Hand safety

Heating safety

Electric safety

Chemical safety

Animal safety

Sharp object

Plant safety

Eye Safety

Wear safety goggles when working around chemicals, acids, bases, or any type of flame or heating device. Wear safety goggles any time there is even the slightest chance that harm could come to your eyes. If any substance gets into your eyes, notify your teacher immediately, and flush your eyes with running water for at least 15 minutes. Treat any unknown chemical as if it were a dangerous chemical. Never look directly into the sun. Doing so could cause permanent blindness.

Avoid wearing contact lenses in a laboratory situation. Even if you are wearing safety goggles, chemicals can get between the contact lenses and your eyes. If your doctor requires that you wear contact lenses instead of glasses, wear eye-cup safety goggles in the lab.

Safety Equipment

Know the locations of the nearest fire alarms and any other safety equipment, such as fire blankets and eyewash fountains, as identified by your teacher, and know the procedures for using them.

Be extra careful when using any glassware. When adding a heavy object to a graduated cylinder, tilt the cylinder so the object slides slowly to the bottom.

Neatness

Keep your work area free of all unnecessary books and papers. Tie back long hair, and secure loose sleeves or other loose articles of clothing, such as ties and bows. Remove dangling jewelry. Don't wear open-toed shoes or sandals in the laboratory. Never eat, drink, or apply cosmetics in a laboratory setting. Food, drink, and cosmetics can easily become contaminated with dangerous materials.

Certain hair products (such as aerosol hair spray) are flammable and should not be worn while working near an open flame. Avoid wearing hair spray or hair gel on lab days.

Sharp/Pointed Objects

Use knives and other sharp instruments with extreme care. Never cut objects while holding them in your hands. Place objects on a suitable work surface for cutting.

Heat

Wear safety goggles when using a heating device or a flame. Whenever possible, use an electric hot plate as a heat source instead of an open flame. When heating materials in a test tube, always angle the test tube away from yourself and others. In order to avoid burns, wear heat-resistant gloves whenever instructed to do so.

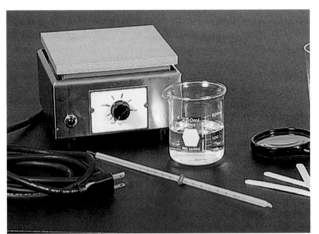

Electricity

Be careful with electrical cords. When using a microscope with a lamp, do not place the cord where it could trip someone. Do not let cords hang over a table edge in a way that could cause equipment to fall if the cord is accidentally pulled. Do not use equipment with damaged cords. Be sure your hands are dry and that the electrical equipment is in the "off" position before plugging it in. Turn off and unplug electrical equipment when you are finished.

Chemicals

Wear safety goggles when handling any potentially dangerous chemicals, acids, or bases. If a chemical is unknown, handle it as you would a dangerous chemical. Wear an apron and safety gloves when working with acids or bases or whenever you are told to do so. If a spill gets on your skin or clothing, rinse it off immediately with water for at least 5 minutes while calling to your teacher.

Never mix chemicals unless your teacher tells you to do so. Never taste, touch, or smell chemicals unless you are specifically directed to do so. Before working with a flammable liquid or gas, check for the presence of any source of flame, spark, or heat.

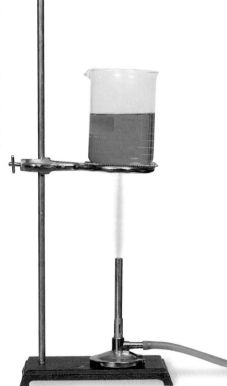

Animal Safety

Always obtain your teacher's permission before bringing any animal into the school building. Handle animals only as your teacher directs. Always treat animals carefully and with respect. Wash your hands thoroughly after handling any animal.

Plant Safety

Do not eat any part of a plant or plant seed used in the laboratory. Wash hands thoroughly after handling any part of a plant. When in nature, do not pick any wild plants unless your teacher instructs you to do so.

Glassware

Examine all glassware before use. Be sure that glassware is clean and free of chips and cracks. Report damaged glassware to your teacher. Glass containers used for heating should be made of heat-resistant glass.

Using the Scientific Method
Teacher's Notes

Time Required
One 45-minute class period

Lab Rating

TEACHER PREP
STUDENT SET-UP
CONCEPT LEVEL
CLEAN UP

MATERIALS
The materials listed on the student page are enough for a pair of students. Students can also work in groups of four. In that case, two students should assume the role of model builders, and the two others should assume the role of core samplers.

Safety Caution
Remind students to review all safety cautions and icons before beginning this lab activity.

Lab Notes
Provide each student group with three pieces of $\frac{1}{2}$ in. PVC pipe cut slightly longer than the height of their models.

Jan Nelson
East Valley Middle School
East Helena, Montana

MAKING MODELS

Using the Scientific Method

Geologists often use a technique called *core sampling* to learn what underground rock layers look like. This technique involves drilling several holes in the ground in different places and taking samples of the underground rock or soil. Geologists then compare the samples from each hole to construct a diagram that shows the bigger picture.

In this activity, you will model the process geologists use to diagram underground rock layers. You will first use modeling clay to form a rock-layer model. You will then exchange models with a classmate, take core samples, and draw a diagram of your classmate's layers.

Materials
- 3 colored pencils or markers
- nontransparent pan or box
- modeling clay in three colors
- 1/2 in. PVC pipe
- plastic knife

Ask a Question

1. Can unseen features be revealed by sampling parts of the whole?

Form a Hypothesis

2. Form a hypotheses on whether taking core samples from several locations will give a good indication of the entire hidden feature.

Test the Hypothesis

3. To test your hypothesis, you will take core samples from a model of underground rock layers, draw a diagram of the entire rock-layer sequence, and then compare your drawing with the actual model.

Build a Model
The model rock layers should be formed out of view of the classmates who will be taking the core samples.

4. Form a plan for your rock layers, and sketch the layers in your ScienceLog. Your sketch should include the three colors in several layers of varying thicknesses.

174

5. In the pan or box, mold the clay into the shape of the lowest layer in your sketch.

6. Repeat step 5 for each additional layer of clay. You now have a rock-layer model. Exchange models with a classmate.

Collect Data

7. Choose three places on the surface of the clay to drill holes. The holes should be far apart and in a straight line. (You do not need to remove the clay from the pan or box.)

8. Use the PVC pipe to "drill" a vertical hole in the clay at one of the chosen locations by slowly pushing the pipe through all the layers of clay. Slowly remove the pipe.

9. Remove the core sample from the pipe by gently pushing the clay out of the pipe with an unsharpened pencil.

10. Draw the core sample in your ScienceLog, and record your observations. Be sure to use a different color of pencil or marker for each layer.

11. Repeat steps 8–10 for the next two core samples. Make sure your drawings are side by side in your ScienceLog in the same order as the samples in the model.

Analyze the Results

12. Look at the pattern of rock layers in each of your core samples. Think about how the rock layers between the core samples might look. Then construct a diagram of the rock layers.

13. Complete your diagram by coloring the rest of the rock layers.

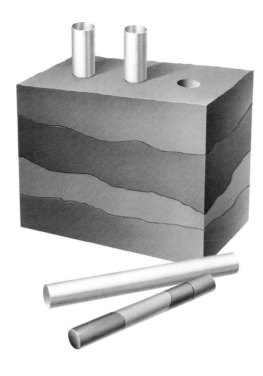

Draw Conclusions

14. Use the plastic knife to cut the clay model along a line connecting the three holes and remove one side of the model. The rock layers should now be visible.

15. How well does your rock-layer diagram match the model? Explain.

16. Is it necessary to revise your diagram from step 13? If so, how?

17. Do your conclusions support your hypothesis? Why or why not?

Going Further

What are two ways that the core-sampling method could be improved?

Answers

15. The rock-layer diagram provides a general overview of the layers. It may not be as specific as the model or provide all the details from the model.

16. Answers will vary. If the model is significantly different than the diagram, students should modify their diagram.

17. Answers will depend on student hypotheses.

Going Further

Answers will vary. Sample answers: More core samples could be taken, the core samples could be taken in specific areas, the core samples could be larger or closer together, or smaller areas could be combined for an overall picture of the layers.

 Datasheets for LabBook

 Science Skills Worksheet "Doing a Lab Write-up"

 Science Skills Worksheet "Using Models to Communicate"

Is It Fool's Gold?— A Dense Situation
Teacher's Notes

Time Required

One 45-minute class period

Lab Ratings

EASY ——————→ HARD

TEACHER PREP ▲▲
STUDENT SET-UP ▲▲▲
CONCEPT LEVEL ▲▲
CLEAN UP ▲▲

MATERIALS

Materials listed on the student page are sufficient for a group of 2–4 students. If your mineral samples are small, the change in volume may be difficult to detect. In that case, replace the beaker in steps 6–7 with a graduated cylinder.

Preparation Notes

Students may need to review density and specific gravity prior to performing this activity.

Lab Notes

- Density is conventionally described as g/cm³, not g/mL.

- Because specific gravity is the ratio of a substance's density to the density of water (1g/cm³), the value will be the same for density. The difference is that specific gravity is a number, and density is a number with the units g/cm³.

- Due to impurities, the density of some minerals is given in ranges. The density of pure gold is 19.3 g/cm³; lower numbers indicate the presence of impurities. The density of

SKILL BUILDER

Is It Fool's Gold?—A Dense Situation

Have you heard of fool's gold? Maybe you've seen a piece of it. This notorious mineral was often passed off as real gold. There are, however, simple tests you can do to keep from being tricked. Minerals can be identified by their properties. Some properties, such as color, vary between different samples of the same mineral. Other properties, such as density and specific gravity, remain consistent from one sample to another. In this activity, you will try to verify the identity of some mineral samples.

Materials

- spring scale
- ring stand
- pyrite sample
- galena sample
- balance
- string
- 400 mL beaker
- 400 mL of water

Ask a Question

1. How can I determine if an unknown mineral is not gold or silver?

Make Observations

2. Copy the data table below into your ScienceLog. Use it to record your observations.

Observation Chart		
Measurement	**Galena**	**Pyrite**
Mass in air (g)		
Weight in air (N)		
Beginning volume of water (mL)		
Final volume of water (mL)		
Volume of mineral (mL)		
Weight in water (N)		

DO NOT WRITE IN BOOK

3. Find the mass of each sample by laying the mineral on the balance. Record the mass of each in your data table.

4. Attach the spring scale to the ring stand.

5. Tie a string around the sample of galena, leaving a loop at the loose end. Suspend the galena from the spring scale, and find its weight in air. Do not remove the sample from the spring scale yet. Enter these data in your data table.

pure silver is 10.5 g/cm³; depending on impurities, that number can be higher or lower.

- Ideally, the values for specific gravity and density obtained in this lab will be identical. Discrepancies will likely result from differences in precision. Students should learn that all scientific measurements involve some margin of error.

CLASSROOM TESTED & APPROVED

Norman Holcomb
Marion Local Schools
Maria Stein, Ohio

6. Fill a beaker halfway with water. Record the beginning volume of water in your data table.

7. Carefully lift the beaker around the galena until the mineral is completely submerged. Be careful not to splash any water out of the beaker! Be sure the mineral does not touch the beaker.

8. Record the new volume and weight in your data table.

9. Subtract the original volume of water from the new volume to find the amount of water displaced by the mineral. This is the volume of the mineral sample itself. Record this value in your data table.

10. Repeat steps 5–9 for the sample of pyrite.

Analyze the Results

11. Copy the data table below into your ScienceLog. **Note:** 1 mL = 1 cm³

12. Use the following equations to calculate the density and specific gravity of each mineral, and record your answers in your data table.

$$\text{Density} = \frac{\text{mass in air}}{\text{volume}}$$

$$\text{Specific gravity} = \frac{\text{weight in air}}{\text{weight in air} - \text{weight in water}}$$

Mineral	Density (g/cm³)	Specific gravity
Silver	10.5	10.5
Galena	*DO NOT WRITE IN BOOK*	
Pyrite		
Gold	19.3	19.3

Draw Conclusions

13. The density of pure gold is 19.3 g/cm³. How can you use this information to prove that your sample of pyrite is not gold?

14. The density of pure silver is 10.5 g/cm³. How can you use this information to prove that your sample of galena is not silver?

15. If you found a gold-colored nugget, how could you find out if the nugget was real gold or fool's gold?

Answers

12.

Mineral	Density (g/cm³)	Specific gravity
Silver	10.5	10.5
Galena	7.4–7.6	7.4–7.6
Pyrite	5	5
Gold	19.3	19.3

13. Because the density of the sample is not 19.3 g/cm³, it is not gold.

14. Because the density of the sample is not 10.5 g/cm³, it is not pure silver. (The sample could contain silver mixed with other minerals.)

15. Sample answer: You could find the density and specific gravity of the gold-colored nugget. If it is pure gold, the density will be 19.3 g/cm³ and the specific gravity will be 19.3, but you would have to perform more tests to prove it was gold. If the sample has a density of 5 g/cm³ and a specific gravity of 5, then it is likely to be pyrite (fool's gold).

 Datasheets for LabBook

Time Required

Two 45-minute class periods

Lab Ratings

EASY —————→ HARD

TEACHER PREP
STUDENT SET-UP
CONCEPT LEVEL
CLEAN UP

MATERIALS

The materials listed are enough for a group of 4–5 students working cooperatively. Using a higher proportion of magnesium sulfate crystals to water will take significantly longer.

Safety Caution

Remind students to review all safety cautions and icons before beginning this lab activity.

Preparation Notes

Samples of igneous rocks may be obtained locally or through various science supply catalogs.

Gordon Zibelman
Drexel Hill Middle School
Drexel Hill, Pennsylvania

Using Scientific Methods

SKILL BUILDER

Crystal Growth

Magma forms deep below the Earth's surface at depths of 25 to 160 km and at extremely high temperatures. Some magma reaches the surface and cools quickly. Other magma gets trapped in cracks or magma chambers beneath the surface and cools very slowly. When magma cools slowly, large, well-developed crystals form. On the other hand, when magma erupts onto the surface, thermal energy is lost rapidly to the air or water. There is not enough time for large crystals to grow. The size of the crystals found in igneous rocks gives geologists clues about where and how the crystals formed.

In this experiment, you will demonstrate how the rate of cooling affects the size of crystals in igneous rocks by cooling crystals of magnesium sulfate at two different rates.

Make a Prediction

1. Suppose you have two solutions that are identical in every way except for temperature. How will the temperature of a solution affect the size of the crystals and the rate at which they form?

Make Observations

2. Put on your gloves, apron, and goggles.

3. Fill the beaker halfway with tap water. Place the beaker on the hot plate, and let it begin to warm. The temperature of the water should be between 40°C and 50°C.
   Caution: Make sure the hot plate is away from the edge of the lab table.

4. Examine two or three crystals of the magnesium sulfate with your magnifying lens. In your ScienceLog, describe the color, shape, luster, and other interesting features of the crystals.

5. Draw a sketch of the magnesium sulfate crystals in your ScienceLog.

Conduct an Experiment

6. Use the pointed laboratory scoop to fill the test tube about halfway with the magnesium sulfate. Add an equal amount of distilled water.

Materials

- heat-resistant gloves
- 400 mL beaker
- 200 mL of tap water
- hot plate
- Celsius thermometer
- magnesium sulfate ($MgSO_4$) (Epsom salts)
- magnifying lens
- pointed laboratory scoop
- medium test tube
- distilled water
- watch or clock
- aluminum foil
- test-tube tongs
- dark marker
- masking tape
- basalt
- pumice
- granite

178

7. Hold the test tube in one hand, and use one finger from your other hand to tap the test tube gently. Observe the solution mixing as you continue to tap the test tube.

8. Place the test tube in the beaker of hot water, and heat it for approximately 3 minutes.
   Caution: Be sure to direct the opening of the test tube away from you and other students.

9. While the test tube is heating, shape your aluminum foil into two small boatlike containers by doubling the foil and turning up each edge.

10. If all the magnesium sulfate is not dissolved after 3 minutes, tap the test tube again, and heat it for 3 more minutes.
    Caution: Use the test-tube tongs to handle the hot test tube.

11. With a marker and a piece of masking tape, label one of your aluminum boats "Sample 1," and place it on the hot plate. Turn the hot plate off.

12. Label the other aluminum boat "Sample 2," and place it on the lab table.

13. Using the test-tube tongs, remove the test tube from the beaker of water, and evenly distribute the contents to each of your foil boats. Carefully pour the hot water in the beaker down the drain. Do not move or disturb either of your foil boats.

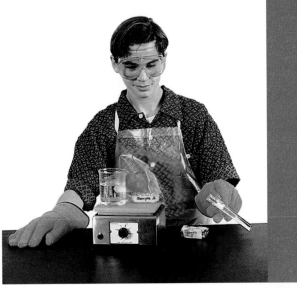

Lab Notes

Some volcanic rocks contain both large and small crystals. This is because the magma cooled for a period of time before erupting. This period of time was long enough for some minerals to crystallize but too short for other minerals to form.

 Datasheets for LabBook

Make Observations

14. Copy the table below into your ScienceLog. Using the magnifying lens, carefully observe the foil boats. Record the time it takes for the first crystals to appear.

Crystal-Formation Table			
Crystal formation	**Time**	**Size and appearance of crystals**	**Sketch of crystals**
Sample 1			
Sample 2			

DO NOT WRITE IN BOOK

Answers

17. Answers will vary. A correct prediction would state that a cool solution will produce crystals more quickly than a warm solution. A correct prediction would also state that the crystals produced in a warm solution will be much larger than those produced in a cool solution.

18. Because the original crystals were small, students may conclude that they formed quickly.

20. Accept all reasonable sketches.

21. See the chart at the bottom of the page.

Going Further

Volcanic rocks that form in the air as the result of a violent volcanic eruption would cool quickly and have small crystals. Volcanic rocks that form from lava oozing out of a volcano would cool more slowly and have larger crystals.

Science Skills Worksheet
"Interpreting Your Data"

15. If crystals have not formed in the boats before class is over, carefully place the boats in a safe place. You may then record the time in days instead of in minutes.

16. When crystals have formed in both boats, use your magnifying lens to examine the crystals carefully.

Analyze the Results

17. Was your prediction correct? Explain.

18. Compare the size and shape of the crystals in Samples 1 and 2 with the size and shape of the crystals you examined in step 4. How long do you think the formation of the original crystals must have taken?

Draw Conclusions

19. Granite, basalt, and pumice are all igneous rocks. The most distinctive feature of each is the size of their crystals. Different igneous rocks form when magma cools at different rates. Examine a sample of each with your magnifying lens.

20. Copy the table below into your ScienceLog, and sketch each rock sample.

21. Use what you have learned in this activity to explain how each rock sample formed and how long it took for the crystals to form. Record your answers in your table.

Igneous Rock Observations			
	Granite	**Basalt**	**Pumice**
Sketch			
How did the rock sample form?			
Rate of cooling			

DO NOT WRITE IN BOOK

Going Further

Describe the size and shape of the crystals you would expect to find when a volcano erupts and sends material into the air and when magma oozes down the volcano's slope.

21.

	Granite	Basalt	Pumice
How did the rock sample form?	when magma cools slowly beneath the Earth's surface	when lava cools quickly on the Earth's surface	when magma is ejected from a volcano during a violent eruption
Rate of cooling	cools slowly; large crystals	cools quickly; small crystals	cools very quickly; very small or no crystals

Metamorphic Mash

Metamorphism is a complex process that takes place deep within the Earth, where the temperature and pressure would turn a human into a crispy pancake. The effects of this extreme temperature and pressure are obvious in some metamorphic rocks. One of these effects is the reorganization of mineral grains within the rock. In this activity, you will investigate the process of metamorphism without being charred, flattened, or buried.

Procedure

1. Flatten the clay into a layer about 1 cm thick. Sprinkle the surface with sequins.

2. Roll the corners of the clay toward the middle to form a neat ball.

3. Carefully use the plastic knife to cut the ball in half. In your ScienceLog, describe the position and location of the sequins inside the ball.

4. Put the ball back together, and use the sheets of cardboard or plywood to flatten the ball until it is about 2 cm thick.

5. Using the plastic knife, slice open the slab of clay in several places. In your ScienceLog, describe the position and location of the sequins in the slab.

Analysis

6. What physical process does flattening the ball represent?

7. Describe any changes in the position and location of the sequins that occurred as the clay ball was flattened into a slab.

8. How are the sequins oriented in relation to the force you put on the ball to flatten it?

9. Do you think the orientation of the mineral grains in a foliated metamorphic rock tells you anything about the rock? Defend your answer.

Going Further

Suppose you find a foliated metamorphic rock that has grains running in two distinct directions. Use what you have learned in this activity to offer a possible explanation for this observation.

Materials

- modeling clay
- sequins or other small flat objects
- plastic knife
- small pieces of very stiff cardboard or plywood

181

Dwight Patton
Carrol T. Welch Middle School
Horizon City, Texas

Going Further

Answers will vary. Two pressures acting on the rock at different times must have pushed on the rock in different directions.

Metamorphic Mash
Teacher's Notes

Time Required
One 45-minute class period

Lab Ratings

EASY ——————————→ HARD

TEACHER PREP 🧪
STUDENT SET-UP 🧪🧪
CONCEPT LEVEL 🧪🧪
CLEAN UP 🧪🧪

MATERIALS
The materials listed in the student page are enough for one student.

Safety Caution

Remind students to review all safety cautions and icons before beginning this lab activity.

Answers

3. The sequins should be lying in a random pattern. Any layering is the result of rolling the ball.

5. The sequins are all horizontal.

6. It represents the pressure that creates metamorphic rock.

7. Before the ball was flattened, the sequins were in a random pattern. Once the ball was flattened, they lined up perpendicular to the pressure.

8. The sequins are aligned perpendicular to the force.

9. Because the grains line up at right angles to the pressure, they are perpendicular to the strongest stress.

 Datasheets for LabBook

Let's Get Sedimental
Teacher's Notes

Time Required

Two 45-minute class periods

Lab Ratings

EASY ——————→ HARD

TEACHER PREP
STUDENT SET-UP
CONCEPT LEVEL
CLEAN UP

MATERIALS

The materials listed are enough for a group of 3–4 students. You may substitute smaller plastic bottles. The amount of sand, gravel, and soil depends on the size of the jar. Each group will need enough of these materials to fill the bottle two-thirds full with a mixture of sand, gravel, and soil.

Safety Caution

Remind students to review all safety cautions and icons before beginning this lab activity. Students should be extremely careful when cutting the sides from the plastic bottles.

Preparation Notes

If the students use larger plastic bottles, it may take several days for the sediment to dry completely. It may be a good idea to ask the students to follow steps 1–5 as an introduction to the chapter. The class can then finish the procedure when the sediment has dried and you have covered all of the concepts in this lab.

Let's Get Sedimental

SKILL BUILDER

How do we determine if sedimentary rock layers are undisturbed? The best way is to be sure that the top of the layer still points up. This activity will show you how to read rock features that say, in effect, "This side up." Then you can look for the signs at a real outcrop.

Procedure

1. Thoroughly mix the sand, gravel, and soil together, and fill the plastic container about one-third full of the mixture.

2. Add water until the container is two-thirds full. Twist the cap back onto the container, and shake the container vigorously until all of the sediment is mixed in the rapidly moving water.

3. Place the container on a tabletop. Using the scissors, carefully cut the top off the container a few centimeters above the water, as shown at right. This will promote evaporation.

4. Do not disturb the container. Allow the water to evaporate. (You may accelerate the process by carefully using the dropper pipet to siphon off some of the clear water after allowing the container to sit for at least 24 hours.)

5. Immediately after you set the bottle on the desk, describe what you see from above and through the sides of the bottle. Do this at least once each day. Record your observations in your ScienceLog.

6. After the sediment has dried and hardened, describe its surface in your ScienceLog.

7. Carefully lay the container on its side, and cut a strip of plastic out of the side to expose the sediments in the bottle. You may find it easier if you place pieces of clay on either side of the bottle to stabilize it.

Materials

- sand
- gravel
- soil (clay-rich, if available)
- 3 L mixing bowl
- plastic pickle jar or 3 L plastic soda bottle with a cap
- water
- scissors
- dropper pipet
- magnifying lens

182

Lab Notes

This lab illustrates the sedimentary (depositional) process of *sorting*. When sediment is suspended in water, the largest, heaviest particles will settle out first, followed by the finer, lighter particles. This process allows scientists and students studying sedimentary rock layers to determine the original orientation of the rock.

Helen Schiller
Northwood Middle School
Taylors, South Carolina

8. Brush away the loose material from the sediment, and gently blow on the surface until it is clean. Examine the surface, and record your observations in your ScienceLog.

Analysis

9. Do you see anything through the side of the bottle that could help you determine if a sedimentary rock is undisturbed? Explain.

10. What structures do you see on the surface of the sediment that you would not expect to find at the bottom?

11. Explain how these features might be used to identify the top of the sedimentary bed in a real outcrop and to decide if the bed has been disturbed.

12. Did you see any structures on the side of the container that might indicate which direction is up?

13. After removing the side of the bottle, use the magnifying lens to examine the boundaries between the gravel, sand, and silt. What do you see? Do the size and type of sediment change quickly or gradually?

Going Further

Explain why the following statement is true: "If the top of a layer can't be found, finding the bottom of it works just as well."

Imagine that a layer was deposited directly above the layers in your container. Describe the bottom of this layer.

Answers

9. Answers will vary. Students should understand that the finest sediments should be at the top layers. This sequence can indicate the top of a sedimentary outcrop. If the layers are not in this order, the rock may have been disturbed.

10. Students might find mud cracks and peels on the top layer. Geologists would not expect to find these features in the bottom of an undisturbed column of sedimentary rock.

11. If features that geologists expect to find only in the top layer are found elsewhere, this indicates that the column has been disturbed. Geologists carefully study the layers for these features so they can determine their original order.

12. Each layer should show finer particles at the top. This pattern can only be seen from the side.

13. Students should see the same grading effect at the boundaries. The changes within each layer will be gradual, but the changes between different layers in the "rock" column may be more dramatic.

Going Further

• Answers will vary. Students should realize that finding the bottom of a layer in an undisturbed column would indicate which direction was down at the time of deposition.

• Students should realize that the bottom of the new layer would match the surface features of the column in their container. Any cracks, for example, would be filled with the new sediment.

 Datasheets for LabBook

Earthquake Waves
Teacher's Notes

Time Required

One 45-minute class period

Lab Ratings

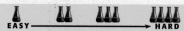

EASY ———→ HARD

TEACHER PREP ▲
STUDENT SET-UP ▲
CONCEPT LEVEL ▲▲▲▲
CLEAN UP ▲

MATERIALS

The materials listed in the student page are enough for two students.

Safety Caution

Remind students to review all safety cautions and icons before beginning this lab activity.

Preparation Notes

Be sure that students understand how to calculate the distance from each city to the epicenter of the earthquake in step 6. These distances must be correct to accurately determine the epicenter of the earthquake on the map.

Emphasize to students that the circles on the map must intersect or come very close to intersecting in order to determine the epicenter of the earthquake. If the circles do not come close to intersecting, tell students that they must check their calculations.

Earthquake Waves

The energy from an earthquake travels as seismic waves in all directions through the Earth. Seismologists can use the properties of certain types of seismic waves to find the epicenter of an earthquake.

P waves travel more quickly than S waves and are always detected first. The average speed of P waves in the Earth's crust is 6.1 km/s. The average speed of S waves in the Earth's crust is 4.1 km/s. The difference in arrival time between P waves and S waves is called *lag time.*

In this activity you will use the S-P-time method to determine the location of an earthquake's epicenter.

Materials

- calculator (optional)
- compass
- metric ruler

Procedure

1. The illustration below shows seismographic records made in three cities following an earthquake. These traces begin at the left and show the arrival of P waves at time zero. The second set of waves on each record represents the arrival of S waves.

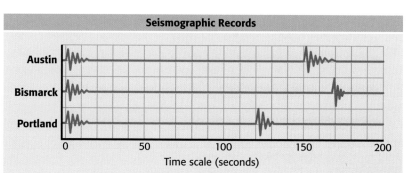

Seismographic Records

Austin

Bismarck

Portland

0   50   100   150   200

Time scale (seconds)

2. Copy the data table on the next page into your ScienceLog.

3. Use the time scale provided with the seismographic records to find the lag time between the P waves and the S waves for each city. Remember, the lag time is the time between the moment when the first P wave arrives and the moment when the first S wave arrives. Record this data in your table.

4. Use the following equation to calculate how long it takes each wave type to travel 100 km:

100 km ÷ average speed of the wave = time

CLASSROOM TESTED & APPROVED

Janel Guse
West Central Middle School
Hartford, South Dakota

5. To find lag time for earthquake waves at 100 km, subtract the time it takes P waves to travel 100 km from the time it takes S waves to travel 100 km. Record the lag time in your ScienceLog.

6. Use the following formula to find the distance from each city to the epicenter:

$$\text{distance} = \frac{\text{measured lag time (s)} \times 100 \text{ km}}{\text{lag time for 100 km (s)}}$$

In your Data Table, record the distance from each city to the epicenter.

7. Trace the map below into your ScienceLog.

8. Use the scale to adjust your compass so that the radius of a circle with Austin at the center is equal to the distance between Austin and the epicenter of the earthquake.

Epicenter Data Table

City	Lag time (seconds)	Distance to the epicenter (km)
Austin, TX		
Bismarck, ND	*DO NOT WRITE*	
Portland, OR	*IN BOOK*	

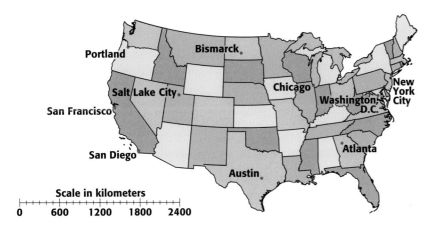

Scale in kilometers
0   600   1200   1800   2400

9. Put the point of your compass at Austin on your copy of the map, and draw a circle.

10. Repeat steps 8 and 9 for Bismarck and Portland. The epicenter of the earthquake is located near the point where the three circles meet.

Analysis

11. Which city is closest to the epicenter?

12. Why do seismologists need measurements from three different locations to find the epicenter of an earthquake?

185

Answers

3. Austin: 150 seconds
   Bismarck: 168 seconds
   Portland: 120 seconds

6. Austin: 1,875 km; Bismarck: 2,100 km; Portland: 1,500 km

11. San Diego, California

12. Seismologists need measurements from three different cities to ensure that the location is accurate. The first two circles intersect in two places. When a third circle is used, all three circles intersect in only one place.

Datasheets for LabBook

Science Skills Worksheet "Grasping Graphing"

Volcano Verdict
Teacher's Notes

Time Required

One 45-minute class period

Lab Ratings

EASY ———————————→ HARD

TEACHER PREP ▲▲
STUDENT SET-UP ▲▲▲
CONCEPT LEVEL ▲▲
CLEAN UP ▲▲

MATERIALS

The materials listed in the student page are sufficient for a pair of students.

Safety Caution

Remind students to review all safety cautions and icons before beginning this lab activity. Students should wear goggles and aprons for this activity.

Preparation Notes

You may want to combine this activity with an activity involving a tiltmeter. Emphasize to students that a gas-emissions tester is just one tool used by volcanologists. These scientists must compare the data gathered through many tests before drawing any conclusions. Other tools include seismographs or satellites that record infrared images of volcanoes over a period of time.

Volcano Verdict

You will need to pair up with a partner for this exploration. You and your partner will act as geologists who work in a city located near a volcano. City officials are counting on you to predict when the volcano will erupt next. You and your partner have decided to use limewater as a gas-emissions tester. You will use this tester to measure the levels of carbon dioxide emitted from a simulated volcano. The more active the volcano is, the more carbon dioxide it releases.

Materials

- 1 L of limewater
- 9 oz clear plastic cup
- graduated cylinder
- 100 mL of water
- 140 mL of white vinegar
- 16 oz drink bottle
- modeling clay
- flexible drinking straw
- 15 mL of baking soda
- 2 sheets of bathroom tissue
- coin
- box or stand for plastic cup

Procedure

1. Put on your safety goggles, and carefully pour limewater into the plastic cup until the cup is three-fourths full. This is your gas-emissions tester.

2. Now build a model volcano. Begin by pouring 50 mL of water and 70 mL of vinegar into the drink bottle.

3. Form a plug of clay around the short end of the straw, as shown below. The clay plug must be large enough to cover the opening of the bottle. Be careful not to get the clay wet.

4. Sprinkle 5 mL of baking soda along the center of a single section of bathroom tissue. Then roll the tissue and twist the ends so that the baking soda can't fall out.

186

Lab Notes

Scientists base their predictions of eruptions on several different kinds of evidence. If a variety of evidence indicates an eruption is imminent, they will recommend evacuation. They are much less likely to make this kind of recommendation if only one kind of evidence suggests an eruption is possible.

CLASSROOM TESTED & APPROVED

Gordon Zibelman
Drexel Hill Middle School
Drexel Hill, Pennsylvania

5. Drop the tissue into the drink bottle, and immediately put the short end of the straw inside the bottle, making a seal with the clay.

6. Put the other end of the straw into the limewater, as shown at right.

7. You have just taken your first measurement of gas levels from the volcano. Record your observations in your ScienceLog.

8. Imagine that it is several days later and you need to test the volcano again to collect more data. Before you continue, toss a coin. If it lands heads up, go to step 9a. If it lands tails up, go to step 9b. Write the step you take in your ScienceLog.

9a. Repeat steps 1–7. This time add 2 mL of baking soda to the vinegar and water. **Note:** You must use fresh water, vinegar, and limewater. Describe your observations in your ScienceLog. Go to step 10.

9b. Repeat steps 1–7. This time add 8 mL of baking soda to the vinegar and water. **Note:** You must use fresh water, vinegar, and limewater. Describe your observations in your ScienceLog. Go to step 10.

Analysis

10. How do you explain the difference in the appearance of the limewater from one trial to the next?

11. What do your measurements indicate about the activity in the volcano?

12. Based on your results, do you think it would be necessary to evacuate the city?

13. How would a geologist use a gas-emissions tester to forecast volcanic eruptions?

Answers

10. Students should realize that carbon dioxide makes the limewater cloudy. If more carbon dioxide is released, the limewater becomes cloudier.

11. The answer to this question depends on which steps the students followed. If the students performed step 9a and used 2 mL of baking soda in the second trial, they should conclude that the volcano is not likely to erupt in the immediate future because it released less gas during the second trial. If the students performed step 9b with 8 mL of baking soda, on the other hand, they should conclude that the volcano is likely to erupt. More gas was released during the second trial, and therefore the pressure must be building.

12. If the students followed step 9a, they should conclude that the city does not need to be evacuated. If they performed step 9b, they should conclude that the city may need to be evacuated.

13. A geologist would use a gas-emissions tester in conjunction with other tests to determine if pressure is building within a volcano. As the pressure builds, the volcano is more likely to erupt.

 Datasheets for LabBook

Concept Mapping: A Way to Bring Ideas Together

What Is a Concept Map?

Have you ever tried to tell someone about a book or a chapter you've just read and found that you can remember only a few isolated words and ideas? Or maybe you've memorized facts for a test and then weeks later discovered you're not even sure what topics those facts covered.

In both cases, you may have understood the ideas or concepts by themselves but not in relation to one another. If you could somehow link the ideas together, you would probably understand them better and remember them longer. This is something a concept map can help you do. A concept map is a way to see how ideas or concepts fit together. It can help you see the "big picture."

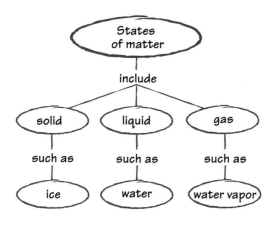

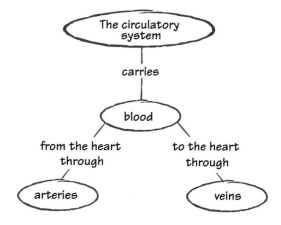

How to Make a Concept Map

❶ Make a list of the main ideas or concepts.

It might help to write each concept on its own slip of paper. This will make it easier to rearrange the concepts as many times as necessary to make sense of how the concepts are connected. After you've made a few concept maps this way, you can go directly from writing your list to actually making the map.

❷ Arrange the concepts in order from the most general to the most specific.

Put the most general concept at the top and circle it. Ask yourself, "How does this concept relate to the remaining concepts?" As you see the relationships, arrange the concepts in order from general to specific.

❸ Connect the related concepts with lines.

❹ On each line, write an action word or short phrase that shows how the concepts are related.

Look at the concept maps on this page, and then see if you can make one for the following terms:

plants, water, photosynthesis, carbon dioxide, sun's energy

One possible answer is provided at right, but don't look at it until you try the concept map yourself.

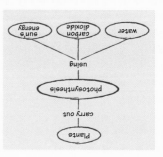

SI Measurement

The International System of Units, or SI, is the standard system of measurement used by many scientists. Using the same standards of measurement makes it easier for scientists to communicate with one another.

SI works by combining prefixes and base units. Each base unit can be used with different prefixes to define smaller and larger quantities. The table below lists common SI prefixes.

SI Prefixes

Prefix	Abbreviation	Factor	Example
kilo-	k	1,000	kilogram, 1 kg = 1,000 g
hecto-	h	100	hectoliter, 1 hL = 100 L
deka-	da	10	dekameter, 1 dam = 10 m
		1	meter, liter
deci-	d	0.1	decigram, 1 dg = 0.1 g
centi-	c	0.01	centimeter, 1 cm = 0.01 m
milli-	m	0.001	milliliter, 1 mL = 0.001 L
micro-	μ	0.000 001	micrometer, 1 μm = 0.000 001 m

SI Conversion Table

SI units	From SI to English	From English to SI
Length		
kilometer (km) = 1,000 m	1 km = 0.621 mi	1 mi = 1.609 km
meter (m) = 100 cm	1 m = 3.281 ft	1 ft = 0.305 m
centimeter (cm) = 0.01 m	1 cm = 0.394 in.	1 in. = 2.540 cm
millimeter (mm) = 0.001 m	1 mm = 0.039 in.	
micrometer (μm) = 0.000 001 m		
nanometer (nm) = 0.000 000 001 m		
Area		
square kilometer (km^2) = 100 hectares	1 km^2 = 0.386 mi^2	1 mi^2 = 2.590 km^2
hectare (ha) = 10,000 m^2	1 ha = 2.471 acres	1 acre = 0.405 ha
square meter (m^2) = 10,000 cm^2	1 m^2 = 10.765 ft^2	1 ft^2 = 0.093 m^2
square centimeter (cm^2) = 100 mm^2	1 cm^2 = 0.155 in.^{2}	1 in.^{2} = 6.452 cm^2
Volume		
liter (L) = 1,000 mL = 1 dm^3	1 L = 1.057 fl qt	1 fl qt = 0.946 L
milliliter (mL) = 0.001 L = 1 cm^3	1 mL = 0.034 fl oz	1 fl oz = 29.575 mL
microliter (μL) = 0.000 001 L		
Mass		
kilogram (kg) = 1,000 g	1 kg = 2.205 lb	1 lb = 0.454 kg
gram (g) = 1,000 mg	1 g = 0.035 oz	1 oz = 28.349 g
milligram (mg) = 0.001 g		
microgram (μg) = 0.000 001 g		

Temperature Scales

Temperature can be expressed using three different scales: Fahrenheit, Celsius, and Kelvin. The SI unit for temperature is the kelvin (K).

Although 0 K is much colder than 0°C, a change of 1 K is equal to a change of 1°C.

Three Temperature Scales

	Fahrenheit	Celsius	Kelvin
Water boils	212°	100°	373
Body temperature	98.6°	37°	310
Room temperature	68°	20°	293
Water freezes	32°	0°	273

Temperature Conversions Table

To convert	Use this equation:	Example
Celsius to Fahrenheit °C ⟶ °F	$°F = \left(\dfrac{9}{5} \times °C\right) + 32$	Convert 45°C to °F. $°F = \left(\dfrac{9}{5} \times 45°C\right) + 32 = 113°F$
Fahrenheit to Celsius °F ⟶ °C	$°C = \dfrac{5}{9} \times (°F - 32)$	Convert 68°F to °C. $°C = \dfrac{5}{9} \times (68°F - 32) = 20°C$
Celsius to Kelvin °C ⟶ K	$K = °C + 273$	Convert 45°C to K. $K = 45°C + 273 = 318\ K$
Kelvin to Celsius K ⟶ °C	$°C = K - 273$	Convert 32 K to °C. $°C = 32\ K - 273 = -241°C$

Measuring Skills

Using a Graduated Cylinder

When using a graduated cylinder to measure volume, keep the following procedures in mind:

1 Make sure the cylinder is on a flat, level surface.

2 Move your head so that your eye is level with the surface of the liquid.

3 Read the mark closest to the liquid level. On glass graduated cylinders, read the mark closest to the center of the curve in the liquid's surface.

Using a Meterstick or Metric Ruler

When using a meterstick or metric ruler to measure length, keep the following procedures in mind:

1 Place the ruler firmly against the object you are measuring.

2 Align one edge of the object exactly with the zero end of the ruler.

3 Look at the other edge of the object to see which of the marks on the ruler is closest to that edge. **Note:** Each small slash between the centimeters represents a millimeter, which is one-tenth of a centimeter.

Using a Triple-Beam Balance

When using a triple-beam balance to measure mass, keep the following procedures in mind:

1 Make sure the balance is on a level surface.

2 Place all of the countermasses at zero. Adjust the balancing knob until the pointer rests at zero.

3 Place the object you wish to measure on the pan. **Caution:** Do not place hot objects or chemicals directly on the balance pan.

4 Move the largest countermass along the beam to the right until it is at the last notch that does not tip the balance. Follow the same procedure with the next-largest countermass. Then move the smallest countermass until the pointer rests at zero.

5 Add the readings from the three beams together to determine the mass of the object.

6 When determining the mass of crystals or powders, use a piece of filter paper. First find the mass of the paper. Then add the crystals or powder to the paper and re-measure. The actual mass of the crystals or powder is the total mass minus the mass of the paper. When finding the mass of liquids, first find the mass of the empty container. Then find the mass of the liquid and container together. The mass of the liquid is the total mass minus the mass of the container.

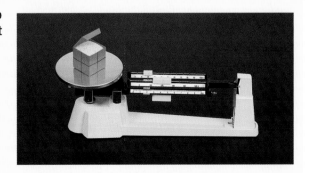

Scientific Method

The series of steps that scientists use to answer questions and solve problems is often called the **scientific method.** The scientific method is not a rigid procedure. Scientists may use all of the steps or just some of the steps of the scientific method. They may even repeat some of the steps. The goal of the scientific method is to come up with reliable answers and solutions.

Six Steps of the Scientific Method

Ask a Question

1 **Ask a Question** Good questions come from careful **observations.** You make observations by using your senses to gather information. Sometimes you may use instruments, such as microscopes and telescopes, to extend the range of your senses. As you observe the natural world, you will discover that you have many more questions than answers. These questions drive the scientific method.

Questions beginning with *what, why, how,* and *when* are very important in focusing an investigation, and they often lead to a hypothesis. (You will learn what a hypothesis is in the next step.) Here is an example of a question that could lead to further investigation.

Question: How does acid rain affect plant growth?

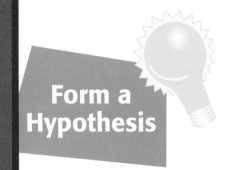

Form a Hypothesis

2 **Form a Hypothesis** After you come up with a question, you need to turn the question into a **hypothesis.** A hypothesis is a clear statement of what you expect the answer to your question to be. Your hypothesis will represent your best "educated guess" based on your observations and what you already know. A good hypothesis is testable. If observations and information cannot be gathered or if an experiment cannot be designed to test your hypothesis, it is untestable, and the investigation can go no further.

Here is a hypothesis that could be formed from the question, "How does acid rain affect plant growth?"

Hypothesis: Acid rain causes plants to grow more slowly.

Notice that the hypothesis provides some specifics that lead to methods of testing. The hypothesis can also lead to predictions. A **prediction** is what you think will be the outcome of your experiment or data collection. Predictions are usually stated in an "if . . . then" format. For example, **if** meat is kept at room temperature, **then** it will spoil faster than meat kept in the refrigerator. More than one prediction can be made for a single hypothesis. Here is a sample prediction for the hypothesis that acid rain causes plants to grow more slowly.

Prediction: If a plant is watered with only acid rain (which has a pH of 4), then the plant will grow at half its normal rate.

3 **Test the Hypothesis** After you have formed a hypothesis and made a prediction, you should test your hypothesis. There are different ways to do this. Perhaps the most familiar way is to conduct a **controlled experiment.** A controlled experiment tests only one factor at a time. A controlled experiment has a **control group** and one or more **experimental groups.** All the factors for the control and experimental groups are the same except for one factor, which is called the **variable.** By changing only one factor, you can see the results of just that one change.

Sometimes, the nature of an investigation makes a controlled experiment impossible. For example, dinosaurs have been extinct for millions of years, and the Earth's core is surrounded by thousands of meters of rock. It would be difficult, if not impossible, to conduct controlled experiments on such things. Under such circumstances, a hypothesis may be tested by making detailed observations. Taking measurements is one way of making observations.

Test the Hypothesis

4 **Analyze the Results** After you have completed your experiments, made your observations, and collected your data, you must analyze all the information you have gathered. Tables and graphs are often used in this step to organize the data.

Analyze the Results

5 **Draw Conclusions** Based on the analysis of your data, you should conclude whether or not your results support your hypothesis. If your hypothesis is supported, you (or others) might want to repeat the observations or experiments to verify your results. If your hypothesis is not supported by the data, you may have to check your procedure for errors. You may even have to reject your hypothesis and make a new one. If you cannot draw a conclusion from your results, you may have to try the investigation again or carry out further observations or experiments.

Draw Conclusions

Do they support your hypothesis?

No

Yes

6 **Communicate Results** After any scientific investigation, you should report your results. By doing a written or oral report, you let others know what you have learned. They may want to repeat your investigation to see if they get the same results. Your report may even lead to another question, which in turn may lead to another investigation.

Communicate Results

Scientific Method in Action

The scientific method is not a "straight line" of steps. It contains loops in which several steps may be repeated over and over again, while others may not be necessary. For example, sometimes scientists will find that testing one hypothesis raises new questions and new hypotheses to be tested. And sometimes, testing the hypothesis leads directly to a conclusion. Furthermore, the steps in the scientific method are not always used in the same order. Follow the steps in the diagram below, and see how many different directions the scientific method can take you.

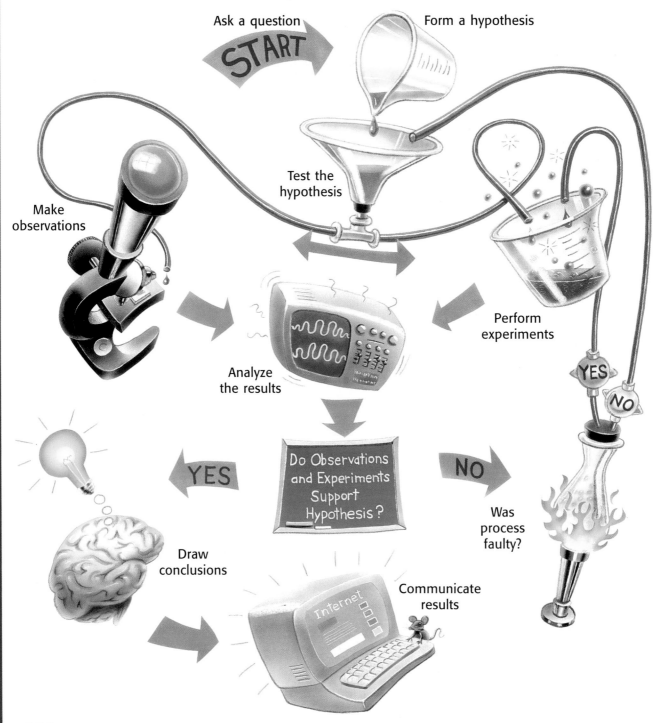

Ask a question — START

Form a hypothesis

Test the hypothesis

Make observations

Perform experiments

Analyze the results

Do Observations and Experiments Support Hypothesis?

YES

NO

YES NO

Was process faulty?

Draw conclusions

Communicate results

Internet

Making Charts and Graphs

Circle Graphs

A circle graph, or pie chart, shows how each group of data relates to all of the data. Each part of the circle represents a category of the data. The entire circle represents all of the data. For example, a biologist studying a hardwood forest in Wisconsin found that there were five different types of trees. The data table at right summarizes the biologist's findings.

Wisconsin Hardwood Trees	
Type of tree	**Number found**
Oak	600
Maple	750
Beech	300
Birch	1,200
Hickory	150
Total	3,000

How to Make a Circle Graph

1 In order to make a circle graph of this data, first find the percentage of each type of tree. To do this, divide the number of individual trees by the total number of trees and multiply by 100.

$$\frac{600 \text{ oak}}{3,000 \text{ trees}} \times 100 = 20\%$$

$$\frac{750 \text{ maple}}{3,000 \text{ trees}} \times 100 = 25\%$$

$$\frac{300 \text{ beech}}{3,000 \text{ trees}} \times 100 = 10\%$$

$$\frac{1,200 \text{ birch}}{3,000 \text{ trees}} \times 100 = 40\%$$

$$\frac{150 \text{ hickory}}{3,000 \text{ trees}} \times 100 = 5\%$$

2 Now determine the size of the pie shapes that make up the chart. Do this by multiplying each percentage by 360°. Remember that a circle contains 360°.

$20\% \times 360° = 72°$ $25\% \times 360° = 90°$
$10\% \times 360° = 36°$ $40\% \times 360° = 144°$
$5\% \times 360° = 18°$

3 Then check that the sum of the percentages is 100 and the sum of the degrees is 360.

$20\% + 25\% + 10\% + 40\% + 5\% = 100\%$
$72° + 90° + 36° + 144° + 18° = 360°$

4 Use a compass to draw a circle and mark its center.

5 Then use a protractor to draw angles of 72°, 90°, 36°, 144°, and 18° in the circle.

6 Finally, label each part of the graph, and choose an appropriate title.

A Community of Wisconsin Hardwood Trees

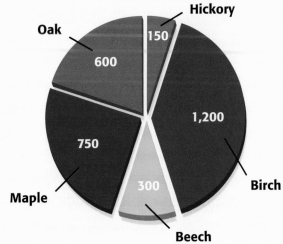

Population of Appleton, 1900–2000	
Year	**Population**
1900	1,800
1920	2,500
1940	3,200
1960	3,900
1980	4,600
2000	5,300

Line Graphs

Line graphs are most often used to demonstrate continuous change. For example, Mr. Smith's science class analyzed the population records for their hometown, Appleton, between 1900 and 2000. Examine the data at left.

Because the year and the population change, they are the *variables*. The population is determined by, or dependent on, the year. Therefore, the population is called the **dependent variable**, and the year is called the **independent variable**. Each set of data is called a **data pair**. To prepare a line graph, data pairs must first be organized in a table like the one at left.

How to Make a Line Graph

❶ Place the independent variable along the horizontal (x) axis. Place the dependent variable along the vertical (y) axis.

❷ Label the x-axis "Year" and the y-axis "Population." Look at your largest and smallest values for the population. Determine a scale for the y-axis that will provide enough space to show these values. You must use the same scale for the entire length of the axis. Find an appropriate scale for the x-axis too.

❸ Choose reasonable starting points for each axis.

❹ Plot the data pairs as accurately as possible.

❺ Choose a title that accurately represents the data.

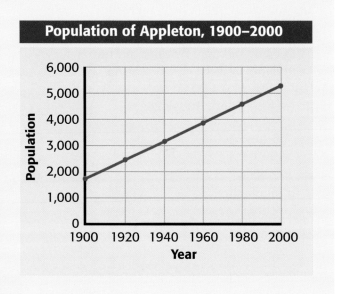

Population of Appleton, 1900–2000

How to Determine Slope

Slope is the ratio of the change in the y-axis to the change in the x-axis, or "rise over run."

❶ Choose two points on the line graph. For example, the population of Appleton in 2000 was 5,300 people. Therefore, you can define point *a* as (2000, 5,300). In 1900, the population was 1,800 people. Define point *b* as (1900, 1,800).

❷ Find the change in the y-axis.
(y at point *a*) − (y at point *b*)
5,300 people − 1,800 people = 3,500 people

❸ Find the change in the x-axis.
(x at point *a*) − (x at point *b*)
2000 − 1900 = 100 years

❹ Calculate the slope of the graph by dividing the change in y by the change in x.

$$\text{slope} = \frac{\text{change in } y}{\text{change in } x}$$

$$\text{slope} = \frac{3,500 \text{ people}}{100 \text{ years}}$$

$$\text{slope} = 35 \text{ people per year}$$

In this example, the population in Appleton increased by a fixed amount each year. The graph of this data is a straight line. Therefore, the relationship is **linear.** When the graph of a set of data is not a straight line, the relationship is **nonlinear.**

Using Algebra to Determine Slope

The equation in step 4 may also be arranged to be:

$$y = kx$$

where y represents the change in the y-axis, k represents the slope, and x represents the change in the x-axis.

$$slope = \frac{change\ in\ y}{change\ in\ x}$$

$$k = \frac{y}{x}$$

$$k \times x = \frac{y \times x}{x}$$

$$kx = y$$

Bar Graphs

Bar graphs are used to demonstrate change that is not continuous. These graphs can be used to indicate trends when the data are taken over a long period of time. A meteorologist gathered the precipitation records at right for Hartford, Connecticut, for April 1–15, 1996, and used a bar graph to represent the data.

Precipitation in Hartford, Connecticut April 1–15, 1996

Date	Precipitation (cm)	Date	Precipitation (cm)
April 1	0.5	April 9	0.25
April 2	1.25	April 10	0.0
April 3	0.0	April 11	1.0
April 4	0.0	April 12	0.0
April 5	0.0	April 13	0.25
April 6	0.0	April 14	0.0
April 7	0.0	April 15	6.50
April 8	1.75		

How to Make a Bar Graph

① Use an appropriate scale and a reasonable starting point for each axis.

② Label the axes, and plot the data.

③ Choose a title that accurately represents the data.

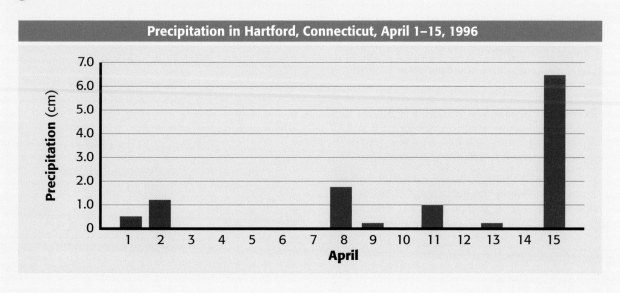

Precipitation in Hartford, Connecticut, April 1–15, 1996

Math Refresher

Science requires an understanding of many math concepts. The following pages will help you review some important math skills.

Averages

An **average**, or **mean**, simplifies a list of numbers into a single number that *approximates* their value.

> **Example:** Find the average of the following set of numbers: 5, 4, 7, and 8.

Step 1: Find the sum.

$$5 + 4 + 7 + 8 = 24$$

Step 2: Divide the sum by the amount of numbers in your set. Because there are four numbers in this example, divide the sum by 4.

$$\frac{24}{4} = 6$$

The average, or mean, is **6.**

Ratios

A **ratio** is a comparison between numbers, and it is usually written as a fraction.

> **Example:** Find the ratio of thermometers to students if you have 36 thermometers and 48 students in your class.

Step 1: Make the ratio.

$$\frac{36 \text{ thermometers}}{48 \text{ students}}$$

Step 2: Reduce the fraction to its simplest form.

$$\frac{36}{48} = \frac{36 \div 12}{48 \div 12} = \frac{3}{4}$$

The ratio of thermometers to students is **3 to 4,** or $\frac{3}{4}$. The ratio may also be written in the form 3:4.

Proportions

A **proportion** is an equation that states that two ratios are equal.

$$\frac{3}{1} = \frac{12}{4}$$

To solve a proportion, first multiply across the equal sign. This is called cross-multiplication. If you know three of the quantities in a proportion, you can use cross-multiplication to find the fourth.

> **Example:** Imagine that you are making a scale model of the solar system for your science project. The diameter of Jupiter is 11.2 times the diameter of the Earth. If you are using a plastic-foam ball with a diameter of 2 cm to represent the Earth, what diameter does the ball representing Jupiter need to be?
>
> $$\frac{11.2}{1} = \frac{x}{2 \text{ cm}}$$

Step 1: Cross-multiply.

$$\frac{11.2}{1} \diagup\!\!\!\!\diagdown \frac{x}{2}$$

$$11.2 \times 2 = x \times 1$$

Step 2: Multiply.

$$22.4 = x \times 1$$

Step 3: Isolate the variable by dividing both sides by 1.

$$x = \frac{22.4}{1}$$

$$x = 22.4 \text{ cm}$$

You will need to use a ball with a diameter of **22.4 cm** to represent Jupiter.

Percentages

A **percentage** is a ratio of a given number to 100.

> **Example:** What is 85 percent of 40?

Step 1: Rewrite the percentage by moving the decimal point two places to the left.

$$_{\curvearrowleft}85$$

Step 2: Multiply the decimal by the number you are calculating the percentage of.

$$0.85 \times 40 = 34$$

85 percent of 40 is **34.**

Decimals

To **add** or **subtract decimals,** line up the digits vertically so that the decimal points line up. Then add or subtract the columns from right to left, carrying or borrowing numbers as necessary.

> **Example:** Add the following numbers: 3.1415 and 2.96.

Step 1: Line up the digits vertically so that the decimal points line up.

$$\begin{array}{r} 3.1415 \\ + \ 2.96 \\ \hline \end{array}$$

Step 2: Add the columns from right to left, carrying when necessary.

$$\begin{array}{r} {\scriptstyle 1\ 1} \\ 3.1415 \\ + \ 2.96 \\ \hline 6.1015 \end{array}$$

The sum is **6.1015.**

Fractions

Numbers tell you how many; **fractions** tell you *how much of a whole.*

> **Example:** Your class has 24 plants. Your teacher instructs you to put 5 in a shady spot. What fraction does this represent?

Step 1: Write a fraction with the total number of parts in the whole as the denominator.

$$\frac{?}{24}$$

Step 2: Write the number of parts of the whole being represented as the numerator.

$$\frac{5}{24}$$

$\frac{5}{24}$ of the plants will be in the shade.

Reducing Fractions

It is usually best to express a fraction in simplest form. This is called *reducing* a fraction.

> **Example:** Reduce the fraction $\frac{30}{45}$ to its simplest form.

Step 1: Find the largest whole number that will divide evenly into both the numerator and denominator. This number is called the greatest common factor (GCF).

factors of the numerator 30: 1, 2, 3, 5, 6, 10, **15,** 30

factors of the denominator 45: 1, 3, 5, 9, **15,** 45

Step 2: Divide both the numerator and the denominator by the GCF, which in this case is 15.

$$\frac{30}{45} = \frac{30 \div 15}{45 \div 15} = \frac{2}{3}$$

$\frac{30}{45}$ reduced to its simplest form is $\frac{2}{3}$.

Adding and Subtracting Fractions

To **add** or **subtract fractions** that have the **same denominator,** simply add or subtract the numerators.

Examples:

$$\frac{3}{5} + \frac{1}{5} = ? \quad \text{and} \quad \frac{3}{4} - \frac{1}{4} = ?$$

Step 1: Add or subtract the numerators.

$$\frac{3}{5} + \frac{1}{5} = \frac{4}{} \quad \text{and} \quad \frac{3}{4} - \frac{1}{4} = \frac{2}{}$$

Step 2: Write the sum or difference over the denominator.

$$\frac{3}{5} + \frac{1}{5} = \frac{4}{5} \quad \text{and} \quad \frac{3}{4} - \frac{1}{4} = \frac{2}{4}$$

Step 3: If necessary, reduce the fraction to its simplest form.

$\frac{4}{5}$ cannot be reduced, and $\frac{2}{4} = \frac{1}{2}$.

To **add** or **subtract fractions** that have **different denominators,** first find the least common denominator (LCD).

Examples:

$$\frac{1}{2} + \frac{1}{6} = ? \quad \text{and} \quad \frac{3}{4} - \frac{2}{3} = ?$$

Step 1: Write the equivalent fractions with a common demominator.

$$\frac{3}{6} + \frac{1}{6} = ? \quad \text{and} \quad \frac{9}{12} - \frac{8}{12} = ?$$

Step 2: Add or subtract.

$$\frac{3}{6} + \frac{1}{6} = \frac{4}{6} \quad \text{and} \quad \frac{9}{12} - \frac{8}{12} = \frac{1}{12}$$

Step 3: If necessary, reduce the fraction to its simplest form.

$\frac{4}{6} = \frac{2}{3}$, and $\frac{1}{12}$ cannot be reduced.

Multiplying Fractions

To **multiply fractions,** multiply the numerators and the denominators together, and then reduce the fraction to its simplest form.

Example:

$$\frac{5}{9} \times \frac{7}{10} = ?$$

Step 1: Multiply the numerators and denominators.

$$\frac{5}{9} \times \frac{7}{10} = \frac{5 \times 7}{9 \times 10} = \frac{35}{90}$$

Step 2: Reduce.

$$\frac{35}{90} = \frac{35 \div 5}{90 \div 5} = \frac{7}{18}$$

Dividing Fractions

To **divide fractions,** first rewrite the divisor (the number you divide *by*) upside down. This is called the reciprocal of the divisor. Then you can multiply and reduce if necessary.

Example:

$$\frac{5}{8} \div \frac{3}{2} = ?$$

Step 1: Rewrite the divisor as its reciprocal.

$$\frac{3}{2} \rightarrow \frac{2}{3}$$

Step 2: Multiply.

$$\frac{5}{8} \times \frac{2}{3} = \frac{5 \times 2}{8 \times 3} = \frac{10}{24}$$

Step 3: Reduce.

$$\frac{10}{24} = \frac{10 \div 2}{24 \div 2} = \frac{5}{12}$$

Scientific Notation

Scientific notation is a short way of representing very large and very small numbers without writing all of the place-holding zeros.

> **Example:** Write 653,000,000 in scientific notation.

Step 1: Write the number without the place-holding zeros.

$$653$$

Step 2: Place the decimal point after the first digit.

$$6.53$$

Step 3: Find the exponent by counting the number of places that you moved the decimal point.

$$6.53000000$$

The decimal point was moved eight places to the left. Therefore, the exponent of 10 is positive 8. Remember, if the decimal point had moved to the right, the exponent would be negative.

Step 4: Write the number in scientific notation.

$$6.53 \times 10^8$$

Area

Area is the number of square units needed to cover the surface of an object.

> **Formulas:**
> Area of a square = side × side
> Area of a rectangle = length × width
> Area of a triangle = $\frac{1}{2}$ × base × height
>
> **Examples:** Find the areas.

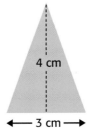

Triangle
Area = $\frac{1}{2}$ × base × height
Area = $\frac{1}{2}$ × 3 cm × 4 cm
Area = **6 cm²**

4 cm   *3 cm*

Rectangle
Area = length × width
Area = 6 cm × 3 cm
Area = **18 cm²**

3 cm   *6 cm*

Square
Area = side × side
Area = 3 cm × 3 cm
Area = **9 cm²**

3 cm   *3 cm*

Volume

Volume is the amount of space something occupies.

> **Formulas:**
> Volume of a cube = side × side × side
>
> Volume of a prism = area of base × height
>
> **Examples:**
> Find the volume of the solids.

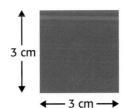

Cube
Volume = side × side × side
Volume = 4 cm × 4 cm × 4 cm
Volume = **64 cm³**

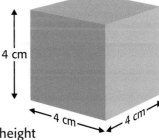

4 cm   *4 cm*   *4 cm*

Prism
Volume = area of base × height
Volume = (area of triangle) × height
Volume = $\left(\frac{1}{2} \times 3 \text{ cm} \times 4 \text{ cm} \right)$ × 5 cm
Volume = 6 cm² × 5 cm
Volume = **30 cm³**

4 cm   *3 cm*   *5 cm*

Periodic Table of the Elements

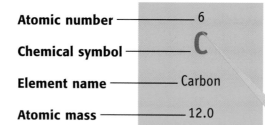

Atomic number ——— 6

Chemical symbol ——— **C**

Element name ——— Carbon

Atomic mass ——— 12.0

Each square on the table includes an element's name, chemical symbol, atomic number, and atomic mass.

The background color indicates the type of element. Carbon is a nonmetal.

The color of the chemical symbol indicates the physical state at room temperature. Carbon is a solid.

Background

Metals

Metalloids

Nonmetals

Chemical Symbol

Solid

Liquid

Gas

Period 1

1
H
Hydrogen
1.0

	Group 1	Group 2
Period 2	3 **Li** Lithium 6.9	4 **Be** Beryllium 9.0
Period 3	11 **Na** Sodium 23.0	12 **Mg** Magnesium 24.3

	Group 1	Group 2	Group 3	Group 4	Group 5	Group 6	Group 7	Group 8	Group 9
Period 4	19 **K** Potassium 39.1	20 **Ca** Calcium 40.1	21 **Sc** Scandium 45.0	22 **Ti** Titanium 47.9	23 **V** Vanadium 50.9	24 **Cr** Chromium 52.0	25 **Mn** Manganese 54.9	26 **Fe** Iron 55.8	27 **Co** Cobalt 58.9
Period 5	37 **Rb** Rubidium 85.5	38 **Sr** Strontium 87.6	39 **Y** Yttrium 88.9	40 **Zr** Zirconium 91.2	41 **Nb** Niobium 92.9	42 **Mo** Molybdenum 95.9	43 **Tc** Technetium (97.9)	44 **Ru** Ruthenium 101.1	45 **Rh** Rhodium 102.9
Period 6	55 **Cs** Cesium 132.9	56 **Ba** Barium 137.3	57 **La** Lanthanum 138.9	72 **Hf** Hafnium 178.5	73 **Ta** Tantalum 180.9	74 **W** Tungsten 183.8	75 **Re** Rhenium 186.2	76 **Os** Osmium 190.2	77 **Ir** Iridium 192.2
Period 7	87 **Fr** Francium (223.0)	88 **Ra** Radium (226.0)	89 **Ac** Actinium (227.0)	104 **Rf** Rutherfordium (261.1)	105 **Db** Dubnium (262.1)	106 **Sg** Seaborgium (263.1)	107 **Bh** Bohrium (262.1)	108 **Hs** Hassium (265)	109 **Mt** Meitnerium (266)

A row of elements is called a period.

A column of elements is called a group or family.

Lanthanides	58 **Ce** Cerium 140.1	59 **Pr** Praseodymium 140.9	60 **Nd** Neodymium 144.2	61 **Pm** Promethium (144.9)	62 **Sm** Samarium 150.4
Actinides	90 **Th** Thorium 232.0	91 **Pa** Protactinium 231.0	92 **U** Uranium 238.0	93 **Np** Neptunium (237.0)	94 **Pu** Plutonium 244.1

These elements are placed below the table to allow the table to be narrower.

This zigzag line reminds you where the metals, nonmetals, and metalloids are.

Group 18

| 2 **He** Helium 4.0 |

	Group 13	Group 14	Group 15	Group 16	Group 17
	5 **B** Boron 10.8	6 **C** Carbon 12.0	7 **N** Nitrogen 14.0	8 **O** Oxygen 16.0	9 **F** Fluorine 19.0	10 **Ne** Neon 20.2

| 13 **Al** Aluminum 27.0 | 14 **Si** Silicon 28.1 | 15 **P** Phosphorus 31.0 | 16 **S** Sulfur 32.1 | 17 **Cl** Chlorine 35.5 | 18 **Ar** Argon 39.9 |

Group 10	Group 11	Group 12

| 28 **Ni** Nickel 58.7 | 29 **Cu** Copper 63.5 | 30 **Zn** Zinc 65.4 | 31 **Ga** Gallium 69.7 | 32 **Ge** Germanium 72.6 | 33 **As** Arsenic 74.9 | 34 **Se** Selenium 79.0 | 35 **Br** Bromine 79.9 | 36 **Kr** Krypton 83.8 |

| 46 **Pd** Palladium 106.4 | 47 **Ag** Silver 107.9 | 48 **Cd** Cadmium 112.4 | 49 **In** Indium 114.8 | 50 **Sn** Tin 118.7 | 51 **Sb** Antimony 121.8 | 52 **Te** Tellurium 127.6 | 53 **I** Iodine 126.9 | 54 **Xe** Xenon 131.3 |

| 78 **Pt** Platinum 195.1 | 79 **Au** Gold 197.0 | 80 **Hg** Mercury 200.6 | 81 **Tl** Thallium 204.4 | 82 **Pb** Lead 207.2 | 83 **Bi** Bismuth 209.0 | 84 **Po** Polonium (209.0) | 85 **At** Astatine (210.0) | 86 **Rn** Radon (222.0) |

| 110 **Uun*** Ununnilium (271) | 111 **Uuu*** Unununium (272) | 112 **Uub*** Ununbium (277) | | 114 **Uuq*** Ununquadium (285) | | 116 **Uuh*** Ununhexium (289) | | 118 **Uuo*** Ununoctium (293) |

A number in parenthesis is the mass number of the most stable form of that element.

| 63 **Eu** Europium 152.0 | 64 **Gd** Gadolinium 157.3 | 65 **Tb** Terbium 158.9 | 66 **Dy** Dysprosium 162.5 | 67 **Ho** Holmium 164.9 | 68 **Er** Erbium 167.3 | 69 **Tm** Thulium 168.9 | 70 **Yb** Ytterbium 173.0 | 71 **Lu** Lutetium 175.0 |

| 95 **Am** Americium (243.1) | 96 **Cm** Curium (247.1) | 97 **Bk** Berkelium (247.1) | 98 **Cf** Californium (251.1) | 99 **Es** Einsteinium (252.1) | 100 **Fm** Fermium (257.1) | 101 **Md** Mendelevium (258.1) | 102 **No** Nobelium (259.1) | 103 **Lr** Lawrencium (262.1) |

*The official names and symbols for the elements greater than 109 will eventually be approved by a committee of scientists.

Physical Science Refresher

Atoms and Elements

Every object in the universe is made up of particles of some kind of matter. **Matter** is anything that takes up space and has mass. All matter is made up of elements. An **element** is a substance that cannot be separated into simpler components by ordinary chemical means. This is because each element consists of only one kind of atom. An **atom** is the smallest unit of an element that has all of the properties of that element.

Atomic Structure

Atoms are made up of small particles called subatomic particles. The three major types of subatomic particles are **electrons, protons,** and **neutrons.** Electrons have a negative electric charge, protons have a positive charge, and neutrons have no electric charge. The protons and neutrons are packed close to one another to form the **nucleus.** The protons give the nucleus a positive charge. Electrons are most likely to be found in regions around the nucleus called **electron clouds.** The negatively charged electrons are attracted to the positively charged nucleus. An atom may have several energy levels in which electrons are located.

Atomic Number

To help in the identification of elements, scientists have assigned an **atomic number** to each kind of atom. The atomic number is the number of protons in the atom. Atoms with the same number of protons are all the same kind of element. In an uncharged, or electrically neutral, atom there are an equal number of protons and electrons. Therefore, the atomic number equals the number of electrons in an uncharged atom. The number of neutrons, however, can vary for a given element. Atoms of the same element that have different numbers of neutrons are called **isotopes.**

Periodic Table of the Elements

In the periodic table, the elements are arranged from left to right in order of increasing atomic number. Each element in the table is in a separate box. An atom of each element has one more electron and one more proton than an atom of the element to its left. Each horizontal row of the table is called a **period.** Changes in chemical properties of elements across a period correspond to changes in the electron arrangements of their atoms. Each vertical column of the table, known as a **group,** lists elements with similar properties. The elements in a group have similar chemical properties because their atoms have the same number of electrons in their outer energy level. For example, the elements helium, neon, argon, krypton, xenon, and radon all have similar properties and are known as the noble gases.

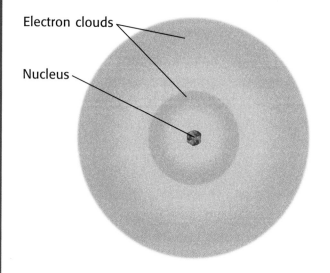

Electron clouds

Nucleus

Molecules and Compounds

When two or more elements are joined chemically, the resulting substance is called a **compound.** A compound is a new substance with properties different from those of the elements that compose it. For example, water, H_2O, is a compound formed when hydrogen (H) and oxygen (O) combine. The smallest complete unit of a compound that has the properties of that compound is called a **molecule.** A chemical formula indicates the elements in a compound. It also indicates the relative number of atoms of each element present. The chemical formula for water is H_2O, which indicates that each water molecule consists of two atoms of hydrogen and one atom of oxygen. The subscript number is used after the symbol for an element to indicate how many atoms of that element are in a single molecule of the compound.

Acids, Bases, and pH

An ion is an atom or group of atoms that has an electric charge because it has lost or gained one or more electrons. When an acid, such as hydrochloric acid, HCl, is mixed with water, it separates into ions. An **acid** is a compound that produces hydrogen ions, H^+, in water. The hydrogen ions then combine with a water molecule to form a hydronium ion, H_3O^+. A **base,** on the other hand, is a substance that produces hydroxide ions, OH^-, in water.

To determine whether a solution is acidic or basic, scientists use pH. The **pH** is a measure of the hydronium ion concentration in a solution. The pH scale ranges from 0 to 14. The middle point, pH = 7, is neutral, neither acidic nor basic. Acids have a pH less than 7; bases have a pH greater than 7. The lower the number is, the more acidic the solution. The higher the number is, the more basic the solution.

Chemical Equations

A chemical reaction occurs when a chemical change takes place. (In a chemical change, new substances with new properties are formed.) A chemical equation is a useful way of describing a chemical reaction by means of chemical formulas. The equation indicates what substances react and what the products are. For example, when carbon and oxygen combine, they can form carbon dioxide. The equation for the reaction is as follows:

$$C + O_2 \rightarrow CO_2.$$

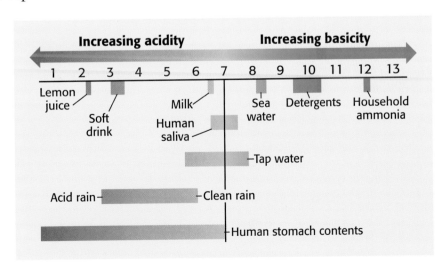

Properties of Common Minerals

Mineral	Color	Luster	Streak	Hardness
Silicate Minerals				
Beryl	deep green, pink, white, bluish green, or light yellow	vitreous	none	7.5–8
Chlorite	green	vitreous to pearly	pale green	2–2.5
Garnet	green or red	vitreous	none	6.5–7.5
Hornblende	dark green, brown, or black	vitreous or silky	none	5–6
Muscovite	colorless, gray, or brown	vitreous or pearly	white	2–2.5
Olivine	olive green	vitreous	none	6.5–7
Orthoclase	colorless, white, pink, or other colors	vitreous to pearly	white or none	6
Plagioclase	blue gray to white	vitreous	white	6
Quartz	colorless or white; any color when not pure	vitreous or waxy	white or none	7
Native Elements				
Copper	copper-red	metallic	copper-red	2.5–3
Diamond	pale yellow or colorless	vitreous	none	10
Graphite	black to gray	submetallic	black	1–2
Carbonates				
Aragonite	colorless, white, or pale yellow	vitreous	white	3.5–4
Calcite	colorless or white to tan	vitreous	white	3
Halides				
Fluorite	light green, yellow, purple, bluish green, or other colors	vitreous	none	4
Halite	colorless or gray	vitreous	white	2.5–3
Oxides				
Hematite	reddish brown to black	metallic to earthy	red to red-brown	5.6–6.5
Magnetite	iron black	metallic	black	5–6
Sulfates				
Anhydrite	colorless, bluish, or violet	vitreous to pearly	white	3–3.5
Gypsum	white, pink, gray, or colorless	vitreous, pearly, or silky	white	1–2.5
Sulfides				
Galena	lead gray	metallic	lead gray to black	2.5
Pyrite	brassy yellow	metallic	greenish, brownish, or black	6–6.5

Silicate Minerals / Nonsilicate Minerals

Density (g/cm³)	Cleavage, Fracture, Special Properties	Common Uses
2.6–2.8	1 cleavage direction; irregular fracture; some varieties fluoresce in ultraviolet light	gemstones, ore of the metal beryllium
2.6–3.3	1 cleavage direction; irregular fracture	
4.2	no cleavage; conchoidal to splintery fracture	gemstones, abrasives
3.2	2 cleavage directions; hackly to splintery fracture	
2.7–3	1 cleavage direction; irregular fracture	electrical insulation, wallpaper, fireproofing material, lubricant
3.2–3.3	no cleavage; conchoidal fracture	gemstones, casting
2.6	2 cleavage directions; irregular fracture	porcelain
2.6–2.7	2 cleavage directions; irregular fracture	ceramics
2.6	no cleavage; conchoidal fracture	gemstones, concrete, glass, porcelain, sandpaper, lenses
8.9	no cleavage; hackly fracture	wiring, brass, bronze, coins
3.5	4 cleavage directions; irregular to conchoidal fracture	gemstones, drilling
2.3	1 cleavage direction; irregular fracture	pencils, paints, lubricants, batteries
2.95	2 cleavage directions; irregular fracture; reacts with hydrochloric acid	minor source of barium
2.7	3 cleavage directions; irregular fracture; reacts with weak acid, double refraction	cements, soil conditioner, whitewash, construction materials
3.2	4 cleavage directions; irregular fracture; some varieties fluoresce or double refract	hydrochloric acid, steel, glass, fiberglass, pottery, enamel
2.2	3 cleavage directions; splintery to conchoidal fracture; salty taste	tanning hides, fertilizer, salting icy roads, food preservation
5.25	no cleavage; splintery fracture; magnetic when heated	iron ore for steel, gemstones, pigments
5.2	2 cleavage directions; splintery fracture; magnetic	iron ore
2.89–2.98	3 cleavage directions; conchoidal to splintery fracture	soil conditioner, sulfuric acid
2.2–2.4	3 cleavage directions; conchoidal to splintery fracture	plaster of Paris, wallboard, soil conditioner
7.4–7.6	3 cleavage directions; irregular fracture	batteries, paints
5	no cleavage; conchoidal to splintery fracture	dyes, inks, gemstones

Glossary

A

absolute dating the process of establishing the age of an object, such as a fossil or rock layer, by determining the number of years it has existed (64)

asthenosphere (as THEN uh SFIR) the soft layer of the mantle on which pieces of the lithosphere move (90)

C

caldera (kahl DER uh) a circular depression that forms when a magma chamber empties and causes the ground above to sink (155)

cast an object created when sediment fills a mold and becomes rock (70)

catastrophism a principle that states that all geologic change occurs suddenly (57)

cinder cone volcano a small, steeply sloped volcano that forms from moderately explosive eruptions of pyroclastic material (154)

cleavage (KLEEV ij) the tendency of a mineral to break along flat surfaces (9)

composite volcano a volcano made of alternating layers of lava and pyroclastic material; also called *stratovolcano* (154)

composition the makeup of a rock; describes either the minerals or elements present in it (31)

compound a pure substance made of two or more elements that have been chemically joined, or bonded together (5)

compression the type of stress that occurs when an object is squeezed (103)

continental drift the theory that continents can drift apart from one another and have done so in the past (95)

convergent boundary the boundary between two colliding tectonic plates (100, 159)

coprolites (KAHP roh LIETS) preserved feces, or dung, from animals (70)

core the central, spherical part of the Earth below the mantle (89)

crater a funnel-shaped pit around the central vent of a volcano (155)

crust the thin, outermost layer of the Earth, or the uppermost part of the lithosphere (88, 159)

crystal the solid, geometric form of a mineral produced by a repeating pattern of atoms (5)

D

deformation the change in the shape of rock in response to stress (103, 121)

density the amount of matter in a given space; mass per unit volume (10)

divergent boundary the boundary between two tectonic plates that are moving away from each other (101)

E

elastic rebound the sudden return of elastically deformed rock to its original shape (121)

element a pure substance that cannot be separated or broken down into simpler substances by ordinary chemical means (4)

eon the largest division of geologic time (75)

epicenter the point on the Earth's surface directly above an earthquake's starting point (126)

epoch (EP uhk) the fourth-largest division of geologic time (75)

era the second-largest division of geologic time (75)

erosion the removal and transport of material by wind, water, or ice (28–29, 62)

extrusive (eks TROO siv) the type of igneous rock that forms when lava or pyroclastic material cools and solidifies on the Earth's surface (36)

F

fault a break in the Earth's crust along which blocks of the crust slide relative to one another due to tectonic forces (105, 120)

fault block a block of the Earth's crust on one side of a fault (105)

focus the point inside the Earth where an earthquake begins (126)

folding the bending of rock layers due to stress in the Earth's crust (104)

foliated the texture of metamorphic rock in which the mineral grains are aligned like the pages of a book (44)

footwall the fault block that is below a fault (105)

fossil any naturally preserved evidence of life (68)

fracture the tendency of a mineral to break along curved or irregular surfaces (9)

G

gap hypothesis states that sections of active faults that have had relatively few earthquakes are likely to be the sites of strong earthquakes in the future (131)

geologic column an ideal sequence of rock layers that contains all the known fossils and rock formations on Earth arranged from oldest to youngest (60)

geologic time scale a scale that divides Earth's 4.6-billion-year history into distinct intervals of time (74)

geothermal energy energy from within the Earth (116)

H

half-life for a particular radioactive sample, the time it takes for one-half of the sample to decay (65)

hanging wall the fault block that is above a fault (105)

hardness the resistance of a mineral to being scratched (10)

hot spot a place on Earth's surface that is directly above a column of rising magma called a mantle plume (159)

I

igneous rock rock that forms from the cooling of magma (30)

index fossil a fossil of an organism that lived during a relatively short, well-defined time span; a fossil that is used to date the rock layers in which it is found (72)

inner core the solid, dense center of the Earth (91)

intrusive (in TROO siv) the type of igneous rock that forms when magma cools and solidifies beneath Earth's surface (35)

isotopes atoms of the same element that have the same number of protons but have different numbers of neutrons (64)

L

lava magma that flows onto the Earth's surface (30, 148)

lithosphere (LITH oh SFIR) the outermost, rigid layer of the Earth that consists of the crust and the rigid upper part of the mantle (90)

luster the way the surface of a mineral reflects light (8)

M

magma the hot liquid that forms when rock partially or completely melts; may include mineral crystals (29)

magnetic reversal the process by which the Earth's north and south magnetic poles periodically change places (98)

mantle the layer of the Earth between the crust and the core (89, 156)

mesosphere literally, the "middle sphere"—the strong, lower part of the mantle between the asthenosphere and the outer core (91)

metamorphic rock rock that forms when the texture and composition of preexisting rock changes due to heat or pressure (30)

meteorite a meteoroid that reaches the Earth's surface without burning up completely (27)

mid-ocean ridge a long mountain chain that forms on the ocean floor where tectonic plates pull apart; usually extends along the center of ocean basins (97, 101, 158)

mineral a naturally formed, inorganic solid with a crystalline structure (4)

Moho a place within the Earth where the speed of seismic waves increases sharply; marks the boundary between the Earth's crust and mantle (135)

mold a cavity in the ground or rock where a plant or animal was buried (70)

N

natural gas a gaseous fossil fuel (106)

nonfoliated the texture of metamorphic rock in which mineral grains show no alignment (44)

nonrenewable resource a natural resource that cannot be replaced or that can be replaced only over thousands or millions of years (15)

nonsilicate mineral a mineral that does not contain compounds of silicon and oxygen (7)

normal fault a fault in which the hanging wall moves down relative to the footwall (105)

O

ore a mineral deposit large enough and pure enough to be mined for a profit (14)

outer core the liquid layer of the Earth's core that lies beneath the mantle and surrounds the inner core (91)

P

period the third-largest division of geologic time (75)

permineralization a process in which minerals fill in pore spaces of an organism's tissues (68)

petrification a process in which an organism's tissues are completely replaced by minerals (68)

plate tectonics the theory that the Earth's lithosphere is divided into tectonic plates that move around on top of the asthenosphere (99)

P waves the fastest type of seismic wave; can travel through solids, liquids, and gases; also known as pressure waves and primary waves (124)

pyroclastic material fragments of rock that are created by explosive volcanic eruptions (151)

R

radioactive decay a process in which radioactive isotopes tend to break down into stable isotopes of other elements (64)

radiometric dating determining the absolute age of a sample based on the ratio of parent material to daughter material (65)

reclamation the process of returning land to its original state after mining is completed (15)

relative dating determining whether an object or event is older or younger than other objects or events (59)

reverse fault a fault in which the hanging wall moves up relative to the footwall (105)

rift a deep crack that forms between tectonic plates as they separate (158)

rock a solid mixture of crystals of one or more minerals or other materials (26)

rock cycle the process by which one rock type changes into another rock type (28)

S

sea-floor spreading the process by which new oceanic lithosphere is created at mid-ocean ridges as older materials are pulled away from the ridge (97)

sedimentary rock rock that forms when sediments are compacted and cemented together (30)

seismic (SIEZ mik) **gap** an area along a fault where relatively few earthquakes have occurred (131)

seismic waves waves of energy that travel through the Earth (124)

seismogram a tracing of earthquake motion created by a seismograph (126)

seismograph an instrument located at or near the surface of the Earth that records seismic waves (126)

seismology the study of earthquakes (120)

shadow zone an area on the Earth's surface where no direct seismic waves from a particular earthquake can be detected (135)

shield volcano a large, gently sloped volcano that forms from repeated, nonexplosive eruptions of lava (154)

silica a compound of silicon and oxygen atoms (150)

silicate mineral a mineral that contains a combination of the elements silicon and oxygen (6)

strata layers of sedimentary rock that form from the deposition of sediment (37)

stratification the layering of sedimentary rock (40)

streak the color of a mineral in powdered form (9)

stress the amount of force per unit area that is put on a given material (103)

strike-slip fault a fault in which the two fault blocks move past each other horizontally (106)

subduction zone the region where an oceanic plate sinks down into the asthenosphere at a convergent boundary, usually between continental and oceanic plates (159)

superposition a principle that states that younger rocks lie above older rocks in undisturbed sequences (59)

S waves the second-fastest type of seismic wave; cannot travel through materials that are completely liquid; also known as shear waves and secondary waves (124)

T

tectonic plate a piece of the lithosphere that moves around on top of the asthenosphere (92)

tension the type of stress that occurs when forces act to stretch an object (103)

texture the sizes, shapes, and positions of the grains that a rock is made of (32)

trace fossil any naturally preserved evidence of an animal's activity (70)

transform boundary the boundary between two tectonic plates that are sliding past each other horizontally (101)

U

unconformity a surface that represents a missing part of the geologic column (62)

uniformitarianism a principle that states that the same geologic processes shaping the Earth today have been at work throughout Earth's history (56)

V

volcano a mountain that forms when molten rock, called magma, is forced to the Earth's surface (148)

Index

A **boldface** number refers to an illustration on that page.

A

absolute dating, 64
active tendon system, **132**
aftershocks, 131
Alaskan Volcano Observatory, 168
amber, 69, **69**
amethyst, 8
ammonites, **70**, 72, **72**
animals, earthquakes and, 144
anticlines, 104, **104**
apatite, **10**
Appalachian Mountains, **107**, 108, **108**, 117
Archean eon, **74, 77**
ash, volcanic, 152, **152**, 153, **153**
asteroid collisions, 58, **58**
asthenosphere, 90–91, **90–91, 94, 97, 99**

B

basalt, **34**
base isolators, **132**
batholiths, **35**
bauxite, **15**
beryl, 15, 206
biosphere, 91
biotite, **6**
birthstones, 43
blocks, volcanic, 152, **152**
Blue Lagoon (Iceland), 116, **116**
bombs, volcanic, 152, **152**
boundaries
  convergent, 100, **100,** 107, 159, **159**
  divergent, 101, **101,** 158, **158**
  transform, 101, **101**
breccia, **38**
burial mounds, 66, **66**
butterflies, 45

C

calcite, **7, 10, 11, 43,** 206
calcium, 38
calcium carbonate, 38. *See also* limestone
calderas, 155, **155**
Candlestick Park (San Francisco), 145
carbon-14 dating, 67

carbon dioxide
  igneous rock and, **33**
  in volcanoes, 161
carbonate minerals, **7,** 206
careers in science
  paleontologist, 85
  seismologist, 120
casts, fossil, 70, **70**
CAT scans, 84, **84**
catastrophism, 57–58
Celsius scale, 158, 190
Cenozoic era, **74,** 76, **76, 77**
chalcopyrite, **15**
chemical reactions, **11**
chlorite, **43,** 206
chromite, 15
cinder cone volcanoes, 154, **154**
clastic sedimentary rock, 38
cleavage, 9, **9,** 207
climate
  changes in, 153
  volcanoes and, 153
collisions, plate, **100,** 159
color (of minerals), 8, 206
Columbia River plateau, 155
composite volcanoes, 154
composition, 31
compounds, 5, 205
compression, 103
computerized axial tomography (CAT), 84
concept mapping, 188
conchoidal fracture, **9**
conglomerates, **32**
contact metamorphism, 42, **42**
continental crust, 88, **88,** 89, 90, 93, **93, 159**
continental drift, **95,** 95–98, 117
convection, plate tectonics and, **99**
convergent boundaries, 100, **100,** 107, 159, **159**
convergent motion, **122–123**
coprolites, 70, **70**
coral, 39, **39**
core
  of Earth, 89, **89, 90–91**
corundum, **7, 10,** 15
craters, 155, **155**
cross braces, **132**
cross-beds, **40**
crust (of the Earth)
  continental, 88, **88, 89,** 93, **93, 159**
  deformations of, **103,** 103–109, **104, 105, 106,** 121, **121**
  oceanic, 88, **88,** 93, **93, 97, 100–101,** 158, 159, **159, 160**
crystals
  formation of, **12–13**
  in minerals, 5
Cullinan diamond, **15**

D

Dante II, 168, **168**
Darwin, Charles, 57
deep mining, 14
deformation, 103, **103,** 121
density, of minerals, 10
diamonds, 9, **9, 10, 15,** 206
dikes, **35**
dinosaurs, 84–85
disconformities, 63, **63**
divergent boundaries, 101, **101,** 158, **158**

E

Earth, *See also* plate tectonics
  composition, 88–89, **88–89**
  core of, 89, **89, 90–91**
  crust of, 88, **88, 89,** 93, **93, 158**
  geologic time scale, **74,** 74–76, **77**
  interior of, 89, **89**
  mantle of, 89, **89,** 156
  structure of, 90–91, **90–91,** 94, **94**
  tectonic plates, **92,** 117
earthquakes, 137
  animals and, 144
  causes of, 121, **121**
  damage by, **121, 131,** 131–132
  Earth's interior and, **135**
  epicenter of, **126,** 126–127, **127**
  focus of, 126, **126**
  forecasting, **130,** 130–131, **131**
  Great Hanshin, 137
  hazard levels and, 129, **129**
  location of, 120, **120,** 126–127, **126–127**
  Loma Prieta (California), 131, 145
  magnitude of, 128, **128**
  on other cosmic bodies, 136–137
  plate motion and, **100–101,** 101, **122–123**
  prediction of, **130,** 130–131, **131**
  preparation for, **133,** 133–134
  strength of, 128, **128,** 130
  types of, 122–123, **122–123**
Effigy Mounds National Monument (Iowa), 66, **66**
elastic rebound, 121, **121**
electromagnetic fields, 144
electron clouds, 204, **204**
elements
  in minerals, 4–5, 7
Enchanted Rock (Llano, Texas), **35**
eons, 75
epicenters, **126,** 126–127, **127**
epochs, 75

Credits

Abbreviations used: (t) top, (c) center, (b) bottom, (l) left, (r) right, (bkgd) background

ILLUSTRATIONS

All work, unless otherwise noted, contributed by Holt, Rinehart & Winston.

Table of Contents: iv(bl), Uhl Studios, Inc.; v(tr), Uhl Studios, Inc.

Scope and Sequence: T11, Paul DiMare, T13, Dan Stuckenschneider/Uhl Studios, Inc.

Chapter One: Page 4(bl), Gary Locke; 5, Stephen Durke/Washington Artists; 12-13(bkgd), Uhl Studios, Inc.; 14(bl), Jared Schneidman Design.

Chapter Two: Page 28-29, Uhl Studios, Inc.; 31(b), Sidney Jablonski; 33, Keith Locke; 34(l), Uhl Studios, Inc.; 35(b), Uhl Studios, Inc.; 38(bl), Robert Hynes; 42(b), Uhl Studios, Inc.; 43(t), Stephen Durke/Washington Artists; 43(b), Uhl Studios, Inc.; 48(br), Sidney Jablonski; 51(cr), Sidney Jablonski.

Chapter Three: Page 56(b), Uhl Studios, Inc.; 58(c), Barbara Hoopes-Ambler; 60(b), Jared Schneidman Design; 61, Uhl Studios, Inc.; 62(b), Jared Schneidman Design; 63, Uhl Studios, Inc.; 64(b), Stephen Durke/Washington-Artists' Represents; 69(br), Will Nelson/Sweet Reps; 70-71(c), Frank Ordaz; 72(c), Uhl Studios, Inc.; 83(tr), Joe LeMonnier.

Chapter Four: Page 88(b), Uhl Studios, Inc.; 89(br), Uhl Studios, Inc.; 90-91, Uhl Studios, Inc.; 92(c), Uhl Studios, Inc.; 93(c), Uhl Studios, Inc.; 94(tl), Uhl Studios, Inc.; 95(tr), Uhl Studios, Inc.; 95(bl), MapQuest.com; 96, MapQuest.com; 97, Uhl Studios, Inc.; 98(cl), Stephen Durke/Washington Artists; 98(cr), Uhl Studios, Inc.; 99(b), Uhl Studios, Inc.; 100-101(b), Uhl Studios, Inc.; 104(tl), Uhl Studios, Inc.; 105(tr), Marty Roper/Planet Rep; 105(cr), Uhl Studios, Inc.; 105(br), Uhl Studios, Inc.; 107(tr), Uhl Studios, Inc.; 108(t), Tony Morse/Ivy Glick; 108(bl), Uhl Studios, Inc.; 112, Uhl Studios, Inc.; 113(cr), Marty Roper/Planet Rep.

Chapter Five: Page 120(b), MapQuest.com; 121(b), Uhl Studios, Inc.; 122(b), Uhl Studios, Inc.; 122-123, Uhl Studios, Inc.; 124, Uhl Studios, Inc.; 125(cl), Uhl Studios, Inc.; 126(bl), Uhl Studios, Inc.; 127(tr), Sidney Jablonski; 129(b), MapQuest.com; 131(t), Jared Schneidman Design; 132, Uhl Studios, Inc.; 135(b), Uhl Studios, Inc.; 136, Sidney Jablonski; 140(br), Sidney Jablonski; 140(cl), Uhl Studios, Inc.; 142(br), Uhl Studios, Inc.; 143(cr), Sidney Jablonski.

Chapter Six: Page 150(tl), Uhl Studios, Inc.; 154(l), Patrick Gnan; 155(tr), Uhl Studios, Inc.; 156(b), Uhl Studios, Inc.; 157(tr), Stephen Durke/Washington Artists; 157(bl), MapQuest.com; 158, Uhl Studios, Inc.; 159, Uhl Studios, Inc.; 160(t), Uhl Studios, Inc.; 167(tr), Ross, Culbert and Lavery.

LabBook: Page 175(tr), Mark Heine; 176(br), Mark Heine; 182, Mark Heine; 184(c), Sidney Jablonski; 185(c), MapQuest.com; 186(t), Marty Roper/Planet Rep; 187(tr), Ralph Garafola/Lorraine Garafola Represents.

Appendix: Page 190(c), Terry Guyer; 194(b), Mark Mille/Sharon Langley; 202, Kristy Sprott; 203, Kristy Sprott; 204(bl), Stephen Durke/Washington Artists; 205(tl), Stephen Durke/Washington Artists; 205(c), Stephen Durke/Washington Artists; 205(b), Bruce Burdick.

PHOTOGRAPHY

Cover and Title Page: Frans Lanting/Minden Pictures

Sam Dudgeon/HRW Photo: Page viii-1, 4, 6(cr), 9(tr,bl), 10(bl), 11(tc,cl), 12(c), 13(b), 19(l), 20(tl), 31(cl), 32(cl), 38(c), 41(cl), 57(all), 59(bl), 65, 103, 133(tr), 134(br), 170, 171(bc), 172(br,cl), 173(tl, b), 177(all), 178, 179, 181, 183, 191(br).

Table of Contents: iv(tl), E. R. Degginger/Color-Pic, Inc.; v(cr), Stephen Frink/Corbis; v(b), Robert Glusic/Natural Selection; vi(tl), E. R. Degginger/Color-Pic, Inc.; vi(bl), Sam Dudgeon/HRW Photo; vii(tr), A. F. Kersting; vii(cr), SuperStock; vii(br), Alberto Garcia/SABA.

Scope and Sequence: T8(l), Lee F. Snyder/Photo Researchers, Inc.; T8(r), Stephen Dalton/Photo Researchers, Inc.; T10, E. R. Degginger/Color-Pic, Inc., T12(l), Rob Matheson/The Stock Market

Master Materials List: T25(bl, c), Image ©2001 PhotoDisc; T26(t), Sam Dudgeon/HRW Photo; T27(t, c), Image ©2001 PhotoDisc

Chapter One: pp. 2-3 Luis Rosendo/FPG International; p. 3 HRW Photo; p. 3 Inga Spence/Tom Stack & Associates; p. 5(br), Dr. Rainer Bode/Bode-Verlag Gmb; p. 6(bl), Pat Lanza/Bruce Coleman Inc.; p. 6(cl, c), E. R. Degginger/ Color-Pic, Inc.; p. 7(top to bottom), (top four), E. R. Degginger/Color-Pic, Inc.; SuperStock; Visuals Unlimited/Ken Lucas; p. 8(tr), Liaison Agency; (tl), Jane Burton/Bruce Coleman, Inc.; Luster Chart (row 1), E. R. Degginger/Color-Pic, Inc.; John Cancalosi 1989/DRK Photo; (row 2), Biophoto Associates/Photo Researchers, Inc.; Biophoto Associates/Bruce Coleman Inc.; (row 3), E. R. Degginger/Color-Pic, Inc.; Biophoto Associates/Photo Researchers, Inc.; (row 4), E. R. Degginger/Color-Pic, Inc.; p. 9(br), Tom Pantages; p. 9(c), E. R. Degginger/Color-Pic, Inc.; p. 9(cl), Erica and Harold Van Pelt/American Museum of Natural History; p. 10(0), Visuals Unlimited/Ken Lucas; 10(0,0,0,0), E. R. Degginger/Color-Pic, Inc.; p. 10(0), Visuals Unlimited/Dane S. Johnson; p. 10(0), Carlyn Iverson/Absolute Science Illustration and Photography; p. 10(0), Mark A. Schneider/Visuals Unlimited; p. 10(0), Charles D. Winters/Photo Researchers, Inc.; p. 10(00), Bard Wrisley/Liasion Agency; p. 11(tl, bc), E. R. Degginger/Color-Pic, Inc.; p. 11(tr), Sam Dudgeon/HRW Photo Courtesy Science Stuff, Austin , TX; p. 11(cr), Tom Pantages Photography; p. 11(br), Victoria Smith/HRW Photo; p. 12(b), E. R. Degginger/Color-Pic, Inc.; p. 12(tl), Victoria Smith/HRW Photo, Courtesy Science Stuff, Austin, TX; p. 13(cr, t), E. R. Degginger/Color-Pic, Inc.; p. 14(c), Wernher Krutein/Liaison Agency; p. 14 (inset), Kosmatsu Mining Systems; p. 14, Index Stock Photography, Inc.; p. 15, Historic Royal Palaces; p. 17 tr Victoria Smith/Courtesy of Science Stuff, Austin, TX/HRW Photo; p. 17 tcr Ken Lucas/Visuals Unlimited; p. 17 cr Charile Winters/HRW Photo; p. 17 (bcr, br) Sam Dudgeon/HRW Photo; p. 19(inset), Kosmatsu Mining Systems; p. 19(tr), Wernher Krutein/Liaison Agency; p. 20(bl), E. R. Degginger/Color-Pic, Inc.; p. 22(bl), Peter Menzel; p. 22(bl), Ralph Wetmore/Stone.

Chapter Two: pp. 24-25 Tom Till; p. 25 HRW Photo; p. 26(c), Kenneth Garrett; p. 26(bc), Fergus O'Brian/FPG International; p. 26(br), Peter Cummings/Tom Stack & Associates; p. 26(bl), Historical Collections, National Museum of Health and Medicine, AFIP; p. 27(bl), A.F. Kersting; p. 27(br), Andy Christiansen/HRW Photo; p. 27(c), Breck P. Kent; p. 27(cr), NASA/Science Photo Library/Photo Researchers, Inc.; p. 31(granite), Pat Lanza/Bruce Coleman Inc.; p. 31(br,cr), E. R. Degginger/Color-Pic, Inc.; p. 31(cl), Walter H. Hodge/Peter Arnold; p. 31(bl), Sp. Harry Taylor/Dorling Kindersley; p. 31(bc), Breck P. Kent; p. 32(c), Dorling Kindersley; p. 32(cr bc), Breck P. Kent; p. 34(br), E. R. Degginger/Color-Pic, Inc.; p. 34(cl, bl, cr), Breck P. Kent; p. 35(tr), Laurence Parent; p. 36(cl), Breck P. Kent; p. 36(cr), Peter Frenck/Bruce Coleman, Inc.; p. 37(br), Robert Glusic/Natural Selection; p. 38(tl), Breck P. Kent/Animals Animals/Earth Scenes; 38(breccia), Breck P. Kent; p. 38(cl), Joyce Photographics/Photo Researchers, Inc.; p. 38(cr), E. R. Degginger/Color-Pic, Inc.; p. 38(br), Breck P. Kent; p. 39(bl), Ed Cooper; p. 39, Stephen Frink/ Corbis; p. 39(bl), Breck P. Kent; p. 39(c), SuperStock; p. 40(cr), Franklin P. OSF/Animals Animals/Earth Scenes; p. 40(tl), Breck P. Kent; p. 41(bl), E. R. Degginger/Color-Pic, Inc.; p. 41(br), George Wuerthner; p. 43(tl), Visuals Unlimited/Dane S. Johnson; p. 43(tlc), Carlyn Iverson/Absolute Science Illustration and Photography; p. 43(tlb), Breck P. Kent; p. 43(tr), Breck P. Kent/Animals Animals/Earth Scenes; p. 43(brc), Tom Pantages; p. 43(br), Breck P. Kent/Animals Animals/Earth Scenes; p. 44(tl), Ken Karp/HRW Photo; p. 44(br), Breck P. Kent; p. 45(tl), E. R. Degginger/Color-Pic, Inc.; p. 45(bl), Ray Simmons/ Photo Researchers, Inc.; p. 45(tc), The Natural History Museum, London; p. 45(bc), Breck P. Kent; p. 46 Peter Van Steen//HRW Photo; p. 47 Peter Van Steen//HRW Photo; p. 48, E. R. Degginger/Color-Pic, Inc.; p. 49, Doug Sokell/Tom Stack & Associates; p. 52(c), Wolfgang Kaehler/Liason International.

Chapter Three: pp. 54-55 Blair Jonathan/National Geographic Society Image Collection; p. 54 Brett Gregory/Auscape International Pty Ltd.; p. 55 HRW Photo; p. 59(br), Andy Christiansen/HRW Photo; p. 66, Tom Till/DRK Photo; p. 67, Courtesy Charles S. Tucek/University of Arizona at Tucson; p. 68(bl), Francois Gohier/Photo Researchers, Inc.; p. 68(cr), p. 147(tr), E. R. Degginger/Color-Pic, Inc.; p. 70(cl), Breck P. Kent; p. 70(bl), The G.R. "Dick" Roberts Photo Library; p. 71(c, cr), Brian Exton; p. 72(tr), Thomas R. Taylor/ Photo Researchers, Inc.; p. 73(br), Mike Buchheit Photography; p. 75, p. 76 (all), American Museum of Natural History; p. 82(tl), Runk/Schoenberger/ Grant Heilman Photography; p. 82(cr), Stone; p. 84(c), Andrew Leitch/©1992 The Walt Disney Co. Reprinted with the permission of Discover Magazine; p. 85(br, tl), Louie Psihoyos/Matrix.

Chapter Four: pp. 86-87 Jock Montgomery/Bruce Coleman, Inc.; p. 86 Courtesy of the Fort Worth Museum of Science and History; p. 87 HRW Photo; p. 89(tr), James Wall/Animals Animals/Earth Scenes; p. 89(bl), World Perspective/Stone; p. 102(cl), ESA/CE/Eurocontrol/Science Photo Library/ Photo Researchers, Inc.; p. 102(tl), NASA; p. 104(br), Visuals Unlimited/ SylvesterAllred; p. 104(bl), The G.R. "Dick" Roberts Photo Library; p. 106(tl), Tom Bean; p. 106(tr), Landform Slides; p. 107(tl), William Manning/ The Stock Market; p. 109, Michelle & Tom Grimm/Stone; p. 110 Sam Dudgeon/HRW Photo; p. 111 Sam Dudgeon/HRW Photo; p. 114, NASA/Photo Researchers, Inc.; p. 116, Bob Krist; p. 117, Martin Schwarzbach/Photo Deutsches Museum Munchen.

Chapter Five: pp. 118-119 Wally Santana/AP/Wide World Photo; p. 118 Haley/SIPA Press; p. 119 HRW Photo; p. 121, Joe Dellinger/NOAA/National Geophysical Data Center; p. 126(cl), Bob Paz/Caltech; p. 127, Earth Images/Stone; p. 130, Peter Cade/Stone; p. 131, A. Ramey/Woodfin Camp & Associates; p. 133(bl), Paul Chesley/Stone; p. 134(tl), Ken Lax; p. 137(cr), NASA; p. 137(tr), SOHO (ESA & NASA); p. 139 Sam Dudgeon/HRW Photo; p. 141, A. Ramey/Woodfin Camp & Associates; p. 142(tl), Chuck O'Rear/ Corbis; p. 144(c), Novaswan/FPG International; p. 145(cr), David Madison/ Bruce Coleman, Inc.

Chapter Six: pp. 146-147 Carl Shaneff/Pacific Stock; p. 146 Darodents/ Pacific Stock; p. 147 HRW Photo; p. 148(cl), Robert W. Madden/National Geographic Society; p. 148(cr), Douglas Peebles Photography; 148(bc), Ken Sakamoto/Black Star; p. 149(b), Breck P. Kent/Earth Scenes; p. 149(tr), Joyce Warren/USGS Photo Library; p. 151(cr), Jim Yuskavitch; p. 151(bl), Karl Weatherly; p. 151(bc), Tui De Roy/Minden Pictures; p. 151(br), B. Murton/

continued on page 216

Self-Check Answers

Chapter 1—Minerals of the Earth's Crust

Page 13: These minerals form wherever salt water has evaporated.

Chapter 2—Rocks: Mineral Mixtures

Page 34: From fastest-cooled to slowest-cooled, the rocks in Figure 10 are: basalt, rhyolite, gabbro, and granite.

Page 42: A rock can come into contact with magma and also be subjected to pressure underground.

Chapter 3—The Rock and Fossil Record

Page 70: Coprolites and tracks are trace fossils because they are evidence of animal activity rather than fossilized organisms.

Chapter 4—Plate Tectonics

Page 105: When folding occurs, sedimentary rock strata bend but do not break. When faulting occurs, sedimentary rock strata break along a fault, and the fault blocks on either side move relative to each other.

Chapter 5—Earthquakes

Page 123: Convergent motion creates reverse faults, while divergent motion creates normal faults. Convergent motion produces deep, strong earthquakes, while divergent motion produces shallow, weak earthquakes.

Page 130: 120

Chapter 6—Volcanoes

Page 157: Solid rock may become magma when pressure is released, when the temperature rises above its melting point, or when its composition changes.